OCR

AS / A2

Applied Science

OCR and Heinemann are working together to provide better support for you

David Ballard, David Baylis, John Bull,
Gill Miller and Ann Simpson
Series editors: David Baylis and Ann Simpson

www.heinemann.co.uk
✓ Free online support
✓ Useful weblinks
✓ 24 hour online ordering

01865 888080

OCR
RECOGNISING ACHIEVEMENT

Heinemann

Official Publisher Partnership

Heinemann is an imprint of Pearson Education Limited, a company incorporated in England and Wales, having its registered office at Edinburgh Gate, Harlow, Essex, CM20 2JE. Registered company number: 872828

www.heinemann.co.uk

Heinemann is a registered trademark of Pearson Education Limited

Text © Pearson Education Limited 2008

First published 2008

12
10 9 8 7 6

British Library Cataloguing in Publication Data is available from the British Library on request.

ISBN 978 0 435692 12 4

Edited by Paul King
Designed by Wearset Ltd, Boldon, Tyne and Wear
Project managed and typeset by Wearset Ltd, Boldon, Tyne and Wear
Illustrated by Wearset Ltd, Boldon, Tyne and Wear
Cover photo © SCIENCE SOURCE/SCIENCE PHOTO LIBRARY
Printed and bound in China (CTPS/06)

The authors and publisher would like to thank the following for permission to reproduce photographs:

pvi Forest; p2 Pascal Goetgheluck/Science Photo Library; p4 T Janine Wiedel Photolibrary/Alamy; p4 B Photononstop/Maximilian Stock Ltd/Photolibrary; p6 Pidjoe/Istockphoto; p8 Alamy Images. Image100/Cumulus; p14 Factoria Singular SL/Istockphoto; p21 Transtock Inc./Alamy; p28 T Richard Smith/Cumulus; p28 B Iofoto/Shutterstock; p30 Digital Vision/Cumulus; p31 Corbis/Cumulus; p32 Corbis/Cumulus; p35 T Associated Press; p35 B Pearson Education Ltd. Trevor Clifford. 2005/Cumulus; p36 T Tomo Jesenicnik/Dreamstime; p36 M Domenico Gelermo/Fotolia; p36 B OlgaLIS/Istockphoto; p36 Wish Photograf/Istock photo; p37 Dr. Joanna Simpson; p38 T Pearson Education Ltd. Devon Olugbena Shaw. 2005/Cumulus; p38 B Martyn F Chillmaid/Science Photo Library; p41 T Pearson Education Ltd. Peter Morris. 2003/Cumulus; p41 B Fancy. Punchstock/Cumulus; p43 T Pearson Education Ltd. Jules Selmes. 2007/Cumulus; p43 B PhotoDisc. PhotoLink. C. Sherburne/Cumulus; p44 Pearson Education Ltd. Gareth Boden. 2005/Cumulus; p45 Sophie-Laure Raphael/Fotolia; p49 James Holmes/Oxford Centre for Molecular Sciences/Science Photo Library; p50 L Ian Goodrick/Alamy; p50 R Manus Manus/Mauritius/Photolibrary; p51 Cre8tive Images/Shutterstock; p52 Mike Powell/Getty Images; p53 John Fryer/Alamy; p54 L PhotoDisc. Jeff Maloney/Cumulus; p54 M Photo Researchers Inc./Photolibrary.com; p55 PhotoDisc. PhotoLink/Cumulus; p56 Walt Adams; p59 Lisa F Young/Shutterstock; p60 L Anatomical Travelogue/Science Photo Library; p60 R Anita/Shutterstock; p62 CNRI/Science Photo Library; p63 R C N Mundy LRPS; p64 Richard Smith/Cumulus; p65 Michael Ross/Science Photo Library; p66 Ian Marlow; p68 Hank Morgan/Science Photo Library; p70 Will & Deni McIntyre/Science Photo Library; p74 L Richard Smith. 2005/Cumulus; p74 R Pearson Education Ltd. Jules Selmes. 2005/Cumulus; p75 James Martin/Getty Images; p77 Samuel Ashfield/Science Photo Library; p78 Ruth Jenkinson/MIDIRS/Science Photo Library; p79 Richard Smith. 2004/Cumulus; p81 kenny123/Bigstockphoto; p82 Alexandar Iotsov/Bigstockphoto; p83 T Wheatley/Bigstockphoto; p83 B PhotoDisc/Cumulus; p84 Horizon International Images Limited/Alamy; p86 Richard Smith/Cumulus; p87 T Konstantin Sutyagin/Shutterstock; p87 B ZTS/Shutterstock; p88 Detail Nottingham/Alamy; p89 Deep Light Productions/Science Photo Library; p90 JSAbbott/Istockphoto; p91 TL Ginae.net/Bigstockphoto; p91 TR Arlene Gee/Bigstockphoto; p91 B Radiation Protection Division/Health Protection Agency/Science Photo Library; p93 Pearson Education Ltd. Gareth Boden. 2003/Cumulus; p97 Dr Jeremy Burgess/Science Photo Library; p98 Dr Gopal Murti/Science Photo Library; p99 Dr Elena Kisevela/Science Photo Library; p100 R Keith C. Flood Photography/Istockphoto; p100 L Sebastian Kaulitzki/Shutterstock; p113 T Associated Press; p113 M Stock Italia/Alamy; p113 B Edward Parker/Alamy; p119 Associated Press; p123 Colin Cuthbert/Science Photo Library; p124 Ed Reschke, Peter Arnold Inc./Science Photo Library; p125 Dennis Kunkel/Phototake Science/Photolibrary; p127 Custom Medical Stock Photo/Science Photo Library; p128 L ISM-/Phototake/Photolibrary; p128 R Astier -/BSIP Medical/Photolibrary; p130 T Sciencephotos/Alamy; p130 B Maximilian Stock Ltd/Science Photo Library; p133 Travismanley/Istockphoto; p136 TEK Image/Science Photo Library; p138 Joseph Helfenberger/Dreamstime; p140 Mauro Fermariello/Science Photo Library; p141 Dragan Trifunovic; p142 David R. Frazier Photolibrary Inc./Alamy; p143 Trufero/Shutterstock; p144 R Andrew Syred/Science Photo Library; p144 L ChriSes/Fotolia; p146 PhotoDisc. Karl Weatherly/Cumulus; p149 T PhotoDisc. PhotoLink/Cumulus; p149 B PhotoDisc. PhotoLink/Cumulus; p150 PhotoDisc. Jim Wehtje/Cumulus; p152 Pearson Education Ltd. Tudor Photography. 2004/Cumulus; p153 John Bull; p154 PhotoDisc. C Squared Studios/Cumulus; p155 TR PhotoDisc. Lawrence M. Sawyer/Cumulus; p155 L PhotoDisc. PhotoLink/Cumulus; p155 BR Professor Harold Edgerton/Science Photo Library; p158 T PhotoDisc. Lawrence Lawry/Cumulus; p158 B Associated Press; p160 Digital Stock/Cumulus; p162 PhotoDisc. Jack Hollingsworth/Cumulus; p166 Andrew Lambert Photography/Science Photo Library; p168 South West Images Scotland/Alamy; p171 Rob Ritchie; p178 Nigel Cattlin/Alamy; p182 Sean Sprague/Alamy; p188 Pearson Education Ltd. Ginny Stroud-Lewis/Cumulus; p196 T Digital Vision/Cumulus; p196 B Digital Vision/Cumulus; p198 T Pearson Education Ltd. Mark Bassett. 2005/Cumulus; p198 B Alamy Images. StockBrazil/Cumulus; p202 Midlands Maintenance & Calibration; p204 PhotoDisc. PhotoLink/Cumulus; p205 PhotoDisc. PhotoLink/Cumulus; p206 Pearson Education Ltd. Tudor Photography. 2004/Cumulus; p212 Chris R Sharp/Science Photo Library; p214 Pearson Education Ltd. Ian Wedgewood. 2007/Cumulus; p218 Corbis/Cumulus; p221 T Associated Press; p221 B Tom Hussey/Getty Images; p224 Shangara Singh/Alamy; p226 L Peter Evans 2003/Cumulus; p226 R Peter Evans 2003/Cumulus; p227 T Brand X Pictures. Morey Milbradt. 2001/Cumulus; p227 B Digital Vision/Cumulus; p229 Dave Baylis; p230 Frank Sochacki; p235 Science Source/Science Photo Library; p246 L The Illustrated London News Picture Library/Cumulus; p246 R PhotoDisc/Cumulus; p248 Pearson Education Ltd. Gareth Boden. 2004/Cumulus; p249 T PhotoDisc. Jim Wehtje/Cumulus; p249 B Pearson Education Ltd. Gareth Boden. 2005/Cumulus; p250 Comstock Images/Cumulus; p252 James Doss/Shutterstock; p253 James Doss/Shutterstock; p254 Ted Kinsman/Science Photo Library; p255 NOAA; p256 TM Martyn F Chillmaid/Science Photo Library; p256 TR Rob Walls/Alamy; p256 BL Dave Ellison/Alamy; p261 Paul Cheyne/Istockphoto; p262 T Alamy Images. Brand X Pictures/Cumulus; p262 B fstop2/Alamy; p268 Jane/Istockphoto; p270 Matjaz Boncina/Istockphoto; p280 Zephyr/Science Photo Library

The authors and publisher would like to thank the following for permission to use copyright material:

p2 Fig 2: Microsoft; p5 Fig 3: reproduced with permission from CLEAPSS; p9 Fig 2: reproduced with permission from CLEAPSS; p75 Fig 2: reproduced with the permission of the Maritime and Coastguard Agency © Crown Copyright; p117 Fig 1: C. Lea, P. Lowrie and S. McGuigan, AS Level Biology for AQA Specification B, Heinemann Educational Publishers, 2000; p193 Fig 2: http://en.wikipedia.org/wiki/Image:Batch_reactor3.jpg; p198 Fig 2: Reproduced courtesy of the Chemical Industry Education Centre, University of York, from their website for schools, www.greener-industry.org; p203 Fig 3: P. Fullick, Physics, Heinemann Advanced Science Series, 1994; p231 Fig 2: C. Lea, S. McGuigan, A. Pauline and P. Lowrie, A2 Biology for AQA, Heinemann Educational Publishers, 2001; p251 Fig 3: Ibarra-Castanedo C. 'Quantitative subsurface defect evaluation by pulsed phase thermography: depth retrieval with the phase,' Ph. D. thesis, http://www.theses.ulaval.ca/2005/23016/23016.html or http://www.theses.ulaval.ca/2005/23016/23016.pdf, Université Laval, 2005; p264 Fig 1: http://www.techoptics.com; p273 Fig 1: J. Pope, Medical Physics: Imaging, Heinemann Advanced Science Series, 1999; p277 Fig 1: J. Pope, Medical Physics: Imaging, Heinemann Advanced Science Series, 1999; p279 Fig 2: J. Pope, Medical Physics: Imaging, Heinemann Advanced Science Series, 1999

Every effort has been made to contact copyright holders of material reproduced in this book. Any omissions will be rectified in subsequent printings if notice is given to the publisher.

Acknowledgements

We would like to thank Margaret Ballard, Tricia Baylis, Alice Bull, Anna Dent, Christina Freeman (Radiographer), Claire Gordon, Les Hopper, David, Jo and Liz Simpson for their invaluable help in the development and trialling of this course.

Websites

There are links to relevant websites in this book. In order to ensure that the links are up-to-date, that the links work, and that the sites are not inadvertently linked to sites that could be considered offensive, we have made the links available on the Heinemann website at www.heinemann.co.uk/hotlinks. When you access the site, the express code is 2124P.

Contents

Introduction

This book will help you during your Applied Science AS and A2 course. It is designed to do two things for you. Firstly, it will encourage you to enjoy this science course and secondly give you support and confidence to complete your portfolio and examined units.

Having chosen to study Applied Science at AS or at A level, you will spend part of your course preparing for one or more externally assessed examinations and the remaining time organising your own work for the portfolio units. This book covers all the material for the externally examined units but it will not provide all the assessment evidence needed for your portfolios. If it did, all the portfolios presented would probably be just rewrites or extracts from the book. Our hope is that this book will help and guide you to develop your own skills. It will give you a base to work from. You will probably be working for your portfolio units with assignment-briefs set by your teachers. This book will help you to meet the demands of those assignments and lead to successfully evidenced portfolios.

The work that you do, as you study this Applied Science specification, will not only improve your knowledge and understanding of a wide range of interesting scientific topics, but also enable you to develop those skills needed to research, select and use appropriate material from text books and the internet. Your organisational skills will improve, allowing you to carry out practical work safely and put together, with knowledge and understanding, a portfolio which reflects your interest in science. You will appreciate and evaluate the impact that science has on society. You should be able to identify ethical issues and appreciate their significance. In the process, you will develop an awareness of the science used in organisations and a realisation of the importance of science in today's world.

Figure 1 Science at work: you should not only be researching at college or school but understanding the nature of science based work. What science goes on at a monkey park?

I think this is an ethical issue.

I think this is a moral issue!

Figure 2 Ethics: what has this to do with science?

About this book

The first part of this book will be useful to you whether you are studying AS or A2. It contains guidance on a range of topics which you will use, principally in the portfolio units, but also in the examined work. This course leads to an advanced qualification and although you will probably study a range of biological, chemical and physical topics you are likely to need guidance on their vocational aspects. There are many text books available as sources of scientific facts, you will probably need to use several of them for some of your portfolio research, but it is hoped that this first section will help you in putting together your portfolio. Here, you will find portfolio tips on organisation, how to use references, how to approach practical work with a vocational slant. Guidance is provided on risk assessment, how to collect and present data, appropriate mathematical and graphical techniques and how to carry out some common, practical techniques you may need to use.

Most of the book is dedicated to providing appropriate factual information, sources of information and guidance for each of the sixteen units in the specification.

The content for the AS examined units, Unit 3 Monitoring the Activity of the Human Body and Unit 4 Cells and Molecules, will contain all the factual information you will need to recall for the examination.

The portfolio units all begin with the assessment criteria. These clearly identify the evidence you will be assessed on and therefore the evidence you need to present to complete your portfolio successfully. It is hoped that the tips given will help you reach the highest mark you can.

In addition for each of the portfolio units you are given some examples to help you to get started in your portfolio work. The information from this book should not just be rewritten. You need to build on the ideas given in the process producing your own, individual work.

The information for the A2 examined units, Unit 9 Sampling and Processing and Unit 16 Working Waves, will help to support your preparation for the examination. Unit 9 is a little different, but you will find case studies to work on and information on how to approach the examination. Working Waves is an A2 unit and hopefully the information given will help you to appreciate the depth to which you need to study this topic if you are to be successful. The A2 portfolio units are set out in the same way as for the AS units and should be used in a similar way but you need to remember that the work you complete for this section and the evidence you present needs to be at A2 level standard.

You will find examination questions for Units 3, 4 and 16. The way Unit 9 is presented in the main body of the book is based on the assessment process and contains plenty of questions, and appropriate answers, of the type you are likely to meet in the examination.

Words in bold and margin boxes

In addition to the facts, ideas and practical guidance, the information provided for each unit in this section of the book contains the following special features.

Some words are printed in **bold**, these are **key definitions** and you will find them either in the spread or in the glossary at the back of this book.

In the margins of the main text are boxes giving you the following information:

- *Assessment tips*

The text includes lots of Assessment tips. These are intended to give you guidance to improve your portfolio work and also things to remember for the examined units.

- *Activity*

You will find lots of Activity boxes throughout the book, these are intended to make you think. They may provoke discussion during your class-work or cause you to think about a particular issue on your own.

- *Case study*

Applied Science is a vocational course and we have tried to link a lot of the work to everyday science or to topics which you may find interesting. You may be able to extend your research using some of these ideas.

- *Sources*

In this specification we are aiming to prepare you for further study and hope to make you skilful in research techniques. The sources given in this book are not the only ones you should use but it is hoped that they will help. Links to useful websites are provided on a dedicated 'hotlinks' page on Heinemann website at www.heinemann.co.uk/hotlinks. When you access this site the express code is 2124P.

Finally we hope that this book will be thought-provoking, encourage you in your research and develop your skills of investigation. However, above all else, we hope that this book gives you the support, guidance and confidence to enable you to work towards a successful qualification in AS/A2 Applied Science.

Key definition

An **artefact** is something that has appeared in a preparation as a result of the preparation technique itself. For example air bubbles appear in a temporary mount because they are easily trapped when the cover slip is lowered over the tissue and water.

Assessment tip

A survey is just a summary of the information you have found out about the organisations you have researched. You need to be careful not to include pages and pages of general information about the organisations.

Activity

Pharmacies are located all over the country and a visit to one, or having a visiting speaker from a pharmacy may enable you to gather information on this service.

Case study

Pilkington's is one of the world's largest manufacturers of glass and glazing products. 'Imagine a world without glass – dark!' Cars would be impractical and there would be no window shopping. The chemistry of glass, the manufacturing process and nanotechnology which is used in glass that cleans itself, is important and interesting science. Scientific knowledge and understanding is needed in this major manufacturing industry.

Sources

Links to useful websites are provided on a dedicated 'hotlinks' page on Heinemann website at www.heinemann.co.uk/hotlinks. When you access this site the express code is 2124P.

Portfolio skills

By the end of this spread, you should be able to:

✱ **understand what needs to be done to make an organised portfolio**

One of the skills needed by a good scientist is organisation. Recording results on scrappy bits of paper, scribbling down observations and then not really knowing what they are related to is not good practice. All assessed, researched and practical work needs to be collated and labelled so that all the work you have completed can be easily located and used if required by the reader. It is not a personal record of what you have completed in your science lessons but it should show the assessment requirements given in the criteria and written appropriately to suit the purpose of the work.

Figure 1 Forensic scientists recording observations at the scene of a crime

Assessment tip

Using a header or footer on your work is easy to do and it will help you to keep a track of your work (see Figure 2). In *Word* just click on *View* on your tool bar and then pull down and click on header and footer. If you then click on Insert Auto Text page/date etc. will be inserted automatically as header/footer into your work.

Assessment tip

A good contents page shows:

Number Name of section Page reference

1 Health and safety at work   10–15

How to be organised when putting together your portfolio

- Check all your work is referenced with your name, unit number and title, also your candidate number and centre number – it is useful to use a header and footer if you are completing an e-file.
- Make sure you have a copy of the assessment criteria at the front of your work.
- Your portfolio needs only to contain the work needed to cover the assessment criteria.
- Number all your pages – make sure you do this as it helps to locate your evidence.
- Generate yourself a contents page.
- Record clearly all the references you have used. It is also useful to include how this information has supported your work. Remember if you do use any information directly taken from a website page you must indicate this. You can show this by including a superscript reference number[1] followed by information where the material was taken from.

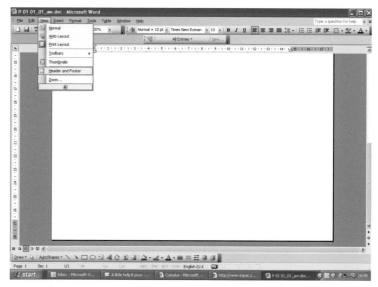

Figure 2 How to find what to do to insert a header and footer

Website references

To record website references correctly do not put 'used Internet'. All the pages of a website share the basic URL. The URL is the World Wide Web address and most web addresses begin with http://www. etc. So you need to reference websites as follows: http://www.ocr.org.uk takes you just to the website – usually the home page. A reference such as http://www.ocr.org.uk/index.html directs you to the index. http://www.ocr.org.uk/pastpapermaterials/pastpapers/index.html directs the reader to the specific page. The last address is usually the amount of detail you need to include when referencing.

Book references

Give the name of the book followed by the author/editor/publisher/ISBN number.

ISBN (International Standard Book Number) is a unique commercial book identifier bar code. The USBN was created in 1966 in the UK by WH Smith. Originally it was a 9-digit number, and as of 1 January 2007, ISBNs became 13 digits long. ISSN numbers are used to identify periodic publications such as magazines.

What to do if you have carried out work in a group

- If you have completed work as a group make sure you have indicated what part was your own individual effort. If you gave a presentation make sure you have evidence that you did this. This could be a video, or an evaluation sheet completed by either the audience to whom you gave the presentation or your assessor.

What is needed to show you have completed the practical work?

- When you include your practical work in your portfolio, check using the assessment criteria exactly what you need to record. It is not always necessary to rewrite standard procedures or methods: original copies attached to your work are usually what is needed. Risk assessments must always be included (see spread P.1.4).
- A good scientist records results in a suitable table as they are completing the practical work; this is good practice and you should be working towards doing this for each practical you do. So before you begin your experimental work think about what you need to measure/observe etc. and draw a suitable format in which to record your results before you begin (see spread P.1.10).
- Also make sure you get a written statement or even a certificate of completion (see spread P.1.2) to show that you have actually carried out the practical activities. A write up of method etc. is not evidence that you actually completed the work.

How to check you have spent enough time on your work

- Deadlines and targets are words you will hear a lot in today's society. In all organisations time is money and staff are expected to complete work to set deadlines and reach targets set on the quality and quantity of work completed. So it is important that you spend the correct amount of time on your work and complete it by the deadline set. Look at the number of marks allocated to each section of the assessment requirements and then link this approximately to the number of hours you need to spend on your work.

Checking work is at the correct level for assessment

- You will find that on the assessment criteria the work is shown in three different columns – these are related to the level of work required. Work at mark band 3 should be at the highest level and if you are aiming to gain A and B grades you should be working towards covering this level of work. Remember at A level D and E grades are still a pass and in order to reach these grades you should be covering work targeted at mark band 1 and mark band 2.
- The quality of the work you produce for your portfolio units needs to be at an appropriate level to reach either an AS or an A2 qualification. The content of the science and the level of the research you carry out at AS level will not be as complex as that needed for A2. Evaluation of your work is a higher level skill and therefore the work which you produce to cover this needs to show higher levels skill (see spreads P.1.2 and 8.1.4).

ISBN 817525766-0

9 788175 257665

Figure 3 Parts of an ISBN bar code

Portfolio skills

Assessment tip

If a section has been allocated a maximum of 7 marks you need to spend about 7–9 hours on this section of your work.

Portfolio skills

By the end of this spread, you should be able to:

✳ know what is needed to complete practical work with a vocational link
✳ know what to include in your portfolio

Figure 1 A forensic scientist giving evidence in court. Accurate practical work is needed

How to make your practical vocational

Following standard procedures and accurate recording of observations and measurements from experimental work is an important skill for scientists in whatever field they work. The practical work you do may be preparative, analytical, using standard or testing procedures or monitoring; all these techniques are used in the work place.
In order to make your work vocational you could:

• Research the topic using the Internet, leaflets or text books in order to find out any historical links, common uses, why such techniques are used and what they are used for.
• Go on a visit where similar practical work is being carried out, compare the technique you use in the laboratory to those used in industry, investigate more about health and safety, practical on a large scale, whether the process is batch or continuous.
• Meet people involved with the work, find out what they do.
• Carry out some work experience in a scientific organisation and put the practical work into context.

Alternatively the practical work might be investigative: looking at health, products we use or rely on in our everyday lives or the work carried out by professionals, e.g. forensic scientists, technicians, analysts. This in itself makes the work vocational.

You will find the words 'linked to a vocational context' popping up in the assessment grids. In order to cover this – make sure that you have included work from the list above. Your practical work needs to have a purpose and be relevant to what happens in scientific organisations or be important to our lives.

Figure 2 Fermentation in industry is carried out on a large scale

What is needed for your portfolio?

The range of procedures and techniques is infinite; whichever practical you chose it is essential you use the following guidelines:

• Check you have the correct instructions for your experimental work and before you begin collect together all the required equipment and chemicals you may need. It is important that scientists working in laboratories are organised and tidy. Include all instructions for your portfolio – you do not need to rewrite given procedures.
• Complete a risk assessment. You may be able to use Hazcards for the information on the chemicals. Ask your teacher/supervisor. You can use a set format, just check the information is directly related to the practical work you are carrying out (refer to spread P.1.4). This should be a working document and you need to use it as you carry out your practical work. You can make additions or alterations as you are working. You always must include risk assessments in your portfolio work.

38A Ethanoic acid, methanoic acid and their salts

Ethanoic acid	Acetic acid; vinegar		CH_3COOH
Corrosive		R10: Flammable. R35: Causes severe burns. Solutions equal to or stronger than 4 mol dm^{-3} should be labelled CORROSIVE. Solutions equal to or stronger than 1.7 mol dm^{-3} but weaker than 4 mol dm^{-3} should be labelled IRRITANT. **Flash point:** 43 °C. **Dangerous with:** CHROMIUM(VI) OXIDE, MANGANATES(VII), NITRIC(V) ACID, PEROXIDES. Violent or explosive reactions may occur. **WEL (mg m^{-3}):** 25 (LTEL), 37 (STEL).	
Store: CLa On cold days, the liquid solidifies. The melting point is 17 °C.		**Disposal:** W1, W4 or W7 W4 Use a fume cupboard. W7 Dilute to less than 0.1 mol dm^{-3} and pour the solution down a foul-water drain.	

Ethanoic acid, methanoic acid and their salts

User	Control measures	Experimental points
Y7	Wear eye protection. Do not inhale the vapours.	Solutions less than 4 mol dm^{-3} ethanoic acid are suitable

Figure 3 Check you chose the correct information from a Hazcard

- Carefully follow the practical instructions. You should make sure that you record any changes you may make to the procedure or if you need to repeat any procedures in order to confirm your results. Always take care when completing the actual practical work as it is important to obtain accurate results.
- Ask your tutor or assessor to record evidence that you have actually carried out the practical work.
- Record all relevant observations or measurements. It is essential that you record the results of your experimental work in a form that can be easily understood by others. If you use a table check that the columns and rows are suitably labelled and don't forget to include: UNITS, and check you record numerical values using CORRECT SIGNIFICANT FIGURES.
- Process any data you may have collected. This may mean you need to plot a graph (refer to page 22) or carry out a number of calculations. You need to make sure you clearly indicate what you have found out from your experimental work. If you have drawn a graph clearly indicate why you have done it and what it shows. If you carried out calculations clearly state the answer, again don't forget UNITS and SIGNIFICANT FIGURES.
- You may need to evaluate your experimental work (refer to spread 8.1.4 for more detail).

Assessment tip

Remember do not quote an answer to more significant figures than can be measured by the instruments or apparatus used.

Assessment tip

When writing an evaluation:
- make a positive statement about your evidence
- include reason for repeats
- comment about errors
- comment about the processing
- suggestions for improvement
- explain why your suggestions could produce better evidence.

This is to confirm that

Has completed practical ________________ *using a risk assessment.*

In addition the following work has been completed:

Risk assessment individually developed and produced

Research into the vocational link of this practical exercise

All work has been carried out safely

All equipment has been used to the appropriate degree of accuracy

Marks Awarded

________________ ________________

Signature *Date*

Figure 4 A certificate of this type could be included in your portfolio – always check you have evidence that you have completed the practical

③ The importance of health and safety when working

By the end of this spread, you should be able to:

✱ understand the importance of health and safety
✱ recognise hazards and risks

Why is health and safety Important?

Every employer and educational provider needs to make sure that all employees, students and pupils work in a safe environment. The **Health and Safety at Work Act** must be followed by both employees and employers. It was set up, and is now supported by, the Health and Safety Commission and the Health and Safety Executive. It was introduced for protection against risks to health or safety in connection with the activities of persons at work, for controlling the keeping and using of dangerous substances, and for controlling harmful emissions into the atmosphere. Both in education and in the workplace, health and safety regulations must always be followed.

Recognising hazards and risks

It is important that before any experimental work, whether it is carried out in a college or school laboratory or scientific organisation, students and employees complete and more importantly use **risk** assessments. Before a risk assessment is completed, all **hazards** involved need to be identified.

Chemical hazards

It is important that when handling chemicals the hazards signs are recognised so the associated risks can be reduced. Remember to note the concentration when using solutions, this does affect the hazard.

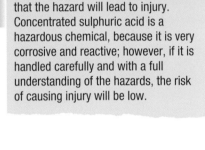

Figure 1 Technician working safely wearing appropriate protective clothing and goggles

Hazard		Risk	Precautions to reduce risk
Flammable		Could catch fire	Keep away from sources of ignition
Corrosive		Can cause chemical burns	Wear protective clothing to avoid contact with skin and eyes Provide good ventilation
Irritant		Can cause skin, eye or respiratory system irritation	Wear protective clothing to avoid contact with skin and eyes
Harmful		May cause harm through skin contact, inhalation of fumes or ingestion	Avoid skin and eye contact Wear gloves or wash hands after use Avoid breathing fumes
Toxic		May cause serious health risks if inhaled, swallowed or penetrates skin	Use in fume cupboard and wear protective clothing Wash hands after use
Oxidising		Produces heat on reaction with other materials and creates a fire risk in contact with flammable or combustible materials	Avoid contact with combustible materials Observe recommendations for storage and use

Table 1 Chemical hazards

Biological hazards

It is important than when biological hazards are encountered the appropriate precautions are taken. These hazards can include bacterial cultures, blood samples and toxic organisms.

Portfolio skills

Hazard		Risk	Precautions to reduce risk
Biohazard		Serious risk to health if inhaled, ingested or penetrates the skin Disease causing organisms – pathogens	Wear protective clothing, avoid contact with skin and respiratory system Wash hands and disinfect any surfaces Ensure safe disposal of any microorganisms

Table 2 Biological hazards

Physical hazards

These may be encountered in the workplace and include working conditions: temperature, lone working, excessive working hours, vibration, and noise. Employers are responsible to ensure that all employees work in safe conditions and the Health and Safety at Work Act is followed. Workers using radioactive sources need to be fully aware of risks and methods to reduce these. All workers who are using radioactive sources daily need to wear badges to monitor the cumulative exposure.

Hazard		Risk	Precautions to reduce risk
Radioactive		Ionising radiation present	Avoid exposure Monitor where appropriate
Dangerous voltage		Risk of electric shock	Follow instructions on use of equipment Check equipment has been suitably tested before use

Table 3 Physical hazards

Supporting safe working in science laboratories

All laboratories have laboratory safety rules. Before you begin any practical work make sure you have a copy of the safety rules for the laboratory you are working in. Accidents, injuries or fires can happen if the correct procedures are not followed. Always work safely.

Experimental work using	What may happen	What to do to reduce risk and be safe
Chemicals	Skin contact – causing irritation, burns, allergic reaction Inhalation of fumes	Check hazards of all chemicals before use and be aware what to do to reduce risk Always wear appropriate protective clothing and goggles Use a fume cupboard when working with toxic chemicals Report any spillages Always follow correct procedures and use stated quantities Smell and test gases with caution Dispose of materials safely after use Clean surfaces after use Keep goggles on when tidying up Wash hands after completing experimental work
Glassware	Cuts due to broken glass Damage caused if dropped or incorrectly heated	Take care when using all glassware, do not put on the edge of the bench – especially thermometers Put all test tubes in racks and other glassware clamp or secure Never clamp glassware too tightly Never use a flame to heat a liquid above its level in the flask Always dispose in glass/sharps containers – not in ordinary bins
Heat	Burns Fire – hair, clothes Scalds	Use correct procedures when heating Flammable liquids – use a water bath or a heating mantle – do not use naked flame When using a Bunsen burner – leave on yellow flame when not in use or turn it off
Electricity	Electric shock Fire	Work safely Do not have wet hands when using electrical equipment or water on your bench Do not use equipment that has not been tested and always check for any broken plugs or broken insulation Check circuits with your supervisor/tutor before you make any connections

Table 4 Safe practice in the laboratory

Current fire extinguisher colour codes

	Water	Powder
USE	Paper, wood, textiles and solid materials fires	Liquid, electrical wood, paper & textile fires
DON'T USE	Liquid, electrical or metal fires	Metal fires

Do not hold horn when operating

	AFFF Foam	Carbon dioxide (CO_2)
USE	Liquid, paper, wood, and textile fires	Liquid and Electrical fires
DON'T USE	Electrical or metal fires	Metal fires

Figure 2 Fire extinguishers in common use – and when to use them

(4) Risk assessments

By the end of this spread, you should be able to:

* ✱ **know what is needed for a risk assessment**
* ✱ **use COSHH data and Hazcards to support risk assessments**

Case study

Accidents and ill health can ruin lives and affect businesses if output is lost or machinery is damaged. In such cases insurance costs increase or cases go to court and businesses can be closed. All employees are legally required to assess the risks in a workplace and ensure a plan is put in place to control the risks.

Why carry out a risk assessment?

Laboratory work may involve you in exposure to chemical, biological or physical hazards. It is important that your working environment is safe in order to protect your health and the health of your colleagues. A risk assessment is a careful review of what in your work could cause you or your colleagues harm. It is essential that you use a risk assessment form and record the information before you carry out any experimental work. The risk assessment information must then be followed during your practical.

Risk assessment

It is advisable to record your risk assessment in a suitable format. There are many different ways, here is one suggestion.

Figure 1 Safe working is important

Risk assessment
Hazard substance (include name and hazard symbol). Also include equipment used
Associated risk
Control measures/safety precautions to reduce risk
Additional information: Be aware: Keep informed: Be responsible and safe What to do in case of accidents

Cuts and burns Get first aid Seek further medical help if required	Fire Sound alarm Evacuate area	Breakage/spillage Follow safe/set procedures Use special bin for disposal Use spillage kit

If contact with hazardous substances occurs: Eyes and skin – wash immediately Inhalation – remove to fresh air Ingestion – do not induce vomiting – seek medical help
When working with microorganisms, in order to prevent the accidental contamination of laboratory cultures or employees/students Aseptic techniques must be used when cells are cultured or used Strict hygiene is needed: wash hands, disinfect work surfaces, cover cuts, as pathogens may be present in cultures. Autoclave unopened cultures

Table 1 Recording risk assessment

Material used or procedure carried out	Hazard involved	What may happen	Safety precautions used	What to do if accident happens	Overall risk Low Medium High

Table 2 Another design for a risk assessment

Use of COSHH data to support risk assessments

COSHH guidelines state that risk assessments arising from the use of hazardous substances must be completed before such substances are used. Measures must be in place to control or prevent the use of hazardous substances.

Why COSHH matters

Using chemicals or other hazardous substances at work can put people's health at risk, so the law requires employers to control exposure to hazardous substances to prevent ill health. They have to protect both employees and others who may be exposed by complying with the Control of Substances Hazardous to Health Regulations 2002 (COSHH).

When you are putting together your risk assessment on the use of hazardous substances you should follow the following guidelines:

- Assess the risks from any hazardous substances you may use.
- Decide what precautions need to be taken.
- Check you are allowed to use the chemicals required for you practical work.
- Ensure that the control measures are used.
- Prepare plans and procedures to deal with accidents, incidents and emergencies.
- Ensure that you are taught how to use equipment and substances used in all your practical activities.

In industry it is important that that exposure to hazardous substances is adequately controlled and monitored. It is also important that where workers are exposed to substances that could be harmful to health they have the appropriate health checks by qualified medical professionals. In schools and colleges it should not be necessary for such substances which are harmful to health to be used.

Use of Hazcards

Individual Hazcards may be available for you to use when putting together your risk assessment. They are very detailed and you need to be able to extract the required information for your practical.

Barium chloride-2-water		$BaCl_2.2H_2O$
Toxic		R25: Toxic if swallowed. R20: Harmful by inhalation. Solutions equal to or stronger than 1 mol dm^{-3} should be labelled TOXIC. Solutions equal to or stronger than 0.1 mol dm^{-3} but weaker than 1 mol dm^{-3} should be labelled HARMFUL. **WEL (mg m^{-3}):** 0.5 (LTEL) 1.5 (STEL) as barium.
Store: T		Disposal: W1, W7, Wspec W7: Dilute to 0.05 mol dm^{-3} before pouring the solution down a foul-water drain. Wspec: Dissolve in water, add sodium magnesium sulfate(VI) solution to precipitate barium sulfate(VI). Filter the barium sulfate(VI) for disposal in normal refuse. Pour the filtrate down a foul-water drain.

Formula of the hydrated chloride	Wear eye protection.	The boiling point of anhydrous barium chloride is 1560 °C. This is much higher than the temperature of the Bunsen-burner flame, so the amount of toxic material in the atmosphere is negligible. Roast the hydrated chloride until all the water is lost. Allow the hot apparatus to cool before reweighing.

Figure 2 Hazcard showing detailed information

Assessment tip

To support your risk assessment:
- Check you have a copy of the laboratory safety rules used in your college or school.
- Check you are aware of the fire procedures and what to do in case of accidents.
  Relevant information can be extracted and used in your risk assessment.

Sources

You can find more on health and safety if you refer to these weblinks:
Health and Safety Executive
Fire Kills
Fire Extinguisher Website
CLEAPSS

Activity

A risk assessment needs to be carried out before a forensic analyst can begin her work. She has been presented with three samples to analyse:

Sample 1: R2341 is a blood sample taken from a suspect involved in a drunken driving charge.

Sample 2: S2342 is an unknown substance possibly a class A drug.

Sample 3: T2343 contains a number of fibres taken from the fingernails of a victim of violent behaviour.

Discuss what the forensic scientist needs to do before beginning her analysis in order to ensure a safe working environment.

Practical techniques used in chemical analysis – 1

By the end of this spread, you should be able to:

✱ **know how to carry out some basic techniques in qualitative analysis**

✱ **analyse results to reach suitable conclusions**

Qualitative analysis

Scientists working in analytical work not only have to follow standard procedures but they also need to be able to use their chemical and biological knowledge to determine what analytical tests need to be carried out, as well as analysing the results. Analysts will work on a wide range of samples ranging from those taken out in the field and tested for environmental reasons to samples prepared in the lab or taken from major production lines, e.g. quality control testing in the manufacture of pharmaceuticals. In addition samples collected from people very often are needed for diagnostic purposes or possibly for forensic analysis.

Tests which you need to be aware of include:

- tests for **organic** functional groups
- tests for **inorganic** compounds – including anion and cation tests
- biochemical tests – details of these tests can be found in Unit 4 Cells and Molecules.

Practical information when testing for organic functional groups:

- Complete a risk assessment before you begin.
- Remember when heating flammable organic compounds to use a water bath (Figure 1).

Key definitions

Organic compounds contain carbon.

Inorganic compounds are not carbon based – except carbon monoxide, carbon dioxide and carbonates.

Assessment tip

Remember each **homologous series** or group of organic compounds has its own functional group:
- alcohols –OH
- aldehydes and ketones –C=O
- carboxylic acids –COOH
- alkenes –C=C–

Testing for	Test	Result
–OH (alcohols) e.g. ethanol	To the organic compound add a few drops of acidified potassium dichromate and warm	Colour change orange to green
–CHO –C=O (aldehydes and ketones) e.g. ethanal, propanone	Add 2,4-dinitrophenyl hydrazine and then a few drops of the organic compound under test	Yellow/orange precipitate
If you need to distinguish between aldehydes and ketones you may need to carry out a further test: warm sample with Fehlings A and B solution – aldehydes form an orange-red precipitate.		
–COOH (carboxylic acids) e.g. ethanoic acid	To the organic compound add sodium carbonate solution or solid and test any gas evolved using limewater	Carbon dioxide gas evolved which turns limewater milky
–C=C– (alkenes) e.g. ethene	To the organic compound add a few drops of bromine water. Shake	Colour change orange to colourless

Table 1 Testing for chemical groups

Following your practical work you should be able to determine the functional groups present in the unknown organic compounds. Full identification may need further analysis. Scientific analysts in industry and in universities not only carry out practical tests on unknown samples but use spectroscopic analysis to determine the full structure of organic compounds.

Practical information when testing for inorganic compounds:

- Complete a risk assessment before you begin – take extra care when using concentrated acids – wear eye protection at all times.
- Make sure if you are testing for the presence of a precipitate you make up a solution of your unknown compound – check it has fully dissolved.

Heating in a water bath

Figure 1 Testing for organic functional groups

- Tests are usually carried out in test tubes; however sometimes if you need to heat a boiling tube is used (check tube is Pyrex – soda glass tubes may crack when strongly heated).

Tests to identify positive ions	Result	Inference
Carry out a flame test	Flame shows a distinctive colour	
Clean a nichrome wire in a hot flame	Yellow	Sodium
Place wire in hydrochloric acid (if concentrated acid used – take extra care!!)	Lilac (still visible if observed through blue glass)	Potassium
Put wire in sample and then in flame	Brick red	Calcium
See Figure 3	Apple green	Barium
	Green	Copper
Use of sodium hydroxide solution		
To a few cm³ of the unknown solution in a test tube add a few drops of dilute sodium hydroxide solution	Blue precipitate	Copper
	White precipitate	Calcium/zinc
Observe the colour of the precipitate	Green precipitate	Iron(II)
	Brown precipitate	Iron(III)
	No precipitate	Sodium/potassium/barium
Sometimes it may be necessary to carry out both a flame test and sodium hydroxide test to determine the cation		

Table 2 Flame testing for positive ions

Tests to identify negative ions	Result	Inference
Test for carbonate or hydrogen carbonate	Carbon dioxide gas evolved which turns limewater milky	Carbonate or hydrogen carbonate present CO_3^{2-} or HCO_3^-
Add dilute hydrochloric acid to sample and warm if no reaction. Test any gas using limewater		$\underset{(aq)}{2H^+} + \underset{(aq)}{CO_3^{2-}} \rightarrow \underset{(g)}{H_2O} + \underset{(g)}{CO_2}$
Test for halides	White precipitate soluble in dilute ammonia solution	Chloride Cl^-
Make a solution of sample using distilled water	Cream precipitate soluble in concentrated ammonia solution	Bromide Br^-
Acidify with dilute nitric acid		
Add a few drops of silver nitrate solution	Yellow precipitate insoluble in ammonia solution	Iodide I^-
If a precipitate forms add ammonia solution (refer to results)		$\underset{(aq)}{Ag^+} + \underset{(aq)}{X^-} \rightarrow \underset{(s)}{AgX}$
Test for sulfate	White precipitate	Sulfate SO_4^{2-}
Make a solution of sample using distilled water		$\underset{(aq)}{Ba^{2+}} + \underset{(aq)}{SO_4^{2-}} \rightarrow \underset{(s)}{BaSO_4}$
Acidifiy with nitric acid		
Add a few drops of barium chloride solution		
Test for nitrate	Brown ring appears where the two layers meet	Nitrate NO_3^-
Make a solution of sample using distilled water		
Add an equal volume of iron(II) sulfate solution then carefully pour concentrated sulfuric acid down the side of the tube		

Table 3 Tests for negative ions

Key definitions

An **inorganic** compound is made up of a positive ion (**cation**) and negative ions (**anions**). In order to identify the compound fully both cations and anions need to be identified.

Assessment tip

Remember whenever you are identifying unknown samples always consider them to be harmful. Never use the same spatula to take samples from different unknowns and always use clean test tubes or nichrome wire (for flame tests).

It may also be useful to repeat tests for confirmation. The presence of sodium can easily contaminate a flame test – so watch out if your flame tests are orange/yellow.

Activity

A technician needed to confirm the presence of:
- sodium carbonate
- potassium chloride
- iron(II) sulfate.

The chemicals were to be given to some new students. Discuss what tests he would need to carry out and what results he would expect.

Portfolio skills

⑥ Practical techniques used in chemical analysis – 2

By the end of this spread, you should be able to:

✳ **know how to carry out some basic techniques in quantitative analysis**
✳ **know the process and record the results obtained**

Quantitative analysis

Quantitative analysis is used in determining *how much* active ingredient or unknown is present in a sample. **Volumetric analysis** is a useful tool to any analytical scientist and these methods can be very accurate. There are two procedures that you need to be aware of: the preparation of a **standard solution** and performing a **titration**.

Preparation of a standard solution

In order to carry out this procedure you will need the following equipment: weighing pot; accurate balance; spatula; volumetric flask and funnel. There are two classes of volumetric flask available depending on the precision required (this is marked on the glassware). Class A measures volume ± 0.06%; Class B ± 0.08%. In addition you will need your sample and distilled water.

A suggested method:
* First weigh a weighing pot and record the mass (this can be a rough weighing).
* Add the approximate mass of the sample to the pot and record weight (this is an accurate weighing).
* Using a funnel carefully tip the sample into the volumetric flask (reweigh the pot with the sample removed: this is an accurate weighing).
* Dissolve the sample in the volumetric flask using sufficient distilled water in order for the sample to dissolve and shake thoroughly.
* Using distilled water make up the solution to the graduation mark on the volumetric flask.
* Remember when you are near to the mark add the distilled water drop by drop.
* Ensure you shake the standard solution thoroughly (check the stopper is in place and invert several times, don't forget to hold the stopper in place).

Key definition

A **standard solution** is one in which the concentration is accurately known.

The concentration of a given solution is the amount of solute per 1 dm^3 of solution.

Units of concentration: $g\ dm^{-3}$; $mol\ dm^{-3}$

In these solutions the solute will be the sample and the solvent distilled water.

A **titration** is a common laboratory method of quantitative analysis used to accurately find the concentration of a solution.

Assessment tip

Please remember before you *begin* any practical activity:
* Write a suitable risk assessment (refer to spread P.1.4).
* Collect together all the equipment you need before you begin.
* Draw out suitable tables in order to record your results and complete these during the practical.

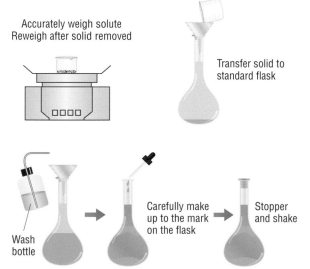

Accurately weigh solute
Reweigh after solid removed

Transfer solid to standard flask

Wash bottle

Carefully make up to the mark on the flask

Stopper and shake

Figure 1 Preparation of a standard solution

Mass of weighing pot + sample	2.432 g
Mass of weighing pot with sample removed	2.041 g
Mass of sample	0.391 g

Figure 2 Table showing examples of recorded weighings to the appropriate degree of accuracy

Solutions you will prepare in the laboratory are usually made in 100 cm³ or 250 cm³ volumetric flasks. As concentrations are given in mol dm⁻³ you will need to work out how much sample is needed for 1000 cm³ (1 dm³).

WORKED EXAMPLE

Calculate the concentration in mol dm⁻³ of a solution of Na_2CO_3 if 2.562 g were made up to a solution of 250 cm³ in a volumetric flask.

A_r values: Na is 23.0; C is 12.0; O is 16.0

Work out the molar mass M (Na_2CO_3) = (23.0 × 2) + 12.0 + (16.0 × 3) = 106.0

Calculate using $n = \dfrac{m}{M}$

The amount in mol n = 2.562 ÷ 106.0 = 0.0242 (this is the amount in 250 cm³)

Calculate the concentration in mol dm⁻³ = 0.0242 × (1000 ÷ 250) = 0.968 mol dm⁻³

Instructions to carry out a titration

In order to carry out this procedure you will need: burette and stand, white tile, pipette, a number of conical flasks, funnel, small (100 cm³) beaker. In addition you will need the samples to be analysed, a standard solution and a suitable indicator.

Remember that before you carry out a titration you need to check all your equipment is clean by washing it carefully with distilled water. The burette and pipette need to be rinsed with the solutions that will be put in them but the conical flasks must only be washed with distilled water.

- Using a funnel fill the burette with a solution of known concentration – check that the end of the burette has solution in it and record the volume of solution in the burette.
- Using a pipette fitted with a safety filler, transfer a fixed volume (an aliquot) of the solution to be analysed in to a conical flask – allow the solution to run out of the pipette and then just touch the pipette on the base of the conical flask. If required add a few drops of a suitable indicator.
- Titrate the aliquot with the solution of known concentration from the burette – make sure you record the initial reading of the solution in the burette before you begin. You need to add the solution until the indicator just changes colour – this is the end point for the titration. The first titration is a rough titration. It is usual to repeat the titrations until **concordant** results are obtained.
- When carrying out a titration it is usual to add the solution 1 cm³ at a time until you reach about 1–2 cm³ from the end point. The solution is then added drop by drop until the indicator changes colour.
- You will need to repeat the titration until concordant results are obtained.

Assessment tip

Scientists use the mole (mol) as a useful way of expressing amounts of chemical substances. To calculate concentrations of standard solutions the mass (g) needs to be converted to mol. In order to do this use

amount in mol $n = \dfrac{mass\ m}{molar\ mass\ M}$

Assessment tip

Molar mass M can be found by adding all the relative atomic masses for each atom in the formula.

M (H_2SO_4) = (1.0 × 2) + 32.0 + (16.0 × 4) = 98 g mol⁻¹

Key definitions

Concordant results are those which are within 0.2 cm³ of each other.

Assessment tip

Acid-base titrations and redox titrations are just two common ways of finding concentrations of unknown substances. You will probably use acid-base titrations for AS work and redox for A2.

Sources

Microbiology online

Richland College

WORKED EXAMPLE

Calculate the concentration in mol dm⁻³ of a solution of vinegar if 23.55 cm³ reacted with 24.00 cm³ of 0.0505 mol dm⁻³ sodium hydroxide solution. There are many ways to complete this calculation. This is just one way.

The ionic equation $H^+_{(aq)} + OH^-_{(aq)} \rightarrow H_2O_{(l)}$ shows the ratio of the reactants

It is possible to use $C_{acid} \times V_{acid} = C_{alkali} \times V_{alkali}$

Rearranging this equation allows you to calculate the unknown concentration

$C_{acid} = \dfrac{24.00 \times 0.0505}{23.55} = 0.0515$ mol dm⁻³

Volume of vinegar	Rough (1)	Accurate (2)	Accurate (3)
Final reading/cm³	23.90	23.60	24.00
Initial reading/cm³	0.10	0.00	0.50
Volume used/cm³	23.80	23.60	23.50
Indicate if used in mean	No	Yes	Yes

Figure 3 Table showing accurate recording of titration result

Portfolio skills

Case study

In 1856 an 18-year-old chemistry research student, William Perkin, was trying to discover how to synthesise quinine, a cure for malaria. His preparation did not work but instead he produced the first synthetic dye. This was a solution which produced an intense purple colour and successfully dyed silk. Perkin patented his dyes which became an instant commercial success. He retired at 35 and just spent his time researching.

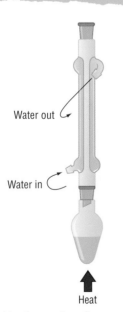

Figure 1 Purple dye

Assessment tip

Remember in a chemical reaction

Reactants → products

By the end of this spread, you should be able to:

✳ **know what techniques are used to prepare organic compounds in the laboratory under safe conditions**

✳ **know what methods are used to assess the purity of organic compounds**

Many organic compounds are manufactured to meet demand in chemical and pharmaceutical industries. Chemists today use their scientific knowledge of preparative techniques and computer aided molecule design to prepare selected compounds in the lab before they are produced on a large scale.

When planning a preparation:

• Knowledge of the chemical reactions needed to prepare the product is required.
• Quantities of reagents – these can be calculated from the reaction.
• Health and safety requirements, risk assessment information (see spread P.1.4).
• Suitable apparatus and techniques needed for preparation and purification.

Organic preparations involve covalent compounds. Reactions are often slow because covalent bonds need to be broken and these are strong. In order to increase the rates of reaction higher temperatures are usually needed. A technique called refluxing is often used in preparing organic compounds. Heating under reflux allows reactions to take place without loss of volatile reagents or products (Figure 2).

Simple distillation is a method that can be used to separate miscible liquids with different boiling points. It is commonly used in organic preparations as a method of collecting the main product from un-reacted reagents (Figure 3).

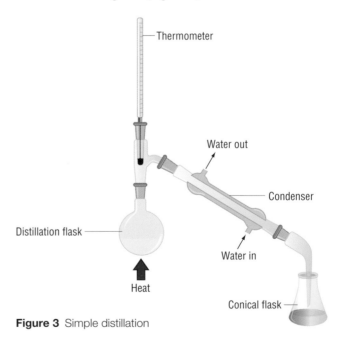

Figure 3 Simple distillation

Figure 2 Heating under reflux

Procedure that can be used for refluxing or distillation

• The liquid reagents need to be placed in a round bottomed or pear shaped flask with a few anti-bumping granules (these are used to encourage smooth boiling).
• Heat is applied until the liquid begins to boil. Check that the correct method of heating is used.

- In the process of refluxing the vapours condense in the condenser and return to the reaction mixture to enable the reaction to take place.
- In distillation when the liquid begins to boil the vapour condenses in the condenser and will be collected in a separate flask. If the main product to be collected boils e.g. at 60 °C there may be small fractions boiling at below and above this value. These need to be collected in a separate collecting vessel and discarded.

Purification techniques – recrystallisation

It is usually necessary when preparing solids to recrystallise. This will ensure that the product is pure.

Before you carry out a **recrystallisation** procedure you need to choose a suitable solvent. The solid to be recrystallised needs to be soluble in hot solvent and insoluble when the solvent is cold.

- Place solid in a conical flask with a small quantity of hot solvent.
- Add warm solvent and continue heating until all solid has dissolved. You are aiming to dissolve your solid in the minimum of solvent. Remember also to check the correct heating method is being used!!
- If there are any insoluble impure particles, you need to remove these by filtration under reduced pressure – tip keep your apparatus warm to prevent solid crystallising.
- Allow solid to cool – the slower the better; however if your crystals don't appear – don't panic, they will appear but you may have added too much solvent so you will need to evaporate, to remove the excess. You could also try scratching the flask with a glass rod. This sometimes helps.

Testing purity

The purity of a solid is indicated by its melting point. Pure solids have definitive melting points (range of 1–2 °C). Impure solids melt below literature values over a wider range. Figure 4 gives you the apparatus that can be used to find melting point.

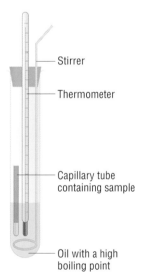

Stirrer

Thermometer

Capillary tube containing sample

Oil with a high boiling point

Figure 4 Melting point apparatus

The purity of a liquid can be indicated by the boiling point. Pure liquids have a boiling point range of 1–2 °C. A distillation apparatus can be used to find the boiling point of a liquid.

Assessment tip

For distillation and refluxing:
- Quickfit glassware is usually used.
- Check ground glass joints fit together tightly.
- Only have flask 1/2 to 2/3 full.
- Heat must not go above level of liquid.

Assessment tip

Methods of heating:
- Bunsen burner and tripod – do not use with flammables.
- Heating mantle and round bottomed flask best to use with organics or flammables.
- Water bath suitable when heating <85 °C

Remember never to heat a mixture in a sealed apparatus.

Definition

Recrystallisation is the process of obtaining pure crystals from an impure sample.

⑧ Practical techniques used in biological work

By the end of this spread, you should be able to:

✱ **know how to carry out some basic techniques to support microscopy and microbiology**

Please remember when you are carrying out any investigative work:
- Check you know the aim of your task.
- Use and follow a suitable risk assessment – especially if you are using microorganisms!!
- Label your equipment and samples wherever necessary.
- Record and label relevant observations and measurements.
- Process your results and evaluate the outcomes.

Using a microscope and preparing a slide

More detailed information on microscopy work can be found in Unit 4. You may want to look at this in addition. You will need to familiarise yourself with the microscope you will be using. Information guidance:
- The eyepiece lens is used to *focus* the specimen or slice of biological material.
- The objective lens produces a *magnified* but inverted image.
- The resolution is the amount of *detail* you see.

If you need to accurately measure specimens you will need to use a microscope graticule. This can give a precision of measurement of 0.5 µm (refer to Unit 4 for more detail).

Slide preparation

Specimens can be living or dead. However the samples need to be attached to a glass microscope slide for observation. Preparation of a temporary slide involves:
- placing a drop of water on the slide, followed by the specimen to be viewed
- lowering a coverslip slowly to avoid air pockets, using tweezers
- absorbing any excess water with filter paper.

A lot of biological matter is not coloured. Stains can be applied to colour cells, tissues, components or metabolic processes. Staining involves:
- immersing the sample in a dye solution
- rinsing and then observing the sample under a microscope.

(Some dyes involve the use of a mordant which is a chemical compound that reacts with the stain to form an insoluble coloured precipitate. The mordant stain remains on the sample and the excess dye solution is then washed away.)

Some common stains include:
- Methylene blue used to stain animal cells to make the nuclei more visible.
- Iodine used as a starch indicator. When in solution starch and iodine turn a dark blue colour.

Biotechnology and techniques used to support work involving microorganisms

Industrially the use of microbes (bacteria and fungi) is used to produce all kinds of fermented foods and drinks, as well as drugs such as antibiotics. Enzymes that break down biological

Key definition

Magnification =
Objective lens × Eyepiece lens

The maximum magnification of most light microscopes is ×1500.

Resolving power is the smallest separation at which two separate objects can be distinguished. The maximum resolving power for a light microscope is 200 nm. This means that anything closer than 200 nm is seen as one point.

Assessment tip

Microscopy and aseptic technique can be used to support work involving:
- cell growth
- microorganisms
- forensic investigations
- effect of disinfectants and antiseptics
- food industry; soy sauce, yogurts, cheese, mycoprotein
- sewage industry and sources of waste.

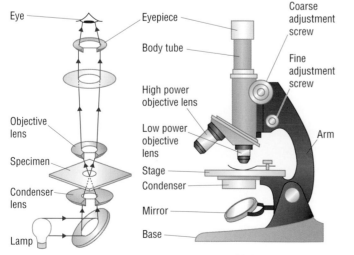

Figure 1 Light microscope showing lenses and light paths

materials are used to produce biological washing powders or can be used to produce a stone washed effect in jeans. Phytase breaks down phosphorus compounds in plants and can be used as an animal feed supplement. Pectinase enzymes are also commonly used in food processing. Pectin, a natural product found in the cell wall of plants, as well as its use in the food industry, is now used in cosmetics where natural ingredients are more and more appreciated by the consumer.

Aseptic technique refers to a procedure that is performed under sterile conditions. In medical terms it refers to practices that help reduce the risk to patients of post-procedure infections. It is achieved by removing or killing all microorganisms from hands and objects and ensuring only sterile equipment and fluids are used during invasive medical procedures. Microbiologists need to use aseptic techniques to prevent microbiological contamination of themselves, which may result in infection or contamination of their working environment or the samples they are analysing.

Aseptic techniques

When you begin your task you need to disinfect your working space and remember that while you are working minimise the time that the bacteria are exposed to the air by keeping tops on all vessels and using flames to kill any bacteria that might enter any of the equipment you may be using.

You may need to carry out the following tasks:

1 Making agar plates – it is important to flame the neck of the bottle containing the molten agar and keep the lid of the Petri dish close to the base and replace it as quickly as possible. Also allow these time to set before you continue.

2 Introducing the bacteria to the agar plates: inoculation – see the sketches in Figure 2.

3 Incubation of the Petri dishes – the Petri dishes need to be sealed, labelled, inverted and incubated. Cultures are usually examined after 24 hours' incubation. The bacteria will be visible as distinct circular colonies.

You may want to extend the practical work you do to:

• Find out the number of viable microorganisms in a fixed amount of liquid, e.g. milk, yeast suspensions or water. A number of serial dilutions could be performed. The number of colonies counted and recorded.

• Test individual bacterial strains against a variety of antibiotics or antiseptics by growing the bacteria as 'lawns' on agar.

Assessment tip

Remember antiseptics are designed to be used for reducing or destroying microorganisms on the skin. They are not used to disinfect objects!!

INOCULATION
If using a broth culture or other liquid source

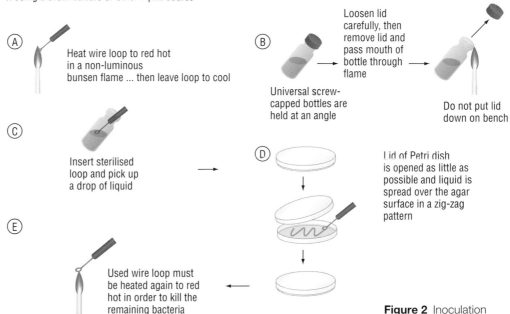

Ⓐ Heat wire loop to red hot in a non-luminous bunsen flame ... then leave loop to cool

Ⓒ Insert sterilised loop and pick up a drop of liquid

Ⓔ Used wire loop must be heated again to red hot in order to kill the remaining bacteria

Ⓑ Loosen lid carefully, then remove lid and pass mouth of bottle through flame

Universal screw-capped bottles are held at an angle

Do not put lid down on bench

Ⓓ Lid of Petri dish is opened as little as possible and liquid is spread over the agar surface in a zig-zag pattern

Figure 2 Inoculation

Case study

Infection by MRSA (methicillin resistant staphylococcus aureus) bacteria is increasingly common in hospitals and there are now cases of bugs which are even showing resistance to vancomycin, an antibiotic traditionally regarded as the 'last line of defence'. A statement was made 'if we get widespread resistance to vancomycin, we will be back to the pre-penicillin era!'

However, maggots might be the answer. Researchers have now evidence that maggots have been able to clear up MRSA from a number of sufferers. It is not fully understood how, although it is thought that they produce chemical enzymes that break up the dead tissue. Maggots were used for medicinal purposes at the beginning of the twentieth century. Now with the rise in antibiotic resistant infections research in this field has started again.

Practical techniques – monitoring and measuring

By the end of this spread, you should be able to:

✳ **know what to do in monitoring human response**
✳ **know how to use some precision instruments and use them in basic techniques**

Sports science and health

Qualified sports and exercise scientists can expect to have a broad technical, physiological, psychological and scientific knowledge. They need to monitor behaviour and fitness and also use precision instruments.

There are a vast range of career opportunities in this field and the British Association of Sport and Exercise Science (BASES) is an association which promotes science within sport and exercise.

You may be expected to carry out monitoring techniques on fellow students or other people. Please remember when you are carrying out any monitoring or testing techniques to:

- check you know how long the task will take
- know how often you need to take readings or monitor progress
- ensure the people involved in the testing have completed suitable risk assessments (see spread P.1.4)
- check you record dates, times and units
- check for repeats – if possible
- process your results and evaluate the outcomes.

Precision instruments

The accuracy and precision of any measurement depend upon the instruments used.

Rulers may be suitable to measure height but vernier callipers, a micrometer screw gauge and a travelling microscope can be used for much more precise measurements. You may be looking at cell structure or measuring the width of strings used in racquets. It is important to use the correct instrument. Vernier callipers measure the nearest 0.1 mm.

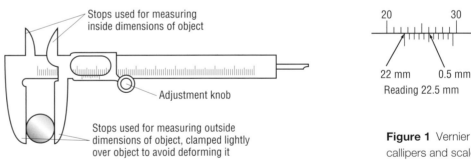

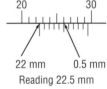

Figure 1 Vernier callipers and scale

The reading of the 0 on the vernier scale gives the approximate distance between the jaws (22 mm). In order to make the reading more precise, look where the mark on the vernier lines up with the line on the main scale (0.5 mm). This makes the final reading 22.5 mm.

A travelling microscope can be used to measure very small lengths. This uses a vernier scale. The diameter of a glass capillary tube could be measured using this instrument.

A micrometer screw gauge is a sensitive instrument useful in measuring diameters of wires, threads. It will measure to the nearest 0.01 mm. You may find it useful to look at one of these instruments. A ratchet in the instruments prevents over-tightening. An accurately threaded screw is rotated until the object to be measured is securely held. Look at the reading on Figure 2. The drum is graduated into 50 divisions each division representing 0.01. The reading is 5.5 + 22 from the moving scale, giving a final reading of 5.72 mm.

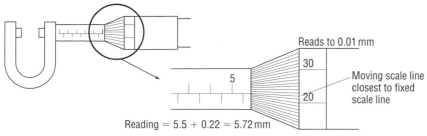

Reads to 0.01 mm

Moving scale line closest to fixed scale line

Reading = 5.5 + 0.22 = 5.72 mm

Figure 2 Micrometer screw gauge and scale

Engineers and material scientists increasingly need to test new products in order to check they are fit for purpose. Steel ropes which support a suspension bridge need to be able to support the variable loads, whereas strings in a racquet need to have suitable elasticity. Knowing values of **Young's modulus** for different materials allows a sufficiently stiff material to be chosen for its use.

Experiment to find the Young's modulus

A simple wire-stretching experiment is shown in Figure 3.

Carry out a risk assessment. This should include assessing the maximum mass that can be safely suspended from the wire, and precautions to avoid being cut in case it should accidentally break.

Clamp a long, thin copper wire held firmly at one end of a bench. Pass the wire over a pulley.

Tie a hanger weight on this end. Make sure that the hanger is just heavy enough to keep the wire taut.

To measure the extension of the wire, *either*: attach a marker to the wire and fix a ruler in position below as shown. *Or*, better, because the extension is very small, use a vernier scale.

Measure the length, *l,* from the clamp to the marker or vernier scale with a simple rule or tape.

Measure the diameter, *d,* with a micrometer.

Increase the mass *m* in 0.05 kg steps up to the maximum safe mass.

You need to record all your readings in suitable formats.

For each mass record the position of the marker or reading of the vernier scale in a table and add columns for extension (i.e. ruler/vernier reading – reading with just the original mass hanger) and the force in N.

In order to calculate Young's modulus you will need to carry out both straightforward and complex calculations.

1 Using the formula $A = \pi\left(\dfrac{d}{2}\right)^2$

Calculate the cross-sectional area of the wire.

Using Young's modulus $E = \dfrac{\text{tensile stress}}{\text{tensile strain}}$

$\text{tensile stress} = \dfrac{\text{tensile force}}{\text{cross-sectional area}}$

$\text{tensile strain} = \dfrac{\text{extension}}{\text{original length}}$

2 Using the values collected in your experiment, plot a graph of force in N against extension in m. You are normally told to plot the dependent variable against the independent variable, but it is normal engineering practice to plot force against extension. This makes subsequent calculations simpler.

The Young's modulus of the sample is given by the gradient of the straight line portion of the graph near the origin. See spread P.1.11 for work on gradients. Find the gradient of the graph.

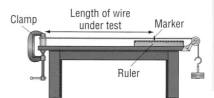

Clamp — Length of wire under test — Marker

Ruler

Figure 3 Wire stretching experiment

Assessment tip

Remember straightforward calculations are substituting numbers in the expressions and calculating the values to the correct significant figures. In complex calculations you need to rearrange, substitute and calculate.

Portfolio skills

Portfolio skills

By the end of this spread, you should be able to:

* **understand the importance of recording accurate data**

It is important that all numerical data is recorded in an internationally accepted way. The convention used by scientists is the SI system (Systeme International d'Unites).

Quantity	Name	Symbol	Quantity	Name	Symbol
Length	metre	m	Electric current	ampere	A
Time	second	s	Amount of substance	mole	mol
Mass	kilogram	kg	Temperature	kelvin	K
Volume	decimetres cubed (litres)	dm^3			

Table 1 Commonly used SI units

Density	kg m^{-3}	Force	newton N	kg m s^{-2}
Concentration	mol dm^{-3}	Energy	joule J	kg m^2 s^{-2}
Velocity	m s^{-1}	Power	watt W	
Acceleration	m s^{-2}			

Table 2 Further units that you may use

As well as units, scientists need to record results *accurately* and to the appropriate *precision*. This is when significant figures are needed as well as prefixes for units. Very often numbers are expressed in standard form and are needed to be given to a stated number of significant figures. Units also need to be quoted with results; if not, values are meaningless.

What does the data mean?

Numerical values can be written in standard form

1000 expressed in standard form is 1×10^3. $10^3 = 10 \times 10 \times 10 = 1000$. $3500 = 3.5 \times 10^3$

0.001 expressed in standard form is 1×10^{-3}. $10^{-3} = 0.1 \times 0.1 \times 0.1 = 0.001$. $0.0035 = 3.5 \times 10^{-3}$

Data can be written:

$1056 \text{ m} = 1.056 \times 10^3 \text{ m} = 1.056 \times 10^6 \text{ mm}$

$0.000065 \text{ dm}^3 = 6.5 \times 10^{-5} \text{ dm}^3 = 6.5 \times 10^{-7} \text{ cm}^3$

Sometimes it is necessary to process data:

$10^2 \times 10^4 = 10^6 = 1\,000\,000$

$10^{-3} \times 10^{-2} = 10^{-5} = 0.00001$

Throughout the varied practical exercises you will perform, it is important that you are aware of the size of the data you record.

Assessment tip

When recording your data check you use the correct symbols:
- Nano   n 10^{-9}
- Micro   μ 10^{-6}
- Milli   m 10^{-3}
- Centi   c 10^{-2}
- Deci   d 10^{-1}
- Kilo   k 10^3
- Mega   M 10^6
- Giga   G 10^9

Nanoscience and Nanotechnology

Nanotechnology probably makes you think of microscopic robots. Although we are not there yet, there are new and exciting developments in this atomic-scale science of nanoparticles. Whereas a human hair is about 80 000 nm, a red blood cell about 700 nm, nanoscience involves research and development on the making and using of structures at an atomic level on a scale of 1–100 nm. Current uses of nanotechnology include:
- sunscreens using microfine and zinc oxide nanoparticles to absorb UV light
- nanomaterials used for thin coatings on self-cleaning windows

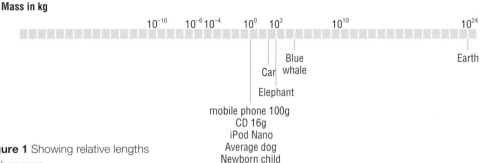

Lengths in m

Diameter of H atom (10^{-10}) · Bacteria (10^{-6}) · Thickness of paper (10^{-4}) · Average height of adult (1.7 m) (10^0) · Electricity pylon (50 m) (10^1 10^2) · Everest (9000 m) (10^4) · 10^7

Mass in kg

10^{-10} 10^{-6} 10^{-4} 10^0 10^3 10^{10} 10^{24}

Car · Blue whale · Earth

Elephant

mobile phone 100g
CD 16g
iPod Nano
Average dog
Newborn child

Figure 1 Showing relative lengths and masses

Figure 2 Nanocomposites used for car bumpers – claimed to be 60% lighter and twice as resistant to scratches and bumps.

Data collection

County analysts and scientific officers provide scientific advice and analytical services. The recording and processing of data is key to enabling accurate and useful decisions to be made. Data collection related to protecting consumers is a major area of research and development, examples include:

- food safety
- environmental protection
- radiation and radioactivity control
- contamination of land and waste disposal.

Collection of data can be done by different methods

- Experimentation by a scientist involves the recording of primary data, measurements and observations. The collection of this data depends on the accuracy of scientists carrying out the work and the precision of the apparatus used. Data is best recorded using tabular format. Volumetric analysis is an example of an experiment using accurate equipment where results can be precisely recorded to four significant figures. Experimental work is usually repeated until results are concordant – within 0.2 cm³ of each other.

	Rough	1	2
Final reading	25.60 cm³	25.60 cm³	25.30 cm³
Initial reading	0.00 cm³	0.50 cm³	0.15 cm³
Volume used	25.60 cm³	25.10 cm³	25.15 cm³
Tick if concordant		✓	✓

Table 3 Repeating results

- Investigative work where the tests are carried out by other people and the scientist records the outcomes. When this data is recorded, information on the sources, the number of participants, the number of tests carried out (and don't forget to do a risk assessment on those taking part in the tests) must all be recorded.
- Collection of samples. The following details should be recorded on collection: date, time, location, habitat details (where appropriate), collecting technique, preservation techniques. This information all needs collating on returning to the laboratory.
- Surveys where information is gathered by using questionnaires: answers need to be collated and presented in a suitable format – may be bar charts, pie charts or in a tabular format.
- Secondary data is that which has been collected or researched by others and which can be reused or processed by a third party.

> **Assessment tip**
>
> When you record your results you need to rember
> - units
> - significant figures
> - need to repeat
> - suitable format – labelled table.

> **Assessment tip**
>
> Remember in any calculation the number of significant figures in the answer must be equal or less than the number of significant figures in the least precise value. If a mean is calculated results need to be quoted to the same number of significant figures measured by the apparatus used in the experiment.
>
> Mean Value $\dfrac{25.10 + 25.15}{2} = 25.13$ cm³
>
> Not
>
> 25.125 cm³ as this has too many significant figures.

(11) Visual presentation of data

By the end of this spread, you should be able to:

* ✱ construct and interpret bar charts, pie charts and histograms
* ✱ translate information between graphical, numerical and algebraic forms
* ✱ plot and interpret graphs of two variables from experimental or other data
* ✱ detect errors involved in collecting data

It is important in presentations that data is clearly shown. **Pie charts**, **bar charts** and **histograms** clearly display data. Graphs are plotted to show relationships between variables and can be used to calculate gradients.

Not only is it useful to know how to plot graphs to illustrate relationships between data but also it is important that you can recognise shapes. Plotting results will allow anomalous data to show. Such values can then be remeasured or experimental work repeated.

Things to remember when plotting a graph

A graph shows the relationship between variables. It is usual for experimental results to plot:

* the independent variable (this is the variable you change in the experiment) on the x-axis
* the dependent variable (the resultant effect) on the y-axis
* sometimes however if a formula is used in order to calculate the gradient the y and x values do not follow the rule stated above (see refractive index example below)
* when you plot a graph remember to plot the points using a pencil
* give graph a heading/title
* label both y-axis and x-axis with quantities *and* units
* choose a suitable and easy to use scale – try and use all the graph paper
* put in error bars or points and circle, these indicate the amount of error for each measurement
* do not join up points – draw lines of best fit or smooth curves.

Key definitions

Bar charts will clearly show visually a comparison of numerical values/percentages. The height of each bar (column) relates to the numerical value and is labelled accordingly.

Histograms differ from bar charts in that the width of each column/bar is not uniform. In a histogram the area is important.

(Area of bar = frequency × standard bar width)

| Basic pie chart in 2D | Basic pie chart in 3D |

Figure 1 Pie chart

Pie charts will display data according to % of each data value. 360° represents 100%. It is useful to know how to use an Excel spreadsheet programme to display data in these ways.

Using gradients

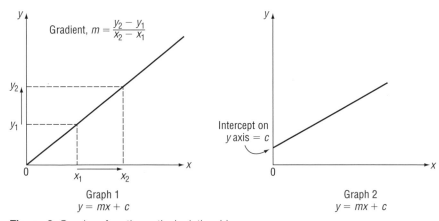

Figure 2 Graphs of mathematical relationships

To find the gradient of a straight line graph

$$\frac{\text{Change in } y \text{ values}}{\text{Change in } x \text{ values}}$$

Units = y units/x units: y units x units^{-1}

To find the gradient of a curve – use a tangent at the point the gradient is to be found.

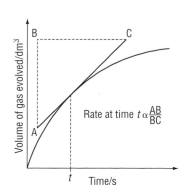

Figure 3 Shows graph of gas evolved. Rate of reaction is the amount of gas evolved over a set time

Rate at time $t \propto \dfrac{AB}{BC}$

Errors and reliability of data

A single measurement in an experimental procedure will not give you a precise result. It is often important to repeat values. Calculating the refractive index of glass is used by forensic scientists to identify a glass sample and refractive index is a property used in classifying gem stones.

$$\text{Refractive index} = \frac{\text{sine } i}{\text{sine } r} \qquad i = \text{angle of incidence} \qquad r = \text{angle of refraction}$$

Refer to page 259 for experimental detail. In order to calculate the refractive index, a number of values of i (angle of incidence) and r (angle of refraction) need to be measured and a graph plotted. Rearrangement of the equation allows the refractive index to be found from the graph.

The reliability of primary data depends on the methods by which it has been gathered. Errors could include:

* Human error.
* Precision error. This depends on the instruments used, e.g. a protractor used to measure an angle probably will only have a precision $\pm 1°$.
* Sampling error, e.g. if data was collected from a sample of the population it may not have been a representative sample – any conclusions drawn would then be inaccurate.
* Where results depend on effects on humans there is a risk of psychological factors, to help overcome this a placebo is often used.

% error

Sometimes it is useful to calculate % error = likely error/value × 100

Value of quantity e.g. length of piece of copper wire = 156 mm using a rule; the smallest unit used in this instrument = 1 mm

The likely error of measurement of rule is ± 0.05 mm (half the unit value)

% error = 0.05/156 × 100 = 0.032%

Compound error

This occurs whenever measurements are combined. It can be estimated by adding the % errors for each measurement.

When secondary data is used it is well worth checking the currency of the data.

Errors on graphs

Data points are often plotted with error bars to show the error in the experimental values (see Figure 4).

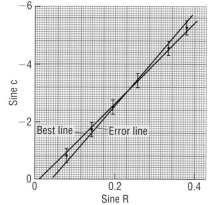

Using V = I R
R can be found from the gradient
The error
If R_1 = value of gradient from best line
R_2 = value of gradient from error line
$$R = R_1 \pm (R_2 - R_1)$$

Figure 4 Shows the value of R from the line of best fit and the errors

Mathematical skills needed by a scientist – 1

By the end of this spread, you should be able to:

✱ **use straightforward and complex calculations**

$Mean = \dfrac{\text{sum of all data values}}{\text{number of data values}}$

Mode is the data value which occurs most often. It is possible to have more than one mode.

Median is the middle value when the data values are placed in ascending order. If there are two values in the middle the mean of the two values is found.

Range is found by subtracting the highest data value from the lowest.

The **frequency** is the number of times a value occurs.

Dealing with data

It is really important that scientists accurately process data. There are a number of basic calculations that are regularly used when data is processed.

In analysis it is always important to repeat results to ensure the appropriate degree of accuracy has been obtained.

Straightforward processing

In a study of 'Active Living', data was collected of the ages of groups of people attending health centre sessions. Data 1: Daytime Sessions (8–9am), Data 2: Evening Sessions (6–7pm).

Data 1	Person	1	2	3	4	5	6	7	8	9	10	11	12	13		
	Age (yrs)	67	66	30	56	55	55	36	40	60	66	66	58	21		
Data 2	Person	1	2	3	4	5	6	7	8	9	10	11	12	13	14	15
	Age (yrs)	23	18	19	21	19	49	50	20	26	19	42	21	20	19	18

The processing of this data could include **mean**, **mode**, **range**, **frequency**, **percentages**. These would all be considered as straightforward calculations.

Process the data of attendance at day and evening sessions to show a comparison of the:

- average age of the people attending
- frequency of the visits of the over-60's
- range of ages
- % of attendees under 21.

Straightforward and complex processing in chemical reactions

Analysts are often asked to look at various commercial products to check percentages of active ingredients.

1 Ear wax is a common problem and one of the reasons that people consult their doctor is when they have ear ache or problems hearing. Ear drops which can be bought from pharmacies will often clear a plug of wax. Sodium hydrogen carbonate ear drops can be analysed by titration with hydrochloric acid. The data collected needs to be processed.

Results of experimental work to find concentration of $NaHCO_3$ in ear drops

25 cm³ samples of ear drops were used in the investigation. HCl concentration 0.1 mol dm⁻³.

The word **percentage** means per hundred. Percentages are another way of representing fractions and decimals. 20% means 20 per 100 or 20/100 or 1/5 or 0.2.

Common percentages

$75\% = \dfrac{75}{100} = \dfrac{3}{4} = 0.75$

$25\% = \dfrac{25}{100} = \dfrac{1}{4} = 0.75$

$1\% = \dfrac{1}{100} = 0.01$

Percentage increase is sometimes needed.

% increase = increase × 100%

Volume of HCl	Rough (1)	Accurate (2)	Accurate (3)
Final reading/cm³	15.80	15.40	15.50
Initial reading/cm³	0.50	0.15	0.20
Volume used/cm³	15.30	15.25	15.30
Tick if used in mean		✓	✓

The processing of this data could be complex or straightforward. If you are given guidance for each step then this is considered to be straightforward, but if you carry out all these steps independently and complete the rearrangement of the expressions yourself then calculations are considered to be complex.

The following guidelines could be used to process this data.
The equation for the reaction studied is:

$$NaHCO_3 + HCl \rightarrow NaCl + H_2O + CO_2$$

Ratio $NaHCO_3$: HCl is 1:1 for straightforward calculations
- Find the volumes of HCl used for each titration.
- Use concordant values and find the mean value for HCl.
- Use the mean volume of HCl, the concentration of HCl and the volume of $NaHCO_3$.
- Rearrange and substitute in this expression $V_{NaHCO_3} \times C_{NaHCO_3} = V_{HCl} \times C_{HCl}$
  (V = volume; C = concentration).

- $C_{NaHCO_3} = \dfrac{V_{HCL} \times C_{HCL}}{V_{NAHCO_3}}$

Activity

Process the data to find the concentration in mol dm^{-3} of $NaHCO_3$ in ear drops.

2 An analyst finding the concentration of Fe^{2+} in a pharmaceutical sample of iron tablets would carry out a redox titration.

25 cm^3 sample of an iron(II) solution made from 10 iron tablets (3.250 g) – crushed and made up to 250 cm^3 of solution with 50 cm^3 of dilute acid and distilled water was titrated with potassium manganate(VII). An average volume of 24.70 cm^3 of 0.01 mol dm^{-3} of potassium managanate(VII) solution was added to give a permanent pink colour to the solution.

The following guidelines could be used to process this data.

The equation for the reaction taking place in the analysis is:

$$MnO_4^-{}_{(aq)} + 5Fe^{2+}{}_{(aq)} + 8H^+{}_{(aq)} + Mn^{2+}{}_{(aq)} + 5Fe^{3+}{}_{(aq)} + 4H_2O_{(l)}$$

- Use the equation to find the ratio of MnO_4^- to Fe^{2+}.
- Calculate the number of moles of MnO_4^- ions used.
- Using the ratio calculate the number of Fe^{2+} ions.
- Find the weight of Fe^{2+} in the sample and then the solution.
- Use the mass of the iron tablets to find the %.

Completion of this task could cover complex calculation work.

Activity

Process the analyst's results to find the concentration of iron(II) in the sample and the % of iron in the tablets.

Physicists carry out a wide range of experimental work and need to process their results by using a range of expressions. It is important that you are able to rearrange formulae and use them in the context of your own experimental work. The science of materials is based on the fact that the properties must be suitable for the use. Science must be able to measure useful properties of materials.

Expressions which you may use.

Density (kg m^{-3}) = $\dfrac{\text{mass (kg)}}{\text{volume (m}^3)}$	Work (J) = force (N) × distance (m)	Kinetic energy (KE) = $1/2 \times mv^2$
Resistance (R) = $\dfrac{\text{voltage (V)}}{\text{current (A)}}$	Resistance (R) = $\dfrac{\text{resistivity ( ) } \times \text{length (m)}}{\text{area (m}^2)}$	Potential energy PE(J) = m (kg) × g (N kg^{-1}) × h (m)
Stress (N m^{-2}) = $\dfrac{\text{force (N)}}{\text{area (m}^2)}$	Power (W) = force (N) × velocity (ms^{-1})	Power (W) = $\dfrac{\text{energy (J)}}{\text{time (s)}}$
Strain = $\dfrac{\text{extension (m)}}{\text{original length (m)}}$	Force (N) = $\dfrac{\text{momentum change (Ns)}}{\text{time taken (s)}}$	Momentum = mass (kg) × velocity (m s^{-1})

Assessment tip

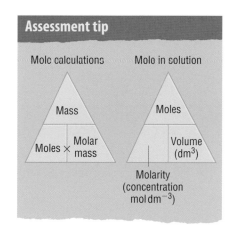

Calculations involving expressions of this type are simple if one step is required. Complex calculation involves two or more steps, e.g. this may include rearrangement of the expression, conversion of units.

Assessment tip

Calculations can be linked to:
- properties of materials
- energy and power.

By the end of this spread, you should be able to:

✻ **use straightforward and complex calculations**

Statistics – why are they useful?

When data is recorded or measurements taken in many biological experiments. e.g. measuring pulse rates, sizes of particular cells, it is not possible to measure every pulse rate or cell size. Instead a representative sample is taken and this allows scientists to come to certain conclusions; however the samples used allow only estimates of wider significance to be made. Statistics is based on probability and enables biologists to base small sample testing on populations.

More complex statistics

The standard deviation is a measure of the variability of the data about the mean.

When all the samples have similar values then the distribution curve is steep and the standard deviation small. When samples show a lot of variation the distribution curve is flat and the standard deviation is large.

Calculating standard deviation

Data collected of height in cm of barley grown in two different environments

Environment 1

90	87	87	91	90

Environment 2

89	89	87	88	87

Table 1

Procedure for calculating standard deviation
- Find the sum of the data.
- Count *n* number of values.
- Calculate the mean.
- Calculate sum of the squares of each value.
- Calculate the sum squared.
- Use the expression for standard deviation to calculate standard deviation.

Statistical testing is used in ecology and psychology experimental work. See Unit 14 and Unit 13. t-tests and chi-square tests are commonly used statistical tests. When you are using these tests you need to work out degrees of freedom.
- For the t-test it is the total number of readings/values in both *data sets* – Figure 2.
- For the chi-square test it is the number of categories/classes of *data* – Figure 3.

t-tests give you a way of looking at the means of two sets of data to see if the difference is significant e.g. perhaps you are comparing growth of two crops in different environments. Chi-square tests indicate whether your expected results are significantly different to your observed result.

Assessment tip

A large standard deviation means there is a lot of variation.

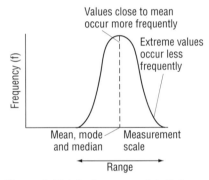

Figure 1 Distribution curve. A bell shape indicates a normal distribution

---

Activity

Process the data to find the standard deviation.

The formula for standard deviation (s) is:

$$s = \sqrt{\dfrac{\sum x^2 = \dfrac{\left(\sum x\right)^2}{n}}{n-1}}$$

s is the standard deviation
Σ means 'sum of'
x is an individual result
n is the total no. of results

Procedure for using a t-test

Construct a **null hypothesis** – an expectation which the experiment was designed to test. If you are analysing crop growth in different locations a suitable hypothesis could be that there would be no difference in height of growth. The t-test will tell you if the data is consistent with this.

The following guidelines could be used to process this data:
- Give data for samples at both locations.
- Calculate the standard deviation for each set of data.
- You then need to calculate the standard error.

Use the mean and standard error to calculate your t-value.
- For this data you would look at a t-table at 8 degrees of freedom. Using this you can determine if your value is significant. If it is you can reject your null hypothesis.

Key definition

A **null hypothesis** is simply something to test against. A t-test helps you to prove that this is right or wrong.

standard error

Where **s** is the **standard deviation** (see above section), and **n** is the **number of results**, for each of the two sets of data.

$$t = \frac{\text{mean of set 1 results} - \text{mean of set 2 results}}{\text{standard error}}$$

DF	t values				
1	3.08	6.31	12.71	63.66	636.62
2	1.89	2.92	4.30	9.93	31.60
3	1.64	2.35	3.18	5.84	12.92
4	1.53	2.13	2.78	4.60	8.61
5	1.48	2.02	2.57	4.03	6.87
6	1.44	1.94	2.45	3.71	5.96
7	1.42	1.90	2.37	3.50	5.41
8	1.40	1.86	2.31	3.36	5.04
9	1.38	1.83	2.26	3.25	4.78
10	1.37	1.81	2.23	3.17	4.59
11	1.36	1.80	2.20	3.11	4.44
12	1.36	1.78	2.18	3.06	4.32
13	1.35	1.77	2.16	3.01	4.22
14	1.35	1.76	2.15	2.98	4.14
15	1.34	1.75	2.13	2.95	4.07
	0.20 (20%)	0.10 (10%)	0.05 (5%)	0.01 (1%)	0.001 (0.1%)

If your value is less than the one in the critical (0.05) probablity accept the null hypothesis; no statistically difference between the means.

Figure 2 Sample of t-table

Procedure for the chi-square test

This can also be used to test a null hypothesis. In the case of the crops the null hypothesis will assume there is no statistically significant difference between the results you would expect to get and those you actually get.

The following guidelines could be used to process this data:
- Record your observed result.
- Record your expected result.
- Use the expression to work out chi-squared.
- Work out the degrees of freedom (number of classes/categories –1) and use a chi-square table to see if you can accept the null hypothesis.

$$\chi^2 = \sum \frac{(O-E)^2}{E}$$

Where:
O = observed result
E = expected result

You would then use chi-square tables like the one in Figure 3.

Degrees of freedom	No. of classes	χ^2 values					
1	2	0.46	1.64	2.71	3.84	6.64	10.83
2	3	1.39	3.22	4.61	5.99	9.21	13.82
3	4	2.37	4.64	6.25	7.82	11.34	16.27
4	5	3.36	5.99	7.78	9.49	13.28	18.47
		0.50 (50%)	0.20 (20%)	0.10 (10%)	0.05 (5%)	0.01 (1%)	0.001 (0.1%)

Critical value

If calculated value is greater than 5% value accept the null hypothesis: that there is no statistically significant difference between expected and observed values.

Figure 3 Chi-square table

Scientific involvement in organisations is wide ranging and varied. The science could be focussed on manufacturing processes or the knowledge and skills needed by scientists who offer science related services.

By the end of this spread, you should be able to:

* **know what you will need to do for this portfolio**
* **be aware of the level of work required**
* **know how you will be assessed**
* **be able to check your portfolio to see if you can improve it**

Assessment objective AO1

There are three strands in this section.

You have to produce:

* evidence of a survey of five science-based organisations (6 marks)
* an in-depth study of one of your chosen science-based organisations (7 marks)
* information on health and safety related to the work you do in this unit (6 marks).

Remember a survey is just a summary of the information you have found out about the organisations you have researched. You need to be careful with this work and not include pages and pages of general information on your organisations. If you choose the NHS you could focus on one department.

Assessment objective AO2

There are two strands in this section.

You have to produce information which:

* shows the impact your chosen organisation has on society (6 marks)
* gives evidence of carrying out and completing a range of calculations (4 marks).

The impact of the organisation can include information about how the organisation affects the everyday lives of people living in the local area or, if it is an international company, its effects world wide. The calculations can be those used to support your practical or based on company statistics or data.

Assessment objective AO3

There are three strands in this section.

You should produce two illustrated, written reports that give:

* evidence that you have safely completed two practical activities each with related risk assessments (8 marks)
* a record of observations and measurements made during your practical activities (6 marks)
* details on processing and interpretation of your results (7 marks).

You can use any practical work as long as it has a 'vocational' link. It is also advisable to do some linked research work to support your practical.

Practical techniques are used in scientific organisations for analysis and investigative work e.g. in pathology, food, material testing or in preparations of products. Alternatively, practical activities could include monitoring exercises e.g. monitoring of fitness as in a health centre or monitoring growth and conditions as in horticultural departments. Investigative and/or preparative work can be used.

Case study

County analysts and scientific advisory services offered by many counties provide scientific advice and analytical services for consumer protection, environmental protection and health and safety purposes. Work involves scientific investigations to ensure food is safe and complies with statutory standards. Staff not only need to produce results from analysis but also need to interpret data and produce reports which are able to stand in court.

Figure 1 The NHS is a science-based organisation where many departments are organisations in themselves e.g. radiography

Assessment tip

Although you may need some guidance you should be showing some independent work and thought in both practical tasks.

Figure 2 Monitoring change is important in health or growth

How did you do?

What grade did you think your work is worth?

Use the following checklists to get some idea of the likely standard at which you are working. Remember that these are only a guide and that you should always aim to work at as hard as you can to improve.

AO	Evidence	Form of evidence	Present	Missing
1a	Information showing a survey on five organisations. Each survey shows: products made or services offered type of work identification of science used legal/health and safety constraints.	Could be: Presentation Leaflet Short report.		
	Your research could be completed as a group activity but your evidence for your portfolio needs to show some individual work. Indicate on your work where you have worked as a team.			
1b	An in-depth study of one organisation including: explanation of the work involved number of people some detail on roles and responsibilities including qualifications required information on science involved how work is supported, quality control, ICT Health and safety links to legislation.	Report.		
1c	A coverage of health and safety. Basic information on hazards and risks. Mention of laws and regulations.	Additions to presentations and reports.		
	You should show selection and presentation of material and not just cut and paste from the Internet. It is important to give the names of the health and safety laws and regulations used.			
2a	Some understanding of the impact of your chosen organisation on society including: economy contribution and costs management of waste ICT use transport and communications effect on community and environment employment impact benefits to society.	Separate report or linked to in-depth study of organisation.		
2b	Calculations based on results of practical or organisation you are studying. Work should include both simple and complex calculations.	Could be worksheet or within results of practical work.		
	Your work should show structure – side headings can be used to check you have included all the points in the report. In your calculations – check you have shown any working.			
3a	The safe completion of two practical tasks. Use of risk assessments. Some research on the vocational link.	Record of safe completion of both tasks.		
3b	A record of relevant observations and measurements from each of the practical tasks.	Suitable tables of results that you have devised.		
3c	Processing of results from the practical work. With some interpretation.	Possibly a graph or calculations.		

Table 1 Assessment objectives checklist

If you have ticked all the 'Present' boxes your work is probably at Grade E or better.

Have you found any areas where you have left something important out?

Are there any ticks in the 'Missing' column? If there are you may have time to do something about it.

What do you need to do to improve your portfolio?

It is likely that the evidence you have presented in your portfolio can be improved.

To improve your work from mark band 1 check you have completed the extra detail. Use the information in the Assessment tip boxes to help you improve.

Internal assessment

Assessment tip

For higher mark bands in AO1a, b and c, your research work needs to:
- show the research you have included is relevant but detailed
- state why you have included your research
- be clear and logical in its presentation
- show the accurate use of scientific terminology
- show a link of the health and safety laws and regulations to your organisations.

Assessment tip

For higher mark bands in AO2a and b, your research and understanding needs to show:
- a report which is comprehensive and fully researched and a check that you have included all the bullet points in the specification.
- explanations of the impact on society of the organisation
- successful completion of complex calculations.

Assessment tip

For higher mark bands in AO3, your practical work should show:
- evidence of safe, independent and accurate use of equipment, supported by your production and use of risk assessments
- research showing that you have linked your practical to a vocational context
- all relevant results recorded to the appropriate precision
- all results accurately processed with conclusions drawn
- work suitably evaluated.

Sources

Further details on producing bibliographical references using Harvard Referencing can be found on the Study Skills site.

By the end of this spread, you should be able to:

✲ **understand how to use your research skills to survey organisations**

What sort of organisations should I survey?

Many organisations may use science but do not employ scientists. It is advisable to think carefully about your choice of organisations. Service organisations with a high scientific involvement could include: pharmacies, NHS departments, opticians, dentists, physiotherapists, colleges, schools, universities, health clubs, zoos, aquariums, garden centres, incinerators, recycling plants, utilities (gas, electricity, water), BNFL, fire service, forensic, telecommunications and waste management.

You may be interested in the armed forces, the army, the navy, the RAF. Science within these services is varied and interesting but a visit or visiting speakers may support your research.

Manufacturing organisations could include: motor vehicle manufacturers; manufacturers of ceramics, cement, fertilisers, food and drink (breweries, bakeries), glass, leather (products), paper, pesticides, photographic products, plastics, rubber, textiles; mining, metals (copper, aluminium, steel) and semiconductors.

What information do I need for my survey?

It is important to know before you decide on your choice of organisations what information you are required to find out. Think about the questions you need to ask and how to find out the answers.

What is the name of the organisation?

Don't forget to record this. It is useful to give some detail on location, size and indicate whether organisation is local, national or international.

For a service organisation: what is the service provided?

You need to find out what your chosen organisations actually provides.

The services provided by organisations differ. Some:
- provide support to the public e.g. pharmacies, fire service, ambulance service
- provide education e.g. universities, schools, colleges
- give a 'hands on service' in order to offer help e.g. doctors, dentists, health clubs
- provide the use of a product e.g. utilities (gas, electricity, water), pharmacies
- provide specialised work e.g. waste management
- offer a leisure activity e.g. zoos, aquariums, museums.

You will need to consider the type of service and research into how it is provided.

What is the type of work taking place?

For this topic area you will need to decide whether you are focusing on the role of one professional or a group of people working together in a particular department.

For example:
- A university science department involves the work of researchers, teaching staff and technical support. You will need to decide whether your focus is going to be on all, or one, of the staff involved.
- For health clubs you may want to focus on the role of one of the health centre personnel and find out the type of support they give and the knowledge they need.
- In the fire service – members of the fire service have specific roles and you may want to focus on these.

Assessment tip

A survey is just a summary of the information you have found out about the organisations you have researched. You need to be careful not to include pages and pages of general information about the organisations.

Figure 1 Interesting science is involved in recycling

Activity

If you were researching the following organisations, discuss the types of questions you would need to ask to find out about the service offered for:
- a pharmacy
- your school or college
- an incinerator.

REMEMBER: Commercial and especially military organisations may not answer some questions asked for various reasons, and sensitivity needs to be exercised when preparing questions.

What is the science involvement?

The science involvement for service providers using science usually requires the people involved having scientific qualifications and they will be required to use this knowledge in their work. This is the case for example with doctors, dentists, science teachers, pharmacists, forensic scientists. You will need to find out what scientific knowledge these professionals need to have. You will also need to find out how they use their scientific knowledge to carry out the service they are involved in.

For a manufacturing organisation: what does the organisation produce?

It may be useful to try and find a local organisation. Food or drink production may be one, e.g. bakeries, dairies, fruit juice producers, yogurt producers; these all involve using scientific knowledge in production of their products. Other examples could be producers or manufacturers of alcohol/beer, metals, plastics, electricity. In all these cases science is involved in the production of these products. Your research should include an explanation of the scientific process involved. Examples could include fermentation, electrolysis or polymerisation.

What are the health and safety issues?

You will need to link the laws and regulations to the organisation you have chosen. Remember HSWA, COSHH, CLEAPSS, PUWER, HCAPP!!! Use spread 1.1.4 to help.

Types of research

When deciding on your organisations try to choose based on your being able you to use a range of research skills.

You can find your information from a variety of sources:
- Visits – make sure you are prepared before you go.
- Talks from professionals (ask within your school and college, employees, parents, governors).
- Use of the Internet – look for websites for local and international companies. Remember to use your own words and reference the website used.
- Use of promotional leaflets and careers.

Figure 2 Pharmacist working

Internal assessment

By the end of this spread, you should be able to:

∗ **know what is needed for an in-depth study for your chosen organisation**
∗ **know how organisations manage their impact on the community and the environment**

Case study

Pilkington's is one of the world's largest manufacturers of glass and glazing products. 'Imagine a world without glass – dark!' Cars would be impractical and there would be no window shopping. The chemistry of glass, the manufacturing process and nanotechnology which is used in glass that cleans itself, is important and interesting science. Scientific knowledge and understanding is needed in this major manufacturing industry.

Figure 1 UK farming

Case study

The National Non-Foods Crops Centre helps to introduce renewable fuels and materials, by linking up different companies – from farming the crops, to manufacturing the products, to the final selling.

Thousands of materials can be made from crops: fuels, drugs, moisturisers, paints, building bricks, insulation, plastics, and these can all be used instead of non-renewable materials.

What to do to extend the work from your survey

You should be able to choose an in-depth study from one of the surveyed organisations, but you need to expand the information especially the science involvement.

Products made

You will need to include in your study:
• How the products are used, e.g. are they consumables, do they support other processes?
• Are testing or quality control procedures needed before they can be sold to the public?
• What quantities are made or sold?

Your chosen organisation may include the production of a wide range of products. Some may be materials which are used in further manufacturing processes e.g. metals (aluminium, steel, copper), glass, plastics, concrete. The food and drink industry supplies a wide range of products obtained from e.g. bakeries, breweries, dairy farms. If you use the farming industry: crops, fruit and vegetables form an important part of our economy and also use science in a range of ways which includes safe use of fertilisers, insecticides, pesticides. GM crop production may also be involved. Some products may used in the production of consumables e.g. CDs, photographic materials, pharmaceuticals.

UK farming contributed £5.6 billion to the economy in 2006. It uses around three-quarters of the UK's land area and employs over half a million people. Not only are crops grown for food purposes, industrial crops are grown for renewable energy fuels and for a wide range of uses in industry ranging from construction to clothing.

Services provided

If your chosen organisation provides a service you will need to explain:
• Work involved in supplying the service. In the majority of these cases the person needs to have sufficient scientific knowledge in order to provide the service. You will need to include an outline of the types of knowledge and understanding such people need to have. These will probably include organisations such as education establishments, armed services, fire service, health service and all related careers, the leisure industry which includes health centres, government agencies e.g. county analysts.
• If your organisation includes provision of electricity, gas, or water you will need to include the science behind the processes used to provide this service. In these cases a lot of the processes are automated and so the job roles are not so important.

British Energy Group plc is a large UK producer of energy, with a workforce of about 6000 skilled professionals. They produce about one-sixth of the nation's electricity.

Yorkshire Water provides 4.7 million residents and businesses in Yorkshire with water and sewage services. They supply 1.2 billion litres of drinking water. Jobs are diverse and include science-related work involving the supply and removal of water in addition employment involving IT, HR and finance.

The science involved

You will need to find out how your product is made or what science is used in its production:

- Look at the production process.
- Find out what the raw materials are. You may need to find out about their extraction or whether they are imported or found in the UK.
- Give the type of reaction that occurs. It could involve any of the following processes: an electrolytic process, a **redox reaction**, fermentation, decomposition, a nuclear reaction.
- Other considerations – catalysts used, specific equipment needed, any control features needed e.g. thermostatic, fertilisers, pesticides.

In the running of the organisation you will need to find out about:

- The energy needed;
- whether the process is batch or continuous; and
- quality checks needed to make sure that the products are fit for purpose.

What type of work takes place

In the manufacture of your chosen product there will be:

- Work involved in supporting the different processes involved in the manufacture.
- Work requiring testing or analysis of the final product.
- Research and development into making new products or finding better ways to manufacture.

Your research should also include the different types of jobs available and what types of qualifications are needed to support these roles.

The impact of an organisation on society

Whatever your chosen organisation, the impact it has on society is important not only to local residents but also to the welfare of the country both now and in the future. When you are researching your chosen organisation finances and economical matters are important in ensuring an organisation can run efficiently and can produce products which can be sold in a worldwide market. Not only are the number of employees important but in many of these science-related organisations the key to success is a skilled workforce. Accessibility of the company needs to be considered not only for providing a service which the public can travel to easily but also for transport of raw materials and products. Consider the following:

Finances:

- stocks and share index on prices of commodities/products/services
- employment costs
- costs of services to consumers.

Employment:

- skilled needs – education of work force
- numbers employed
- affect on transport.

Input and output needs:

- energy requirements
- waste management
- recycling facilities.

It may be relevant to include the importance of the products to every day life, how they contribute to the health of the nation, may be used for pleasure or may be something we eat or drink every day.

Internal assessment

References to support research

Websites to support the case studies:

Pilkington Glass
British Glass
British Energy
Yorkshire Water

A useful site which gives the websites of all the water companies throught the UK and Northern Ireland:

Water UK

A useful tool if the focus of your organisation is on manufacture of materials from crops:

National Non-food Crops Centre

Health and safety in the workplace

By the end of this spread, you should be able to:

✳ understand the importance of health and safety laws and regulations in science organisations
✳ understand how this information can be used for your portfolio

Case study

Becoming ill or being hurt through work is something no one wants to happen. Before 1974 approximately eight million employees had no legal safety protection at work. The introduction of the Health and Safety at Work Act in 1974 has led to a substantial reduction in work-related injury rates. From 1974 to 2006 the number of:
• fatal injuries fell by **76%**
• reported non-fatal injuries fell by **68%**.

Why have health and safety laws and regulations?

Health and safety laws and regulations have been introduced to provide guidelines for organisations to work to. Implementing and monitoring the correct health and safety measures at work not only save lives and prevent injuries but make the workplace much safer. The Health and Safety Executive checks that health and safety regulations are being followed for manufacturing, construction and industrial organisations. Other service organisations, offices etc. are checked by the Environment Agency.

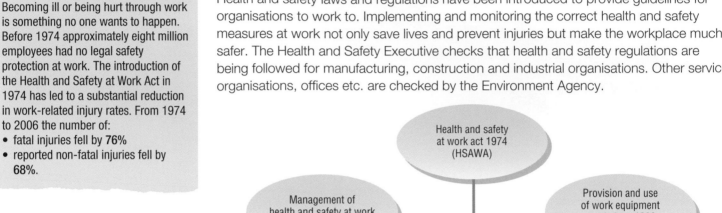

Figure 1 Some important areas of legislation

The Health and Safety at Work Act (HSAWA)

This Act aims to make sure that high standards of health and safety are maintained in the workplace. Everyone has to follow the terms of this Act. Employers need to provide:
• information and training for health and safety to all staff
• and maintain safety equipment and protective clothing
• a safe place of employment and ensure safety signs are provided and maintained
• a safe working environment, providing emergency procedures and first aid facilities
• a written safety policy and suitable risk assessments.

Employers also need to:
• ensure materials are properly stored, handled, used and transported
• control the keeping and use of explosive or highly flammable or otherwise dangerous substances
• control the emission into the atmosphere of substances.

Employers should also consult with either a health and safety representative or employees if there is any change which may affect health and safety at work, e.g. the introduction of new technology and in the planning of health and safety.

Employees have specific responsibilities as well. They must:
- take care of their own health and safety and that of other people
- cooperate with their employers
- not interfere with anything related to providing health and safety protection.

Management of Health & Safety at Work Regulations 1992 (MHSWR)

The MHSWR was developed together with the Health and Safety at Work Act to specify the roles of employers and employees to help keep the work place safe.

All major food manufacturing organisations are very concerned about food safety. The Foods Standards Agency promotes the microbiological safety of food.

Hazard and Critical Control Points as part of the Food Safety Act 1990

The Food Safety (General Food Hygiene) Regulations 1995 require all food businesses to identify activities that are critical to ensuring food safety and to ensure that adequate safety procedures are identified, implemented and maintained. The Hazard Analysis Critical Control Point (HCAPP) concept is a system for assuring the safety of food and is used by the larger food manufacturers. It involves:
- Listing potential food hazards.
- Identification of points where hazards may occur.
- Deciding which points are critical to ensuring food safety.
- Identification and implementation of effective control and monitoring procedures at critical points.
- Implementation and checks.

Provision and Use of Work Equipment Regulations 1998 (PUWER)

These regulations require risks to people's health, and safety from equipment that they use at work, to be controlled. The regulations require that equipment provided for use at work is:
- suitable for its intended use
- safe for use and suitably maintained
- used by people who have received training
- accompanied by suitable protective devices, warnings and instructions.

The Consortium of Local Authorities for Provision of Science Services (CLEAPSS)

CLEAPSS is an advisory service providing support in science and technology for a consortium of local authorities and education establishments. CLEAPSS provides advice for teachers, technicians, science advisers, health and safety advisers, other local authority officers and school governors.

CLEAPSS covers health and safety including risk assessment; chemicals, living organisms, equipment; sources of resources; laboratory design, facilities and fittings; technicians and their jobs; and some D&T facilities and fittings.

CLEAPSS materials are intended for teachers and technicians. Individual Hazcards can be given to students if appropriate but students should not be given access to other CLEAPSS documents except the Student Safety Sheets, which were intended for students.

Figure 2 Safety at work in the food industry

Figure 3 Health and safety at college

Internal assessment

By the end of this spread, you should be able to:

∗ **know what you will need to do for this portfolio**
∗ **be aware of the level of work required**
∗ **know how you will be assessed**
∗ **check your portfolio to see if you can improve it**

In order for organisations to become both profitable and efficient, they are now required to produce and implement energy management strategies. Energy policies form part of these strategies, and include organisations working to reach targets involving energy efficient measures which include energy efficient design of buildings, development of a culture of energy awareness and accountability and the use of equipment which uses renewable energy and supports carbon reduction.

Assessment objective AO1

There are three strands in this section.
You have to produce a report which includes:
• a study of one organisation's energy policy (6 marks)
• consideration of energy efficiency (6 marks)
• the economic and environmental impacts (7 marks).

Assessment objective AO2

There are two strands in this section.

You have to produce information which:
• shows energy transfers involved in the generation of electricity and quantitative information on costs of different fuels (5 marks)
• gives evidence of completing a range of calculations on costs involved in the generation of electricity and a comparison of large scale and small scale electrical generation (5 marks).

The majority of the UK's electricity comes from burning fossil fuels (coal, oil, gas). There are effective alternatives to fossil fuels which will never run out; sun, wind, water or fuels which are replaceable; crops and waste products. Renewable fuels include biomass, hydropower, wind power and solar (PV) photovoltaic.

Assessment objective AO3

There are three strands in this section.

You should produce three reports giving evidence that you have carried out four practical analyses:
• a report of two practical activities (one using chromatography and one colorimetry) (8 marks)
• a report of a qualitative chemical analysis (6 marks)
• a report of a quantitative chemical analysis (7 marks).

The analysis work studied in this unit needs to indicate how the different techniques are used to solve a variety of problems and analyses in industrial or service provider organisations. Chromatography is an important technique used either to separate or identify mixtures that are or can be coloured. Thin layer chromatography (TLC) is often used in the determination of pigments in plants, detection of pesticides or insecticides in food or the dye composition in fibres in forensics. Colorimetry also uses colour as an analytical tool and this method is used in the determination of concentrations of chemicals in solutions. There are two types of analysis, qualitative and quantitative. Qualitative analysis aims to find out what is present in a sample whereas quantitative analysis is the determination of the amount of the given element/compound etc. in the sample.

Figure 1 Wind speed increases with height, so it is best to have the turbines high

Figure 2 Colorimetry – a useful technique

Internal assessment

How did you do?

What grade did you think your work is worth?

Use the following checklists to get some idea of the likely standard at which you are working. Remember that these are only a guide and that you should always aim to work at as hard as you can to improve.

AO	Evidence	Form of evidence	Present	Missing
1a	Information related to the energy policy of one organisation. A clear description is needed.	Report Presentation Leaflet		
1b	Energy efficiency to include what it means and how it has been considered.	Report Leaflet		
1c	An assessment of the economic and environmental impacts of your chosen organisation.	Report Leaflet		
	You should include references to show where you have found information on your energy policy: it could be a website/company policy or obtained from a visit.			
2a	Work which includes: diagrams and explanations on energy transfers which occur in the generation of electricity information on costs of fuels both renewable and non renewable.	Your study can be presented as: report, poster presentation.		
2b	Work which includes: calculations on costs involved in the generation of electricity a comparison of relative benefits and problems of large scale and small scale electrical generation.	Your study can be presented as: report, poster presentation.		
	Evidence should be well structured and should show evidence of individual research work. Take care in calculations to be accurate and to record all answers to the correct number of significant figures. You should be aiming to use researched data: don't forget to indicate the source.			
3a 3b 3c	Each report must include: a link to a vocational context a risk assessment evidence that you have actually completed the practical work a copy of the instructions you followed (you do not need to rewrite these) all relevant measurements or observations evidence of processing your results with some interpretation some evaluation of your work.	Report 1 Report 2 Report 3		
	Although you may need some guidance you should be showing some independent work and thought in the practical tasks. It will also support your work if you have included some researched information on the vocational link of your practical.			

Table 1 Assessment objectives checklist

• If you have ticked all the 'Present' boxes your work is probably at Grade E or better.

Have you found any areas where you have left something important out?

Are there any ticks in the 'Missing' column? If there are you may have time to do something about it.

What do you need to do to improve your portfolio?

It is likely that the evidence you have presented in your portfolio can be improved.

Use the information in the Assessment tip margin boxes to increase the chance of your getting a better grade. There is an Assessment tip box for each of the assessment objectives. The advice given, if taken, could improve your grade up to Grade A.

Internal assessment

Assessment tip

For higher mark bands

AO1 Your research and report needs to:
• show detailed and relevant information on the energy policy – no cut and paste
• show how efficiency has been considered and evaluated
• show detailed evidence of both environmental and economic impacts of organisation
• include accurate use of scientific terminology.

Assessment tip

For higher mark bands

AO2 Your study needs to show:
• detailed work on energy transfer involved in the generation of electricity
• well displayed information on the costs of different fuels
• complex calculations using data on costs
• a comparison of large and small scale electricity generation.

Assessment tip

For higher mark bands

AO3 Completion and presentation of four practical tasks should show:
• you have carried out detailed research which shows links to a vocational context
• evidence that in your practical work you have made measurements to the appropriate precision and accuracy and you have checked significant figures
• you have made all relevant results and processed them accurately
• high level evaluative work.

By the end of this spread, you should be able to:

* produce a report on the energy policy of an organisation you have chosen to study
* explain what is meant by the efficiency of a system
* investigate steps that could be taken by a non-domestic consumer to maximise their efficiency of electrical supply
* consider the economic and environmental impacts of the energy policy

Climate change is increasingly becoming a major challenge. It is now accepted that green house gas (GHG) emissions caused by humans are having a bad effect on the environment. The 'Carbon Footprint' of organisations is the total set of GHG emissions produced. Organisations are now trying to reduce their 'Carbon Footprint' by looking at fuel and vehicle usage, electricity bills and travel.

The UK has promised to reduce carbon dioxide emissions by 20% by 2010 and 60% by 2050. There are a number of plans to help do this. These include the Energy Efficiency Commitment and the Climate Change levy.

Making a formal statement of their energy policy helps companies to make sure that all employees do what they are supposed to do. It also makes staff keener to save energy at times when commercial pressures might tempt them not to.

The policy statement

In the past, some companies didn't care how much energy they used as long as they made a profit. Nowadays most organisations recognise that it is in their interest, and good for the planet, to use less energy. Many find the best way to do this is to start by agreeing a formal energy policy.

Try to find an organisation with a *clearly stated* energy policy. Summarise the main points of the policy. Comment on them.

You might add detail to your account by noting good practice (e.g. double glazing was installed last year). However, this should not be a substitute for a proper policy statement.

Some points to consider when researching and describing the energy policy:
* Does the policy set targets for reducing energy consumption?
* Does the policy indicate how energy savings will be achieved?
* Has the organisation thought about all aspects of the business?
* How well is the policy carried out in practice? If possible, visit your organisation.

Energy efficiency

Include a scientific definition of efficiency. You can give this either as:

* $\text{efficiency} = \dfrac{\text{power out}}{\text{power in}} \times 100\%$ or

* $\text{efficiency} = \dfrac{\text{useful work done in a given time}}{\text{energy supplied in the given time}} \times 100\%$

People also talk about efficiency in the context of reducing the amount of fuel used to keep a building at a certain temperature. Since all the heat in the central heating pipes eventually escapes we can't use the expression above. That doesn't mean that it's not a good idea to reduce the heat losses.

Internal assessment

Assessment tip

The specification requires that you should report on the policy of a non domestic consumer rather than a producer of electricity.

Source

Weblinks give examples of universities that publish their energy policy on the Internet.

Assessment tip

Don't confuse an energy policy with an environmental policy.

In the third strand of the assessment you are expected to include the environmental impact of the energy policy. But this report should not be about how they avoid polluting the local river – even if that is good news!

Activity

1 Calculate and compare the efficiency of different kinds of light bulb from their light output and electrical power rating.
2 Find out how much of the chemical energy in boiler fuel is usefully transferred to heat the water in the central heating system. How much is wasted up the chimney?

If visiting your organisation:

- Politely ask if they can tell you how much fuel or money they have saved due to their policy. Don't demand this information! It may be 'commercially confidential' (that means secret to you or I!) or the spokesman may simply not have access to the figures.
- Look to see if they are taking simple measures to save energy e.g. energy saving light bulbs, doors kept shut, double glazing.
- Find out if employees know about the policy.
- Find out if the company vehicles are fuel efficient.

Economic and environmental impacts

Some actions save energy and therefore reduce costs with little or no investment. For example keeping doors shut normally costs nothing. Replacing light bulbs with energy saving versions (Figure 1) requires little or no investment.

Some energy saving measures require capital investment. Examples are:

- installing of some form of insulation (Figure 2)
- recycling waste heat from production plant to heat offices.

The economic advantage of these measures can be assessed from the pay-back time. If you use the savings in fuel costs to pay back the cost of the investment, how many years will it take? A company accountant would probably include the interest costs in their calculations.

Some organisations may have parts of their policies that will reduce their use of fossil fuels even though this will actually cost them money. For example they may decide to buy electricity generated from 'green' sources (Figure 3). This may be done truly for the good of the planet.

Figure 1 Energy saving light bulb

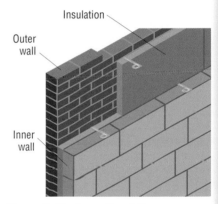

Figure 2 Cavity wall insulation, one simple way of reducing energy loss

Figure 3 Wind farm

Some companies may say that their shareholders expect them to make as much profit as possible. Even these may decide that it is good publicity to be seen to be 'green'. They may, for example, put up a wind generator in their car park.

Case study

Carbon emissions are a shortened term for carbon dioxide emissions used in international climate change negotiations.

1 tonne of carbon when combined with oxygen will produce 3.67 tonnes of carbon dioxide.

By the end of this spread, you should be able to:

✱ assess simple data on calorific values and fuel prices
✱ describe the forms of energy transfer involved in the generation of electricity

In order to compare the costs of energy from different sources, you need to be able to calculate them. It is not enough just to look at prices. You may get more energy from a kilogram of one fuel than another. In any case fuels are priced in different units. Some are sold by volume, others by mass.

Energy from most renewable sources doesn't actually have a fuel cost. However, it is not free. There are costs in converting energy into a form we can use.

Source

The calorific values of most common fuels can be found on the Kaye and Laby website.

Case study

One other small complication – the volume conversion factor – has recently been added to gas bills.

Ofgas (that's the people who make sure that the gas companies don't over-charge us) noticed that the amount of gas in a cubic metre depends on temperature and pressure, and this may be different at your house than when the gas is put into the pipe.

The solution is to multiply the volume measured by the meter (gas units in Figure 1) by a volume conversion factor (1.0226400 on this bill).

This is explained more fully in the prnewswire web link.

Calorific values

Look at the gas bill in Figure 1.

→ Gas you've used - in detail

Previous reading	Recent reading	Gas units	Kilowatt hours used	Pence per kWh
04533 14 Jul 07 we read your meter	04768 10 Oct 07 we read your meter	235	2613.02 over 89 days	First 1102.00 kWh at 4.266 pence Next 1511.02 kWh at 2.173 pence

How we convert gas units used to kilowatt hours:
kWh used = Gas Units
$\times$ 1.0226400 (volume conversion factor)
$\times$ 39.1431 (calorific value)
$\div$ 3.6 (kilowatt hour conversion factor)

Figure 1 Gas bill

The calorific value of the gas is given near the bottom as 39.1431. No unit is given on the bill, but it is in megajoules per cubic metre (MJ m^{-3}). You will remember that joules are the SI unit of energy. The calorific value tells us how much energy is in each cubic metre of gas supplied.

The calorific value of gas is given in MJ m^{-3}, because gas meters measure the volume of gas used. The calorific value of solid fuels is usually given in megajoules per kilogram (MJ kg^{-1}). It is easier to measure coal by mass.

Case study

Looking at Figure 1 in more detail you can see that the charge is about 4p per kWh to start with then about 2p per kWh after the first 1102 kWh each quarter.

(Gas and electricity bills are usually sent out every three months i.e. a *quarter* of a year.)

Fuel prices

Domestic gas and electricity

The prices of domestic gas and electricity are not charged in SI units. Instead the unit of energy used is called the kilowatt-hour (see Figure 1) 1 kWh = 3.6 MJ).

In Figure 1 you can see that this customer's gas costs about 2p or 4p per kWh.

Electricity is more expensive than gas. The same supplier charges about 8p or 14p per kWh for electricity. By the time you read this, prices will almost certainly have changed. You should find out how much gas and electricity cost now in your area, either by looking at a recent bill or at a supplier's website.

Diesel, petrol and heating oil

Liquid fuels are normally priced by volume. You will need to look up their density if you wish to combine them with calorific values expressed in MJ kg^{-1}.

Solid fuels

You can find the cost of coal and anthracite from your local supplier.

Renewables

Wind, tidal, wave and solar energy have no fuel costs, but the electricity they produce is not free because of capital and other costs. The British Wind Energy Association website shows that offshore wind energy is significantly more expensive than onshore.

Biofuels are also renewable, but do have a calorific value. See Sources.

Energy transfers

Much of our electricity is obtained from chemical and nuclear energy which are forms of potential energy. Solar energy starts off as nuclear energy in the Sun. Some is converted into heat on the Earth. Some of the heat is converted into chemical energy by plants. Some of the Sun's energy is converted into kinetic energy of the wind and waves. Tidal energy comes from the gravitational potential energy of the moon.

One way of showing the transfers of energy from one form to another in processes such as the generation of electricity is by means of diagrams such as Figure 4.

Figure 2 Petrol and diesel are priced in litres

Sources

The petrol prices website will tell you your local petrol and diesel prices (see web link). Or you could simply look at the sign outside your local petrol station!

The oil price check website will give you prices for heating oil.

The British Wind Energy Association website gives a detailed breakdown of costs of setting up installations and consequent energy prices compared to other sources.

A good place to start your research into current biofuels costs is the Defra website.

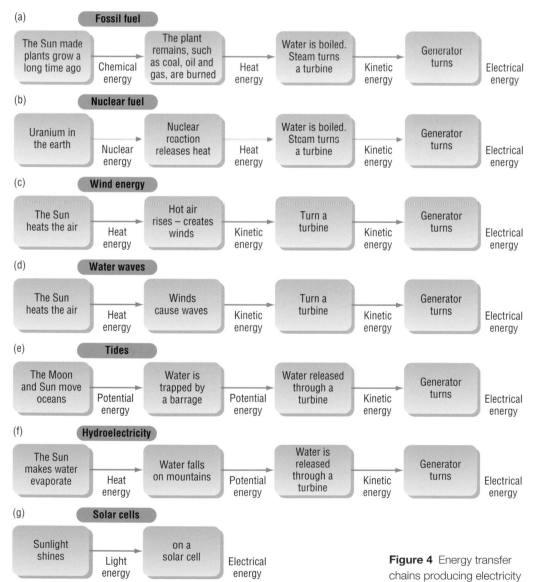

(a) **Fossil fuel**

The Sun made plants grow a long time ago → *Chemical energy* → The plant remains, such as coal, oil and gas, are burned → *Heat energy* → Water is boiled. Steam turns a turbine → *Kinetic energy* → Generator turns → *Electrical energy*

(b) **Nuclear fuel**

Uranium in the earth → *Nuclear energy* → Nuclear reaction releases heat → *Heat energy* → Water is boiled. Steam turns a turbine → *Kinetic energy* → Generator turns → *Electrical energy*

(c) **Wind energy**

The Sun heats the air → *Heat energy* → Hot air rises – creates winds → *Kinetic energy* → Turn a turbine → *Kinetic energy* → Generator turns → *Electrical energy*

(d) **Water waves**

The Sun heats the air → *Heat energy* → Winds cause waves → *Kinetic energy* → Turn a turbine → *Kinetic energy* → Generator turns → *Electrical energy*

(e) **Tides**

The Moon and Sun move oceans → *Potential energy* → Water is trapped by a barrage → *Potential energy* → Water released through a turbine → *Kinetic energy* → Generator turns → *Electrical energy*

(f) **Hydroelectricity**

The Sun makes water evaporate → *Heat energy* → Water falls on mountains → *Potential energy* → Water is released through a turbine → *Kinetic energy* → Generator turns → *Electrical energy*

(g) **Solar cells**

Sunlight shines → *Light energy* → on a solar cell → *Electrical energy*

Figure 4 Energy transfer chains producing electricity

Figure 3 Solar power – the fuel is free, but money is needed to set up solar panels

Fuel calculations and power generation scales

By the end of this spread, you should be able to:

✳ **do calculations of fuel costs from data researched**
✳ **include a comparison of relative benefits and problems of large-scale and small-scale electrical generation**

Fuel calculations

To compare fuel costs you need to convert them all to the same unit. Electricity and gas bills are charged per kilowatt-hour. You *could* choose to work out all costs in these units. However it is *better* scientific practice to us the SI unit of energy – the joule (J). Since this is a comparatively small amount of energy we will use the SI prefix for a million and work out cost in megajoules (MJ).

Values used here are examples. Prices will vary. You should do your own calculations using values you have researched.

Electricity

The electricity meter in your home measures how much you use in kW hr. Prices are stated in pence per kW hr.

Prices are complicated because companies sometimes make a 'standing charge' to meet the cost of providing cables to your home even if you use very little electricity. Alternatively they may charge a much higher price for the first so many units you use.
1 kW hr = 3 600 000 J = 3.6 MJ
So if 1 kW hr costs 8.00p

1 MJ costs $\frac{8}{3.6}$ = 2.22p.

Gas

If you use mains gas at home, the gas meter measures the volume of gas you have used in m³. However, prices are stated in pence per kWh, so you can calculate cost per MJ in the same way as the electricity example above. As with electricity there may be a standing charge or variable rates.

If you use bottled gas you usually pay per kg. The calculations are done in a similar way to those for coal (see the next spread).

Liquid fuels

Petrol and diesel are priced per litre at the pump.

Figure 1 Cooking with gas

Heating oil delivered to you home is priced for typically 500 L or 900 L. (In science we usually call a litre 1 dm³, or 0.001 m³, but in this section we will use the name of the unit used by the suppliers.) The more you buy the cheaper it is. (This is because the supplier has to pay for the lorry to go to your home however much they deliver.)

If 500 L costs £200 (20 000p), 1 L costs $\frac{20\,000}{500}$ = 40p

The calorific value is 47 MJ kg⁻¹; density of kerosene = 817 kg m⁻³ (see SI metric web link)

So calorific value = 47 × 817 = 38 399 MJ m⁻³

1 m³ = 1000 L; so calorific value = $\frac{38\,399}{1000}$ = 38.4 MJ L⁻¹

1 MJ costs $\frac{\text{cost per L}}{\text{calorific value per L}} = \frac{40}{38.4}$ =1.04p.

Solid fuels

A 25 kg sack of coal costs £7.05 = 705p, delivered to your home.

If the calorific value is 36 MJ kg^{-1}

1 MJ costs $\dfrac{\text{cost per kg}}{\text{calorific value per kg}} = \dfrac{705 \div 25}{36} = \dfrac{28.2}{36} = 0.78p.$

Wind energy

You can calculate the cost of wind energy per MJ as for general electricity prices using the costs per kW hr given in the BWEA web link.

Biofuels

Suppose 1 m^3 of logs costs £100.

However 1 m^3 supplied will not be solid wood. There will be spaces between the logs. Let's assume that only 70% of the volume is wood.

0.7 m^3 of wood costs £100. 1 m^3 of wood costs £142.86. Calorific value = 15 MJ kg^{-1}

Densities of wood vary. Assume density = 600 kg m^{-3}. So calorific value = 15 × 600 = 9000 MJ m^{-3}

1 MJ costs $\dfrac{\text{cost per }m^3}{\text{calorific value per }m^3} = \dfrac{14286}{9000} = 1.59p.$

Comparison of scale in electricity production

You are asked to compare the benefits and problems of electricity production at different scales.

The specification suggests wind energy as an example of small scale production. But today wind energy provides a good example of an energy source that is used on both large and small scale.

Example 1: Wind

It is possible to buy a small wind turbine to supply a single house. You can research how much this would cost and how much less you would have to pay the electricity company. Increasing numbers of large wind farms are being built, both on land and offshore. The BWEA website will tell you a lot of what you need to know.

Example 2: Oil

Small scale diesel powered generators are used in a number of situations, for example, contractors working on sites with no mains supply, back-up generators in places like hospitals and key computer installations where a break in supply can have serious consequences and buildings not yet connected to the mains supply.

Large scale oil-fired power stations contribute about 2% of UK electrical supply.

Example 3: Solar

Solar power is installed on a small scale in individual buildings.

Find out the current progress of plans to set up large scale plant in the deserts in America and Africa.

Internal assessment

Assessment tip

Remember that you are comparing the different scales of electricity production, not different fuels.

So you should compare, for example, large scale wind power with small scale wind power, or large scale oil fuelled generation with small scale diesel generators.

Case study

The Birlot tide mill on the Island of Brehat, France was once used to grind wheat, barley and buckwheat. Theoretically the water wheels could be replaced by a turbine to generate electricity on a small scale.

Figure 2 Birlot tide mill

The proposed Severn barrage would produce electricity on a large scale, but cause significant environmental damage.

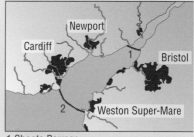

1 Shoots Barrage
2 Cardiff Weston Barrage

Figure 3 Two possible schemes for the proposed Severn barrage

By the end of this spread, you should be able to:

* be aware of the practical techniques required for physical analysis
* be aware of some industrial links with each method
* know how to complete suitable reports

Assessment tip

When carrying out colorimetric work take care to ensure that you check whether you are using transmittance (how much light passes through the sample) or absorbance (how much light is absorbed).

Case study

Colorimetry can be used in the analysis of water samples. Nitrite NO_2^- ions and nitrate NO_3^- ions occur in many surface and ground water supplies formed as a product of the oxidation of nitrogen from ammonia. The presence of large quantities of these ions is indicative of waste water pollution. A level ideal for marine fish is between 0.01 and 0.04 ppm nitrite and 0.1 and 0.2 ppm nitrate. Although these ions are colourless they produce a pink colour when treated with a suitable dye, which then allows analysis by colorimetry.

Physical analysis: Colorimetry

Colorimetry is a technique that can be used to measure the concentration of coloured solutions. In a colorimeter a light sensitive cell gives a reading linked to the amount of light absorbed or transmitted through a sample. The reading is related to the concentration of the coloured compound in the solution.

The colorimeter is calibrated using known concentrations of a coloured solution. A calibration curve of absorbance vs concentration is plotted and used to find out the concentration of the unknown sample. The absorbance value from the unknown sample is used to find the concentration of the unknown.

Physical analysis: Chromatography

Chromatography is a useful physical method for analysing complex mixtures, by separating the chemicals present. The components to be separated are always distributed between two phases: a stationary phase and a mobile phase. The components in a mixture are separated by this method because of the difference in the adsorption between the stationary and mobile phases. The mobile phase carries the mixture through the stationary phase. The component is attracted to both phases: a component strongly attracted to the stationary phase is held back whereas one strongly attracted to the mobile phase moves on. Separation of the various components occurs. There are many different types of chromatography.

Chromatography	Mobile phase	Stationary phase
Paper	Solvent (l)	Water trapped in the paper.
TLC (Thin Layer)	Solvent (l)	A thin layer of adsorbent particles such as alumina or silica supported on a glass or metal plate.
Column	Solvent (l)	Small solid adsorbent particles.
HPLC (High Performance Liquid Chromatography)	Solvent (l) Forced through column at high pressure	A powdered adsorbent solid silica or resin particles 10 μm diameter packed into a column.
GLC (Gas–Liquid Chromatography)	Gas (g): N_2, Ar	A liquid coating the surface of a solid

Table 1 Types of chromatography

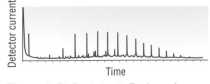

Figure 1 GLC print-out. Each peak indicates the retention time of the component

Analysts working on GLC and HPLC instruments can provide both qualitative and quantitative data. Although GLC and HPLC equipment is expensive it has high resolution. Different components travel through the column at different speeds. The time each component takes is called the retention time. The retention times can be used to identify components and the peak heights give a measure of the amounts. This type of chromatography has wide ranging use for detection of contaminants in water and is sensitive to a wide range of organic compounds.

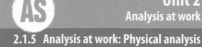
TLC is a technique applied both in drug synthesis and research. It can be used to monitor the progress of a chemical reaction as well as identification in forensic work. Sometimes the components are not visible to the naked eye and in these cases the components are identified using UV light or exposing the plates to iodine. These are just some of the methods used to expose the spots. TLC and paper chromatography are the types that you will need to carry out in the laboratory. Each component has a distinctive R_f value and you can use this as a method of identification.

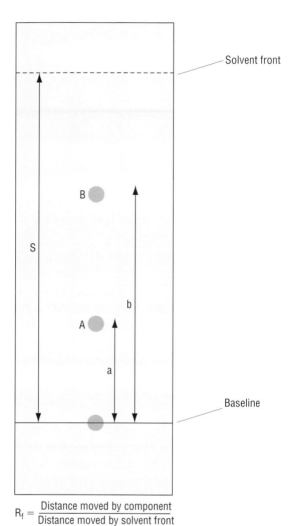

$$R_f = \frac{\text{Distance moved by component}}{\text{Distance moved by solvent front}}$$

R_f values: A=a/s; B=b/s

Figure 2 Calculation of R_f values

TLC and paper chromatography can be used in the analysis of a range of mixtures. Discuss what solvents you would need and what techniques you need to carry out if you were to analyse the following:
- the pigments chlorophyll, carotene, xanthophylls found in green leaves
- the active ingredients in a range of painkillers such as Anadin, paracetamol, aspirin, ibuprofen.

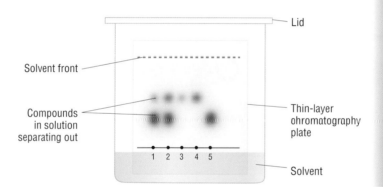

Figure 3 Thin Layer Chromatography – as the solvent travels up the plate the components will separate depending on their attraction for the different phases

The work needed for the report

Your work needs to include:
- How these two techniques are linked to a vocational context. The information in this spread starts to give you some ideas. You will need to focus on each method and support the work with additional research. Colorimetry and chromatography are excellent analytical techniques used widely in both research and analyses.
- Information on the practical method you completed.
- A record all measurements and observations.
- What you found out from each practical activity.

Assessment tip

Don't forget that for:
- the colorimetry experiment you need a table showing all the data for your calibration curve
- chromatography calculate the R_f values.

Internal assessment

By the end of this spread, you should be able to:

* be aware of the practical techniques required for qualitative and quantitative analysis
* be aware of some industrial links with each method
* know how to complete suitable reports

Qualitative and quantitative analysis are the standard tools of any analytical scientist. Recognising the meaning of these two terms will be expected throughout any work you study in science.

Planning in qualitative analysis

Qualitative analysis can be used to detect and identify either **inorganic** or **organic** compounds. In order to do this it is necessary to be able to carry out basic tests. Remember an inorganic compound is made up of a **cation** and **anion** and in order to identify the compound fully both cation and anion need to be detected

Inorganic testing

Here are a series of steps you could use to try and identify the cation and anion of an unknown inorganic compound. Experimental details for these tests and results can be found in spread P.1.5.

1 The first tests will allow you to identify the cation: carry out a flame test with the unknown compound and observe the colour (Figure 2). If the cation is identified go to 4. If not carry on.
2 Make a solution of unknown compound using distilled water and then test using sodium hydroxide and observe the colour of the precipitate. If the cation is identified go to 4. If not carry on.
3 Try testing for the presence of ammonium ions, using sodium hydroxide and warming. You should now have identified the cation. *If the cation is now identified continue, if not it may be worth consulting your tutor or repeating some of the tests.*

The following tests will allow you to identify the anion:

4 Start to test for a carbonate by using dilute hydrochloric acid and test any gas using limewater. If your test is not positive continue to 5 (Figure 2).
5 Test for halides – chloride/bromide/iodide – by adding dilute nitric acid followed by silver nitrate solution. Formation of a precipitate suggests halide ions are present. If this test is not positive continue to 6.
6 Test for sulfate – by adding dilute hydrochloric acid followed by barium chloride solution. Formation of a white precipitate suggests sulfate is present. If this test is not positive continue to 7.
7 Test for nitrate – add iron(II) sulfate solution followed by concentrated sulfuric acid and look for a brown ring – you need to take extra care doing this test – and do it in the fume cupboard.

This plan is just a guide to help you identify unknown inorganic compounds; you will however need to use it with detailed experimental procedures.

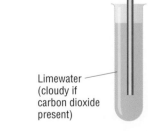

Sample and dilute hydrochloric acid

Colour of flame yellow/orange for sodium identifies cation

Limewater (cloudy if carbon dioxide present)

Figure 2 Flame tests and testing for carbon dioxide

Organic testing

Qualitative organic analysis is often used to identify the presence of organic functional groups. Alcohols, carboxylic acids, sugars can easily be identified. You will need section P1.5 for the practical details and the table to identify any positive results. Again a plan is needed in order to identify an unknown organic compound.

1 Smell may help to put you in the right direction, but you must take care! Just waft the vapour carefully towards your nose, do not breathe in the fumes.
2 Test the solubility in water and pH. These may also give you some ideas.
3 It is then useful to start with tests which support your ideas in steps 1 and 2.

Remember when identifying organic compounds it is the functional group you need to identify. Tests available include the test for:

- alkenes (functional group C=C) – bromine water
- alcohols (functional group C–OH) – acidified potassium dichromate and warm
- carboxylic acids (functional group COOH) – sodium carbonate and test for carbon dioxide
- aldehydes and ketones (functional group C=O) – 2,4 dinitro phenylhydrazine – in excess
- reducing sugars – Benedict's solution and warm.

This plan is just a guide to help you identify unknown organic compounds, you will however need to use it with detailed experimental procedures.

Using techniques for quantitative analysis

Quantitative analysis uses the techniques of **volumetric analysis** to find unknown concentrations. This includes the preparation of standard solutions and titrations. Detailed experimental procedures are given in spread P.1.6.

The titrations you may be using for your tasks include:
- Acid-base titrations where accurate concentrations of acids or alkalis can be found. These reactions are monitored using a suitable acid-base indicator. Indicators in common use include phenolphthalein, screened methyl orange, or methyl red. You will need to check the colour changes of these indicators and make sure you know the colour at the 'end point' of the reaction.
- Redox titrations involve reduction and oxidation. Titrations involving acidified potassium manganate (VII) solution are often used when investigating concentrations of unknowns involving redox reactions. Potassium manganate (VII) is a purple solution and therefore an indicator is not necessary. In this case the reaction is complete when the solution turns to a very pale pink.

The work needed for the report

You will need to write a report for both the qualitative and the quantitative analysis.

For both reports you will need to include:
- the vocational link and why it is important to carry out the analysis
- suitable risk assessments
- information on the practical methods you completed
- records of all measurements and observations
- balanced equations to support your conclusions
- what you found out from each practical activity
- calculations where appropriate.

Modern analytical laboratories usually have a range of analytical instruments. A mass spectrometer can be used to determine the relative mass of a compound and skilled scientists can use the unique mass spectrum of a compound to determine chemical structure. Although mass spectrometers are expensive they only need small samples and can be used to obtain detailed information. Two other important types of spectroscopy include infrared (IR) and ultraviolet (UV). Infrared spectroscopy can be used to identify types of bonds present and therefore identify functional groups. Ultraviolet spectroscopy is used mainly for quantitative analysis as it only provide limited evidence on chemical structure.

Internal assessment

Activity

A forensic scientist has been given a blue liquid to analyse. It was found at the scene of a crime. It was suspected to be an alcohol containing copper sulfate. Plan a series of tests that the forensic scientist may use to identify the unknown liquid.

Activity

In scientific organisations volumetric analysis can be used in investigative work. Discuss what solutions and techniques you would need to carry out if you were to analyse the following:
- water samples to check pollution control
- acid content of vinegars, citric fruit, lemonade
- lactic acid in milk
- active ingredients in antacid tablets
- iron content in iron tablets/ lawn sand.

By the end of this spread, you should be able to:

* compare respiration and the burning of fuels
* describe the circulatory and respiratory systems as part of the respiration process
* explain why respiration is so important to the functions of all cells in the body

Respiration and the burning of fuels

You may remember from earlier studies that burning and respiration are similar chemical processes.

Both processes release some of the energy found inside molecules. How much of the energy is released will vary. It will depend on the conditions under which the chemical changes take place. You will know that some things burn better under some conditions than others. **Respiration** can be either aerobic or anaerobic. The following word equations summarise burning and respiration.

Burning

fossil fuel + oxygen = carbon dioxide + water + heat and light

Figure 1 Woodland bonfire

Figure 2 Charcoal burning heap

Aerobic respiration

glucose + oxygen = carbon dioxide + water + energy available for cells to use

Anaerobic respiration

glucose = lactic acid + energy available for cells to use

How the circulatory and respiratory systems work together

The word equations for aerobic and anaerobic respiration given above simply state the substrates (raw materials) and the products for the processes. Both processes are, in reality, complicated biochemical pathways. Many stages have been missed out and 'replaced' by the '=' sign.

The biochemical changes involved in anaerobic respiration take place in the cytoplasm of a cell. The **enzymes** that promote these changes are found within the cytoplasm.

The biochemical changes that occur in aerobic respiration take place in special structures called mitochondria (singular: **mitochondrion**).

Assessment tip

When you are asked to make comparisons or highlight differences do not simply make two statements and expect the reader to make the comparison. Try to use link words such as 'whereas' or 'on the other hand'. As an example aerobic respiration produces carbon dioxide and water as wastes *whereas* anaerobic produces lactic acid.

Key definition

A **mitochondrion** is a cell organelle, i.e. a microscopic structure that is found inside a cell. Mitochondria contain the enzymes for the biochemical changes associated with aerobic respiration. They are elongated structures about 1 µm long.

Glucose for respiration has its origin in the food eaten. Oxygen is in the air breathed into the human body. Most respiring cells inside a human body are a long way away from the gut and the lungs. A continuous supply of glucose and oxygen must be made available to a cell if it is to stay alive. Similarly, the toxic (poisonous) waste products of respiration must be removed from the cell to be excreted. Breathing supplies oxygen for the body and removes carbon dioxide from the body. The circulatory system delivers oxygen to respiring cells and takes carbon dioxide away from the cell to be released from the lungs. It also transports the energy released as heat or in chemical form to those parts of the body that require it.

Energy is made available for cells to use in the form of **ATP (adenosine triphosphate)**.

Why respiration is so important

Growth, sensitivity, nutrition, movement, excretion and reproduction all involve chemical changes that require energy. Respiration provides the energy in the form of ATP, required by these life processes.

Examples include energy for:

- muscle contraction
- swimming of sperms
- nerve impulse transmission
- the separation of chromosomes during nuclear division
- the uptake and loss of ions and other particles
- active transport.

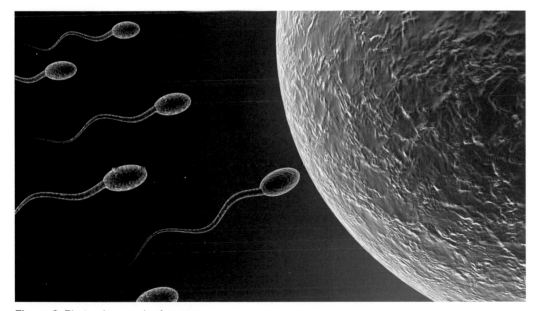

Figure 3 Photomicrograph of sperms

ATP is also important in that when it breaks down to form ADP and in turn AMP (adenosine monophosphate) the phosphate groups may be transferred to other molecules making them 'more reactive' and making chemical change more likely. For example ATP provides energy for chemical change in the liver or for chemical change in the retina of the eye making visual pigments.

One form of AMP is also an important messenger molecule in the body. Cyclic AMP activates enzymes. The enzymes make chemical change more likely.

The way it works is summarised as follows. A **hormone** triggers the production of cyclic AMP. Cyclic AMP activates (turns-on) the enzymes associated with the biochemical pathways associated with that hormone. As a result the hormonally controlled changes happen in the body.

> **Key definition**
>
> A molecule of **ATP** is formed when three phosphate groups are attached to a molecule called adenosine. Energy is required to attach the phosphates, particularly the third. Respiration provides this energy. ATP is produced during respiration. When ATP is broken down e.g. ATP to ADP (adenosine diphosphate) this energy is released. ATP is used as a means to transfer energy from one process to another.

External assessment

51

By the end of this spread, you should be able to:

* state the differences between aerobic and anaerobic respiration in terms of substrates, products and quantity of energy made available to a respiring cell
* relate cellular activity to what happens in a muscle cell during various levels of physical activity
* explain how monitoring a person's circulatory and respiratory systems and analysing their blood provides information about a person's state of health or fitness

All of the ATP used by long distance runners is likely to be produced by aerobic respiration.

100 m sprinters generate their ATP during the race by anaerobic respiration. Weightlifters, gymnasts, basketball players and wrestlers are also towards the 'anaerobic end' of the scale. Where on the scale are joggers likely to appear?

Cells obtain the energy they need, in order to work, in different ways depending on the conditions. This is of interest and value to sports scientists and to the trainers of sportsmen and women.

Differences between aerobic and anaerobic respiration

Aerobic respiration goes on only in the presence of oxygen. Anaerobic respiration can take place in the absence of oxygen.

Table 1 summarises the differences between anaerobic and aerobic respiration in muscles cells.

Feature	Anaerobic	Aerobic
Substrates	Glucose	Glucose and oxygen
Products	Lactic acid	Carbon dioxide and water
Quantity of energy: molecules of ATP per molecule of glucose	2	38

Table 1 The differences between anaerobic and aerobic respiration in muscles cells

Muscles in action

Some sporting activities rely more heavily on aerobic than anaerobic respiration. In others the muscles produce the required energy by respiring anaerobically for most of the action.

Figure 1 Photo finish 100 m sprint

Muscle cells will respire aerobically while the supply of oxygen is adequate. Intensive activity quickly causes the demand for oxygen to exceed the rate at which it can be supplied to the muscles. The cells are obliged to respire anaerobically if they are to continue contracting. Ventilation (breathing) rate and circulatory (heart) rate usually increase to meet the demand for extra oxygen. Carbon dioxide is produced as waste and its concentration increases in the muscle. This is continuously removed by the circulatory system but the pH in the muscle will be relatively acidic. Muscle activity generates heat. Increase in acidity and temperature encourages release of oxygen from **oxyhaemoglobin**. If anaerobic conditions develop lactic acid is formed instead of carbon dioxide and the concentration of this will increase in line with activity.

AS

Unit 3
Monitoring the activity of
the human body

3.1.2 Using energy

ATP credit – oxygen debt

The lactic acid produced during anaerobic respiration is transported to the liver. Here it is converted into a 3-carbon compound which can be used to produce ATP when the oxygen balance is restored. Have you ever wondered why your breathing rate continues to be faster than usual, for a time, after you've finished exercising? The extra oxygen being breathed in is used to oxidise the lactic acid formed during the exercise. You had ATP on credit and the extra oxygen is to pay-back the oxygen debt.

Figure 2 Recovering after a race

Monitoring the activity

You can monitor the effect that a period of activity has on the body by recording:

- breathing rate
- heart rate
- blood oxygen concentration
- blood lactic acid concentration.

The ways that heart rate and breathing can be monitored are described in spreads 3.4.1 and 3.4.3.

It is possible to take blood samples from an athlete during a period of physical activity. Blood-solute concentration changes can be monitored. It is possible to monitor oxygen transport and lactic acid production in this way.

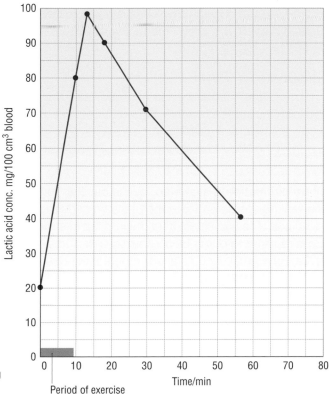

Figure 3 Graph of lactic acid concentration during and after activity

Assessment tip

'Comparisons' and 'differences' can be identified using two pieces of data. To identify a 'trend' will require reference to a wider range of data – either vertically within one column of a table or across a range of columns in a table. Make sure that you actually quote data in data analysis questions. Marks are often allocated for referring to specific relevant data.

By the end of this spread, you should be able to:

✳ describe the structure of the heart, the roles of the four chambers and the valves in double circulation

✳ describe the characteristic features of arteries, veins and capillaries

Figure 1 Athlete using an exercise machine

Case study

In the gym recently a potential member, working-out on an exercise-bike, was being assessed by one of the supervisors. The supervisor was over-heard to say 'I'm checking the most important muscle in your body'. She was taking the person's pulse.

Activity

Look at Figure 3. Find the valves. List the valves and their positions.

Activity

Look at Figure 3. Compare the walls of the right and left ventricles. Use a ruler to measure the thickness of the muscle. What is the ratio of thickness for the two sides?

Is the heart the most important 'muscle' in your body?
Structure of the heart

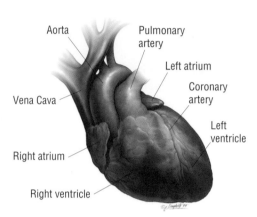

Figure 2 External features of the human heart

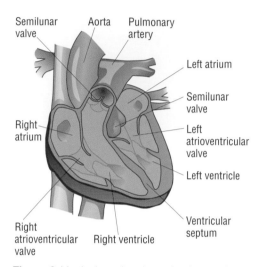

Figure 3 Vertical section through a human heart

The human heart has four muscular chambers. There are two atria (singular **atrium**) and two **ventricles**. When you are standing up blood can pass from the right atrium into the right ventricle below it, similarly on the left of the heart. The atrium and ventricle on each side of the heart are separated by a valve – an **atrioventricular valve**. The same thing will happen if you are upside-down. This is possible because blood moves under pressure and back-flow is prevented by the valves. There are valves at the places where blood enters or leaves the heart.

Double circulation

You can think of the heart as having two functions. These are to pump blood:

* to and from the lungs to enable oxygen to be picked up and to excrete carbon dioxide – the pulmonary circuit
* to and from the body to meet the needs of the cells in body tissues – the systemic circuit.

Pulmonary circulation is 'powered' by the **cardiac muscle** of the right hand side of the heart. The left hand side provides the pressure needed to push blood around the systemic circuit. The two sides of the heart differ in structure as a consequence. Greater pressure is required to pump blood from the heart to all of the body's organs and to return it. Under normal circumstances much of the return journey in the human blood system is against gravity too.

Contraction of the cardiac muscle in the walls of the atria moves blood past the atrioventricular valves into the ventricles. The tricuspid valve is on the right and bicuspid (also known as the mitral valve) on the left. Ventricular contraction moves blood through the semilunar valves of the pulmonary artery and aorta. In a healthy heart this arrangement keeps oxygenated and deoxygenated blood apart improving the efficiency of the circulatory system.

Blood vessels

AS

Unit 3
Monitoring the activity of
the human body

3.2.1 The vascular system

Figure 4 Weightlifter in action

Part of your circulatory system becomes more obvious when you exert yourself. Look at the weightlifter in Figure 4. The blood vessels are prominent. These are veins. They show up because they are quite near to the surface. Their role is to return blood to the heart. The blood in them is under relatively low pressure.

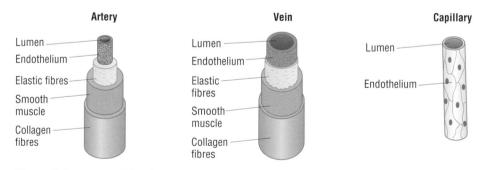

Figure 5 Structure of blood vessels

Blood, going out to the muscles, travels in arteries. These are more deep-seated vessels conducting blood under higher pressure. Arteries are surrounded by the tissues and organs of the body. This helps to confine them and prevent their being over-inflated. This is important. The pressure in the arteries is, as a result, more likely to push the blood forwards and not cause the arteries to 'balloon'.

Positioned between the arteries and veins, linking the two systems, are some very small, tubular, structures called capillaries. Their walls are one-cell thick and have spaces between the cells making the tube 'leaky'. This is where blood solutes, such as oxygen, sugars, waste products and hormones, 'get on' and 'get off' the transport system.

External assessment

By the end of this spread, you should be able to:

✱ **explain how heart rate is affected by nervous and hormonal inputs**

In-built rhythm

The human heart beats, on average, about 70 times every minute. To do its job efficiently the heart muscle needs to contract in a controlled way. This ensures that blood is pumped continuously through the circulatory system at a steady rate. Occasionally, particularly as a person ages, the rhythmic beating of their heart goes wrong. To overcome the problem, they may have to have a pacemaker fitted (see Figure 1).

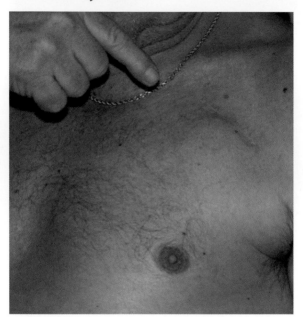

Figure 1 Pacemaker

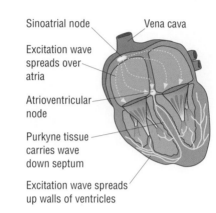

Sinoatrial node
Vena cava
Excitation wave spreads over atria
Atrioventricular node
Purkyne tissue carries wave down septum
Excitation wave spreads up walls of ventricles

Figure 2 Control centres of the heart

Assessment tip

One way to remember the two phases is to think of constriction and dilation – contraction (systole) and relaxation (diastole).

The pattern of muscular activity of a healthy heart is called the **cardiac cycle**. The cycle involves two phases – **systole** and **diastole**. The muscular chambers of the heart contract (systole) and relax (diastole). Atrial systole is usually about 0.15 s, ventricular systole about 0.30 s and diastole about 0.40 s in length.

The timing of the cardiac cycle is controlled by a particular section of the heart muscle known as the **SAN**.

The way that the cardiac cycle is controlled is summarised as follows:
- the muscle cells of the SAN act as the natural pacemaker
- each time they contract they generate impulses
- this wave of excitation spreads out rapidly over the atrial walls
- both atria contract
- at the same rhythm as the SAN
- a band of fibres (**septum**) between the atria and ventricles prevents the wave of excitation from triggering-off ventricular contraction at the same time as atrial contraction
- the wave spreads into the ventricles through a patch of conducting fibres called the **AVN**
- after a delay of about 0.1 second
- it passes to a bunch of conducting fibres called Purkyne fibres, also known as the Bundle of His
- which run down the septum between the ventricles
- the excitation wave travels very rapidly to the base of the heart at the apex of the ventricles
- it spreads upwards and outwards through the ventricle walls
- as the excitation wave passes through the ventricular wall it causes the muscle cells to contract from the apex up.

Key definitions

The **SAN** (sinoatrial node) is myogenic, as is all cardiac muscle, having an inbuilt ability to generate action potentials or impulses. It sets up, as a result, its own rhythm of contraction. It does not require nerve impulses to do so.

The **AVN** (atrioventricular node) is the position where the wave of excitement is allowed to pass through the septum that separates the atria from the ventricles.

External assessment

Changing the rhythm

The rate of the cardiac cycle described above can vary. You may have been aware of occasions when your heart has been beating faster than usual. This is a common outcome of physical activity. It also happens when you are startled by something – sudden noise or threatening event. There must be other factors at work here overriding the SAN in some way. Heart rate can be affected by nervous and hormonal inputs.

Why change the rhythm?

During periods of increased activity the muscles involved require a faster and greater blood supply. This is to provide extra oxygen and blood sugar to service the increase in aerobic respiration to supply the ATP required. Larger concentrations of carbon dioxide are produced that have to be removed from the active muscle. The heart attempts to do this by increasing its output – cardiac output. This is achieved in two ways. The heart rate can increase in terms of beats per minute. The volume of blood pushed out, stroke volume, can be increased in terms of cm³ per stroke. Cardiac output can be calculated using the following equation:

Cardiac output = heart rate × stroke volume (volume per unit time)

How does the body's activity bring about the change? These changes are partly under nervous control and partly hormonal.

Nervous control

The heart receives impulses from two types of nerve over which you have no conscious control. These are:

- a parasympathetic nerve called the vagus delivers impulses to the SAN and the AVN
- sympathetic nerves deliver impulses to many areas of the heart's walls.

Sympathetic stimulation of the heart speeds up the heart rate and increases the stroke volume. Impulses arriving at the heart in the vagus nerve cause the heart rate to fall and the stroke volume to decrease. Prior to physical activity your brain will get your heart ready for action by sympathetic nerve stimulation.

Hormonal control

Adrenaline, a **hormone** secreted by the adrenal glands, has an effect on the heart similar to sympathetic stimulation. When you are really excited or very scared you can feel the change – a sudden rush, racing pulse, thumping heart beat.

How is the need for change monitored and regulated?

The cardiovascular centre in the medulla oblongata region of the brain regulates heart activity and breathing.

Two types of receptors are found in the walls of the aorta close to the heart and the carotid bodies:

1 Chemoreceptors monitor concentrations of oxygen, carbon dioxide and hydrogen ions in the blood flowing through them. If oxygen concentration is lower than normal and carbon dioxide and hydrogen ion concentrations are higher than normal the cardiovascular centre is 'informed' by nerve impulses. Sympathetic stimulation of the heart, adrenal glands and in particular the muscles associated with breathing brings about an increased cardiac output and breathing rate.

2 Baroreceptors (stretch receptors) register changes in the walls of the blood vessels caused by change in blood pressure. High blood pressure stretches the wall. Impulses are sent to the cardiovascular centre which in turn sets off impulses in the vagus (parasympathetic) nerve to the heart to slow it down and reduce its stroke volume. This helps to lower the blood pressure. The opposite effect results from sympathetic stimulation if the baroreceptors register lower than normal blood pressure.

> **Key definition**
>
> Hormones are chemical messengers. They are made in one place and have their effect somewhere else (on target cells). They are distributed by means of the bloodstream. Their effects are often slower and longer lasting than nervous communications.

External assessment

By the end of this spread, you should be able to:

✳ describe the structure of the lungs, trachea and bronchial tubes
✳ describe how ventilation is brought about by muscles

Structure of the human ventilation system

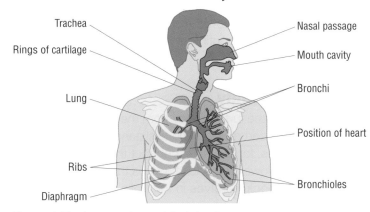

Figure 1 The lungs and associated structures

Air enters the human ventilation system through the mouth and nose. It is moved along the trachea and enters the bronchial tree. Look at Figure 1. You will see why the arrangement of airways is compared to a tree – you'll have to turn the book upside down to get the full effect. The trachea divides to form the left and right **bronchi** (singular bronchus). Each bronchus divides forming smaller branches called **bronchioles**. The bronchioles branch to form even narrower tubes. The dead ends of the narrowest bronchioles are air-sacs called **alveoli** (singular alveolus). The alveoli are close to capillaries of the pulmonary arteries and veins (see spread 3.2.5, Figure 1).

As you will see below air is moved in and out of the airways as a result of pressure changes. If the pressure within a flexible tube is reduced it is possible that the tube will collapse. Also if two thin, smooth, moist surfaces are allowed to come into contact they tend to stick together. You may well have used cling-film and be aware of this principle. It is important therefore that the surfaces of the airways are kept apart. One way in which this is achieved is by the presence of cartilage in the wall of the structure concerned. The trachea has 'C-shaped' rings of **cartilage** to prevent collapse but at the same time retain flexibility.

> ### Key definition
>
> **Cartilage** is a hard but flexible supporting tissue. Living cartilage cells are set in a mass composed of a variety of substances including the protein collagen. Nutrients and other required substances can diffuse to the cartilage-forming cells.

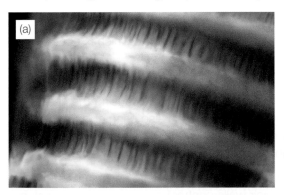

Figure 2 a Photo of close-up of trachea. **b** Photo of vacuum-cleaner hose

Particles of dust and microorganisms are usually present in inhaled air. It is important that these are removed to protect the delicate gas exchange surfaces, particularly in the alveoli. Goblet cells are found in the airways of the ventilation system. These cells secrete **mucus** which is sticky. Airborne particles and potentially damaging microorganisms are trapped in the mucus. The mucus is moved up and out of the airways by the rhythmic action of **cilia**. The mucus, together with the trapped material, is brought to the back of the throat to be swallowed. The debris ends up in the acidic content of the stomach.

Contraction of involuntary, smooth muscle in the wall of an airway causes the airway to become narrower. This restricts air flow. This can be a problem and is one of the causes of an asthmatic attack.

The special features shown by parts of the airways are summarised in Table 1. A '✓' in the table means that the feature is shown by the structure and an '✗' indicates that it is not.

Structure	Feature			
	Cartilage	**Goblet cells**	**Smooth muscle**	**Cilia**
Trachea	✓	✓	✓	✓
Bronchus	✓	✓	✓	✓
Large bronchiole	✗	✓	✓	✓
Alveolus	✗	✗	✗	✗

Table 1 Special features of the airways

How humans breathe

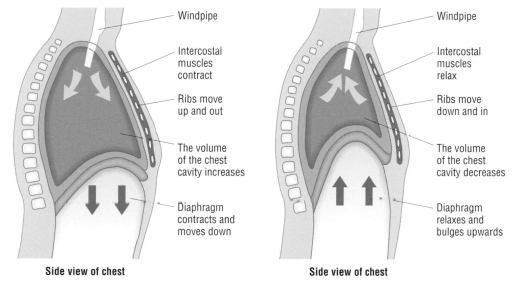

Side view of chest   Side view of chest

Figure 3 Side views of thorax to show changes taking place during inhalation and exhalation

Feature	Inhalation	Exhalation
Ribs and sternum	Raised by contraction of external intercostal muscles	Lowered by gravity and contraction of internal intercostal muscles
Diaphragm	Pulled down by contraction of muscle fibres in diaphragm	Diaphragm moves up due to contraction of abdominal wall muscle, elastic recoil or resistance offered by gut
Volume of thorax	Increases	Decreases
Air pressure inside thorax	Decreases	Increases
Air movement	From the atmosphere to the lung air space	From the lung air space to the atmosphere

Table 2 Relationships between breathing in and breating out

Key definitions

Mucus is a glycoprotein – a large molecule formed from a protein and a sugar. The molecules are long and fibrous. In water the long molecules interact to form networks. This makes the solution thick and sticky.

A cilium (plural **cilia**) is an elongated, hair-like structure found as part of a specialised cell. Cilia are able to beat. An unattached ciliated cell can move. Its cilium beats in such a way that the cell moves through the liquid that surrounds it. If ciliated cells are anchored, fixed as part of a tissue as is the case in the human airway, when the cilia beat the cells stays where they are and the mucus moves.

Case study

Cystic fibrosis sufferers produce extra thick, very sticky mucus. This can accumulate in the lungs and pathogens that would normally be removed in the mucus by cilia remain and may cause infection. The cilia are unable to move the mucus and physiotherapy is required to get rid of it.

Key definition

Intercostal muscles are found between the ribs. There are two sets acting as antagonistic pairs. The external set contract to enable inhalation and the internal set reverse the movement.

External assessment

By the end of this spread, you should be able to:

＊ **explain how gases are exchanged between the atmosphere and the blood through the respiratory surfaces of the lungs**
＊ **explain how oxygen and nutrients reach the cells within tissues**
＊ **explain how carbon dioxide is removed from the cells and from the bloodstream**

Gas exchange in the lungs
What makes a good gas exchange surface?

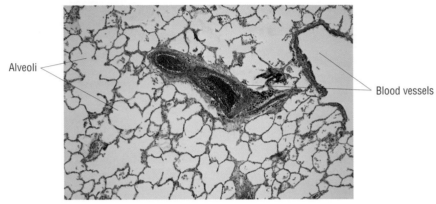

Alveoli

Blood vessels

Figure 1 Diagram of alveoli and associated blood vessels

Cells in the body require a continuous supply of oxygen for respiration and a means to remove the waste, carbon dioxide. Oxygen enters and carbon dioxide leaves the human body through the lungs. Both respiratory gases are transported to and from the lungs by the bloodstream. Gas exchange will therefore take place between the lung air space and pulmonary capillary networks and between the blood in systemic capillary networks and the cells close to them. This section will focus on the processes that take place in the lungs but the principles involved will be the same at both sites.

The alveoli, blood and capillary network of the human lung provide an efficient gas exchange surface. The lung system shows the following features:

* Very large surface area – in a young adult estimated to be about 70 m² compared to total body surface area approximately 18 m².
* Barriers are very thin – alveolar wall and pulmonary capillary wall are both about 0.1 μm to 0.5 μm thick.
* Permeable to the gases involved – alveolar and capillary walls are permeable to water, oxygen and carbon dioxide.
* Moist – the surface of the alveoli and the capillary walls have liquid on them that includes water so that the gases can dissolve and cross the membranes in solution.
* About 80% of the total alveolar surface is in contact with a pulmonary capillary.
* Red blood cells are flexible and when forced through very narrow capillaries will change shape, curving into contact with the capillary wall – the diffusion distance is therefore very small.
* **Diffusion gradients** exist – maintained in the correct direction.
* Close to a transport system – the gases in the alveolar spaces are continuously changed as a result of ventilation and the blood in the capillaries is continuously changed as a result of blood circulation.

Air brought into the lungs, when you breathe in, diffuses into the alveolar spaces. Blood arriving at the gas exchange surface has less oxygen and more carbon dioxide in it than the air at the exchange surface. The diffusion gradient for oxygen is such that oxygen will

Activity

Wet, thin surfaces stick together like cling-film. Why don't alveolar surfaces stick together?
Why is the possibility of alveoli sticking together a problem for premature babies?

Key definition

A **diffusion gradient** gives an indication of the rate of diffusion between two areas. It depends on the difference in concentration of the same particle e.g. ion Cl⁻ or molecule e.g. O₂ found in the two areas. Where the difference in concentration is large the gradient will be steep and the diffusion rate will be much higher, from high to low than low to high. When the gradient is zero, the concentration is the same in each area and the rate of diffusion between the two areas is the same in both directions. A state of equilibrium exists.

AS
Unit 3
Monitoring the activity of
the human body
3.2.5 Gas exchange

diffuse from the air space to the blood faster than in the other direction. Net exchange for oxygen will be from air to blood. The converse is true for carbon dioxide. More carbon dioxide will leave the blood for the air space than in the opposite direction in the same time. The net result here is for more carbon dioxide to leave the blood than enter it.

The percentage composition of gases in inhaled and exhaled air is summarised in Table 1.

Gas	Inhaled (%)	Exhaled (%)	Approximate change
Oxygen	21.00	17.00	20% decrease
Carbon dioxide	0.04	4.00	100-fold increase
Nitrogen	79.00	79.00	nil

Table 1 Percentage composition of gases in inhaled and exhaled air

Transport to cells
Transport of oxygen
Oxygen is transported around the bloodstream in the red blood cells. **Haemoglobin** present in the blood cell will combine with oxygen to form **oxyhaemoglobin**. This is a reversible reaction. The position of equilibrium is determined by the concentration of free oxygen surrounding the haemoglobin.

haemoglobin + 4 molecules of oxygen ⇌ oxyhaemoglobin

In areas of high oxygen availability the reaction proceeds from left to right. In areas where oxygen availability is limited the reverse occurs and oxyhaemoglobin breaks down to release its oxygen.

One area where there will be a lot of oxygen available is in the lungs. Here, red blood cells will become highly saturated with oxygen. The reverse will occur when they arrive, for example, at an area of high respiratory activity such as an exercising muscle. Low oxygen availability there will cause the oxyhaemoglobin to break down releasing its oxygen.

Transport of nutrients
Dissolved nutrients such as blood glucose, amino acids, fatty acids and glycerol are added to the bloodstream by diffusion, facilitated diffusion or **active transport** from the small intestine after a meal. Some of these will be put to use, as required, by respiring cells. Those nutrients surplus to requirement will be stored, to be released/for use at a later date. Nutrients travel to their point of use as solutes in blood plasma.

Transport away from cells
Transport of carbon dioxide
Carbon dioxide diffuses from a respiring cell into the blood plasma to be transported in one of three different ways:
- 5% dissolves in the blood plasma as molecular carbon dioxide.
- 10% leaves the plasma to enter red blood cells where it combines with haemoglobin to form **carbaminohaemoglobin**.
- 85% diffuses into red blood cells where it combines with water to form carbonic acid, the process being catalysed by the enzyme carbonic anhydrase. Carbonic acid breaks down inside the red blood cell to form hydrogen carbonate ions and hydrogen ions. The hydrogen ions combine with haemoglobin to form haemoglobinic acid. The hydrogen carbonate ions diffuse out of the red blood cells travelling to the lungs in solution in the plasma.

Excretion at lung surface
When the red blood cells arrive at the lungs the chemistry goes into reverse. The carbon dioxide diffuses into the alveoli to be excreted from the lungs when you breathe out.

Figure 2 Patient with nasal cannulae in place

Case study
Carbon monoxide is a product of the combustion of petrol or a poorly ventilated or inefficient gas appliance. It is also a component of tobacco smoke. Inhaled carbon monoxide combines irreversibly with haemoglobin to form carboxyhaemoglobin. Red blood cells exposed to the high concentration of this gas in the lungs of a smoker who inhales tobacco smoke will no longer be able to transport oxygen. Poorly serviced and maintained gas appliances can lead to fatalities.

External assessment

By the end of this spread, you should be able to:

* explain why you need to know the average values that are regarded as normal for physiological indicators for male and female adults at rest
* describe how blood counts can be useful in diagnosis e.g. red blood cells and anaemia, and white cells and leukaemia
* state the principles of how blood sugar monitoring is useful in the treatment of diabetes
* state the principles of how breathing tests of e.g. tidal volume and peak flow rate are used in the treatment of asthma

Vital signs

A physical assessment is likely to be one of the first things that happen to you when you go to see a doctor or go into hospital. The doctor or nurse will 'give you a check-up'. Your vital signs are measured and recorded. Vital signs are indicators of health. They include temperature, pulse, breathing actions and blood pressure. Together this data provides a baseline for medical staff to work from. The data indicate your state of health. Factors around and within you may cause these vital signs to change. Examples could include one or more of the following: how active you are physically, what the temperature is around you, whether you are physically or psychologically ill. Changes may take the vital signs outside the normal, 'average' range and indicate a need for medical or nursing care. They will also, of course, indicate the effectiveness or otherwise of the medical and nursing therapies.

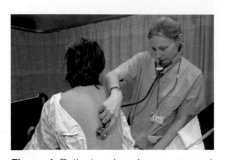
Figure 1 Patient undergoing assessment in hospital

Vital sign	Subject/condition	Value/range
Blood glucose	Fasting	3.5–7.5 mmol dm³
	Glucose in urine	9.0 mmol dm³
Breathing	Rate, typical range	15–18 per min
	Tidal volume	0.4–0.5 dm³
	Vital capacity (male)	6.0 dm³
	Vital capacity (female)	4.25 dm³
	Peak flow	400–600 dm³ min⁻¹
Blood pressure	Typical 18-year-old adult	120/80 mmHg
	Male, 20 years old	125/80 mmHg
	Female, 20 years old	123/80 mmHg
	Male, 40 years old	135/85 mmHg
	Female, 40 years old	133/85 mmHg
Pulse	Rate, typical range	60–80 beats per min
Body temperature	Normal, typical range	36.5–37.2 °C
	Death	below 25 °C
	Hypothermia	32 °C
	Fever	Above 37.2 °C
	Hyperthermia/heat exhaustion/heat stroke	Likely if above 38 °C in the absence of infection
	High temperatures that would lead to death	Above 43 °C

Table 1 Normal values or ranges

AS

Unit 3
Monitoring the activity of
the human body

3.3.1 Vital signs

Blood cell counts and diagnosis

Check-ups by your doctor can often result in your having to have a blood sample taken for analysis. These are used to identify, confirm or reject possible conditions. For example, a doctor may suspect that an individual has anaemia. Individuals suffering from anaemia for example have a blood-haemoglobin concentration lower than normal. This may be due to (i) too few red blood cells being produced, (ii) some of those produced being destroyed or (iii) by blood loss (bleeding) having taken place. A blood sample investigation would be helpful to distinguish between the first two possible causes. Abnormality in terms of cell count can be assessed by doing a full blood count where a sample is tested with an automated analyser (see spread 4.4.2). In addition a blood smear might be used. This could provide a significant amount of information including abnormality of blood cell structure. See also spread 4.5.1.

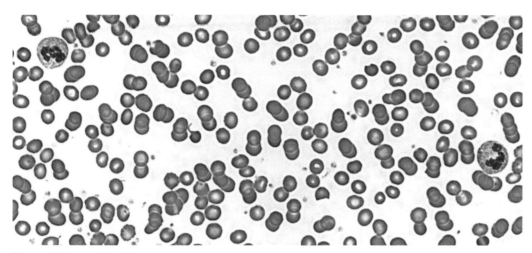

Figure 2 Human blood smear

Similarly, a full blood count indicating increased **leucocyte** cell count above the normal $4\text{--}11 \times 10^9/dm^3$ might indicate the disease leukaemia. See also spread 4.5.1.

Diabetics need to check their blood-sugar level

Diabetes is a disease that appears to be on the increase. Diabetics have to inject insulin in order to control their blood-glucose concentration. They must do this in a controlled way – the quantity injected should relate to the blood-glucose demand. In a healthy individual the blood-glucose concentration is regulated by two hormones, insulin and glucagon.

Both these hormones are secreted by the pancreas in response to the level of glucose in the blood. To regulate the blood-glucose concentration artificially, therefore, it is necessary to know what the blood-glucose concentration is, in order to administer the appropriate amount of insulin. Diabetics can do the monitoring using clinisticks or a sugar metering device (see spread 3.4.5).

Breathing tests and asthma management

Another disease on the increase is asthma. As you may have seen earlier (see spread 3.2.4) one of the direct causes of this disease is the contraction of smooth muscle in the walls of the airways. This constricts the tube and restricts the passage of air. Consequently the individual suffers from shortness of breath. Drugs are available to try to control these attacks. The effectiveness of the therapy can be monitored and the disease managed by measuring and recording breathing test data. One test commonly used is the peak flow test (see spread 3.4.3). Alternatively, breathing rate and tidal volume data acquired by spirometry may be of value to medical staff responsible for an asthmatic patient's care.

Key definition

Leucocytes are white blood cells. There are several different types including neutrophils, lymphocytes, monocytes, eosinophils and basophils.

Source

Hormonal control of diabetes

External assessment

65

By the end of this spread, you should be able to:

* state the principles of how blood tests are used to find the following chemicals in the blood: alcohol, a named recreational drug and a named performance enhancing drug

When do we have to take blood–drug tests?

There are a variety of situations where it is necessary to test blood for drugs. Some of these are listed below:

- accident testing
- health/life insurance medicals
- pre-employment screening
- evidence of illegality
- comply with drug rehabilitation programme
- sports related drug abuse.

Figure 1 Police and medical team at an accident

Which drugs are described as recreational drugs?

Name of drug	Type of drug
Alcohol	Depressant
Amphetamines (whizz, pills, speed)	Stimulant
Amyl nitrate (poppers)	Stimulant
Ecstasy (e's)	Hallucinogenic
Barbiturates (downers)	Depressant
Cannabis (pot, hash, spliff, weed, green, puff)	Depressant
Cocaine (Columbian marching powder)	Stimulant
GHB (liquid e, liquid x)	Anaesthetic
Ketamine	Anaesthetic (veterinary use)
Khat	Stimulant
Heroin (morphine, smack, h, brown)	Analgesic
Methadone	Analgesic
THC	Hallucinogenic

Table 1 Common recreational drugs

Source

Web link to drug index: Drug Scope

External assessment

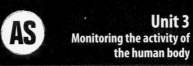

AS

Unit 3
Monitoring the activity of
the human body

3.3.2 Drugs and drug testing

Which drugs are described as performance enhancing drugs?

Name of drug	Type/action
Anabolic steroid	Substance related to testosterone
Erythropoietin (EPO)	Hormone, stimulates red blood cell production
Modafinil	Stimulant, promotes wakefulness
Nandrolone	Anabolic steroid
Testosterone	Anabolic steroid
Tetrahydrogesterone (THG, The Clear)	Anabolic steroid
Trenbolone	Anabolic steroid, veterinary use

Table 2 Common performance enhancing drugs

What happens to you when you give a blood sample?

A simple procedure is carried out to obtain a blood sample.

- Blood samples are usually obtained from the veins at the elbow.
- A band, called a tourniquet, is placed around the upper arm.
- This stops blood leaving the veins in the arm. The veins at the elbow become much more obvious and filled with blood.
- The surface of the skin is cleaned.
- A hypodermic needle is inserted into vein.
- A low pressure bottle or a syringe is attached to the needle and blood is withdrawn.
- The blood is transferred to the bottle if a syringe has been used and the bottle sealed.
- Pressure is applied to the puncture wound with a small ball of cotton wool.
- Adhesive tape may be placed over the dressing.
- The hypodermic and syringe are placed into the designated waste container.
- The blood sample is sent to the appropriate laboratory for analysis.

What happens to the blood when it gets to the laboratory?

A variety of techniques are available to test a blood sample for the presence of drugs and their concentrations. Methods of detection and assessment commonly applied to **assay** a blood sample include one or more of the following:

- gas chromatography (GC)
- high performance liquid chromatography (HPLC)
- UV absorption (UVA)
- mass spectrometry (MS).

> **Key definition**
>
> An **assay** is a quantitative/qualitative analysis of a substance especially on ores and drugs to determine its components and concentration. Assay techniques are often used to compare measurements with known concentrations as in colorimetry.

Case study

A blood sample will need to be prepared before it undergoes assessment. Blood cells for example will be removed. The liquid component is presented to the machine for analysis. As a mixture passes through a chromatographic process, solutes and solvents pass through the stationary material in the column. Some substances are retained more than others. Any substance will behave in the same way under the same conditions. Its retention value is one of its characteristics. A gas chromatography machine may be used to produce a graph showing the various components. An HPLC system could be used to produce a graph showing retention values for the components of the sample. Part of the HPLC system involves a UV detector. Some HPLC systems are linked to a mass spectrometer. When a component is recognised by the UV detector some of the detected substance is sent to the mass spectrometer for analysis. The whole process is linked to a computer.

Different compounds have different retention times, UV absorption values, fragmentation patterns. Database records are available, for these values, for a very large number of compounds. This enables rapid and automated identification of any drugs present in a blood sample.

The concentration of the substance in the sample can be calculated by the computer. Most UK labs use the same concentration value for a 'positive' test result. A result is considered to be positive if the concentration of the drug present is above a specified concentration for that particular drug. Follow guidelines from Substance and Mental Health Services Administration (SAMHSA).

External assessment

By the end of this spread, you should be able to:

✳ **state the principles of how blood tests, including ELISA tests, are used to find antibody indicators for diseases, e.g. hepatitis and AIDS**

Key definitions

Antigens are molecules which a cell recognises as foreign. They could be part of a pathogen, a pollen grain or a dust particle. They initiate an immune response.

An **antibody** is a protein produced in response to an antigen. The relationship between an antigen and its antibody is extremely specific.

An **enzyme** is a protein which alters the rate of a chemical change. Sometimes they are described as biological catalysts.

An **isotope** is one form of a chemical element. Isotopes differ in terms of the number of neutrons in their nucleus. They have the same number of electrons and protons. Examples include C^{12} and C^{14}. C^{14} is radioactive.

Fluorescent and **chemi-luminescent** compounds give off light.

Blood tests have been developed that use the principle of antigen–antibody specificity. These are called immunoassays. Disease organisms possess specific antigens. Each **antigen** is recognised by its own. Specific antibody and forms an antigen–antibody complex with it. The antigen indicates the presence of the pathogen, the **antibody** locates the antigen and the antigen–antibody complex confirms its presence.

So if you can find the antigen–antibody complex and make it show up you can demonstrate that the pathogen is in the sample.

The antibodies used in the test can be labelled so that they can be located.

Antibodies are labelled in one of three ways.

The antibody can be linked to:
• an **enzyme**
• a radioactive **isotope**
• a **fluorescent** or **chemi-luminescent** compound.

The 'enzyme–antibody–antigen' complex usually converts a colourless substrate into a coloured product. If there is a colour change, the complex, and therefore the antigen, must be there. How much colour is produced, measured by colorimetry, gives an indication of the quantity. ELISA is an enzyme-linked immunosorbent assay.

Radioactive antibody–antigen complexes will act as a radioactive source and can be registered using a Geiger-Muller counter.

The fluorescent or chemi-fluorescent assays are recorded using fluorometers. They can also be viewed using microscopy.

Radioimmunoassay is the least commonly used.

When you have an infection your body reacts to the presence of the pathogen's antigen by producing antibodies. Therefore presence of antibodies of a specific type in blood serum will also indicate that the pathogen has been around and that you have, or have had, an infection. This is the most common way in which immunoassays are employed.

Figure 1 Technician setting up ELISA

ELISA can be used to test a patient to see whether they have a disease, for example hepatitis or HIV. In an ELISA the enzyme-linked antibody (monoclonal antibody) you add to the sample is 'looking for' an antigen which is itself an antibody. The one being looked for is the one the sample-provider's body will have made in response to the infection if they were infected. Let's call the antibody in the sample IgG. This is, for example, the HIV- or hepatitis-specific antibody. The enzyme-linked anti-IgG is added to the sample. If the HIV antibody IgG is there, the anti-IgG will attach to it. If the colourless substrate is added the enzyme will promote the change and a colour will appear but only if the HIV antibody was there to start with.

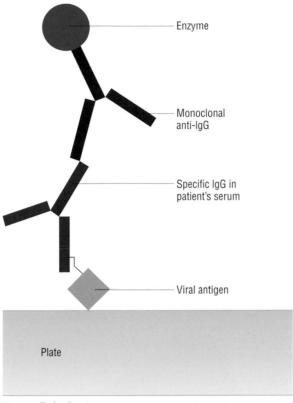

Figure 2 Antibody–enzyme– antigen linkage in ELISA

ELISA tests are carried out in special plates. The plates have an ordered arrangement of wells on their surface. The following list summarises one way in which an ELISA can be carried out to test for a particular antigen found in someone's blood serum.
- Antibodies specific for the antigen in question are added to bind to the bottom of the wells.
- The wells are washed to get rid of surplus antibodies.
- An agent is added that binds to those areas of the walls of the wells not occupied by antibody.
- The wells are washed again to get rid of surplus binding agent.
- The patient's serum sample is added to the wells.
- Any of the specific antigen present in the serum binds to the antibodies fixed to the walls of the wells.
- The wells are washed to get rid of surplus serum.
- Antibody–enzyme complex is added to the wells.
- This complex binds to any antigen trapped in the wells.
- Surplus complex is washed away.
- Substrate appropriate for the enzyme linked to the antibody is added.
- If the enzyme is there the enzyme promoted reaction occurs.
- An observable change occurs (probably a colour change) and intensity measured if the test is positive.

Case study

Pregnancy test kits work on the same principle. Human chorionic gonadotrophin (HCG) is found in the urine after conception. Anti-HCG monoclonal antibodies are present in the test device. A urine sample is wicked into the device. If HCG is present the hormone links to the anti-HCG, a particular sequence of events takes place and a 'positive result' shows up indicating pregnancy. If HCG is not present, a different outcome leads to a negative result.

External assessment

Sphygmomanometers and electrocardiograms have their uses

By the end of this spread, you should be able to:

* state that a sphygmomanometer can be used to monitor blood pressure; an electrocardiogram can be used to monitor the activity of the heart
* recognise a normal trace, or the average value in the case of a sphygmomanometer, and describe what it shows for each of the instruments
* recognise traces for normal heart, sinus tachycardia, bradycardia, sinus arrhythmia and ventricular fibrillation
* describe what sphygmomanometer and electrocardiogram readings show about the probable physiological status of people
* use graphs to monitor changes in blood pressure and pulse rate (from spreads 3.4.1 and 3.4.2)

Sphygmomanometer

There are two types of sphygmomanometers. These are digital and manual. Digital (electronic) sphygmomanometers are easier to use and do not involve listening to the blood flow but are less accurate and are not used for patients with certain conditions. They calculate mean arterial pressure. Manual versions include mercury and aneroid sphygmomanometers. A manual sphygmomanometer is used to measure blood pressure indirectly by using a **stethoscope** to register changes in pressure by changes in sound.

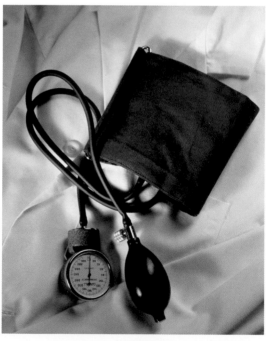

Figure 1 Manual (aneroid) sphygmomanometer

Many factors affect blood pressure readings. These include age, diurnal variation (changes over the course of a 24-hour day), medications and stress. Values considered to be normal are often stated in the media but are obliged to be generalisations. (See values stated in Table 1, spread 3.3.1.)

Blood pressure values are used as indicators of physiological status and are useful in patient assessment. It is however important that the factors mentioned in the previous paragraph are taken into account when interpreting blood pressure readings. For example, if someone

AS

Unit 3
Monitoring the activity of
the human body

3.3.4 Sphygmomanometers and
electrocardiograms have their uses

who might be expected to record a blood pressure reading of 120/80 mmHg actually presented with a value of 150/90 mmHg this would be cause for concern. On its own this would not necessarily indicate hypertension but it would probably prompt further monitoring. Systolic values less than 90 mmHg are normal for some people but for the majority this would probably indicate hypotension and some form of illness.

Electrocardiogram

An electrocardiogram is a device that produces a graphical representation of your heart's activity.

Figure 2 shows the traces produced by individuals showing normal heart activity, sinus tachycardia, bradycardia, sinus arrhythmia and ventricular fibrillation.

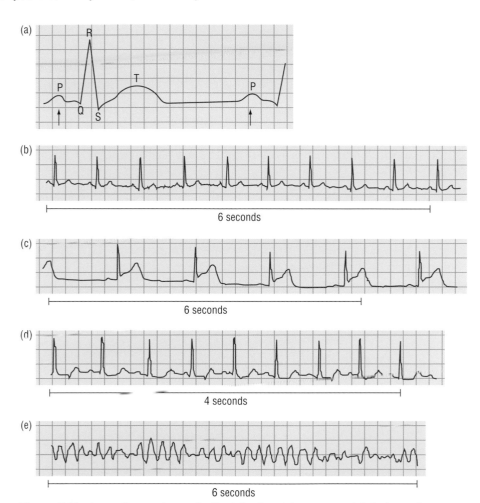

Figure 2 Electrocardiogram traces for the following states: **a** normal, **b** tachycardia, **c** bradycardia, **d** arrhythmia and **e** ventricular fibrillation

Traces that show abnormally elevated heart rate, above 100 beats per minute in adults, indicate a state called tachycardia. When the heart rate is abnormally depressed, below 60 beats per minute in adults, this indicates a state described as bradycardia.

Any deviation from the normal heart rate rhythm is covered by the general term arrhythmia. Tachycardia may happen as a result of exercise, emotion or fever. Athletes commonly show bradycardia. Sinus arrhythmia often shows up in young people as a change in rhythm with ventilation. Heart rate increases with inspiration and decreases with expiration. The term ventricular fibrillation is used to describe the condition when the ventricular contractions are irregular and uncoordinated. This results in ineffective cardiac output. As a result the individual rapidly loses consciousness and death occurs unless immediate effective treatment is started.

By the end of this spread, you should be able to:

✱ state that a spirometer and peak flow meter can be used to monitor the activity of the lungs
✱ recognise a normal trace for a spirometer and the average value in the case of a peak flow meter, and describe what it shows for each of the instruments
✱ describe what spirometer traces and peak flow meter readings show about the probable physiological status of people

Spirometer

A spirometer is used to assess lung volumes. The following volumes and capacity can be assessed using a spirometer.

- Tidal volume – the volume of air that is ventilated during either the inspiratory or the expiratory phase of each breathing cycle.
- Inspiratory reserve volume – the volume of the extra air that can be inspired at the end of tidal inspiration.
- Expiratory reserve volume – the volume of the extra air that can be expired at the end of tidal expiration.
- Inspiratory capacity – maximum volume of air that can be inspired following tidal expiration.
- **Vital capacity** – maximum volume of air that can be expired after a maximum inspiration.
- Residual volume – the volume of gas left in the lungs after maximum expiration.

It is possible to measure these as static measurements or as volume–time traces. The spirometer can also be used to measure rate of oxygen consumption. This is indicated by the fall of the marker as it travels across the grid.

Key definitions

A **lung capacity** is composed of two or more lung volumes. For example:

Vital capacity = tidal volume + inspiratory reserve + expiratory reserve.

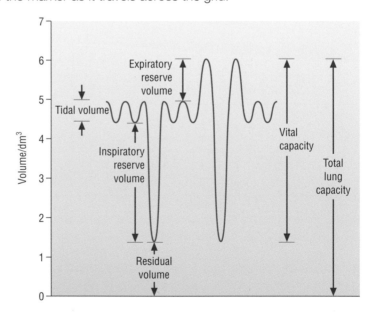

Figure 1 Typical lung volumes and **lung capacities** at rest

Lung volumes which are abnormally low (particularly residual volume) indicate restrictive lung disease e.g. pulmonary fibrosis, lung cancer and pneumonia. Asthma is described as an obstructive lung disease and asthmatics usually have normal lung volumes (except for residual volume) but their flow rate is reduced. People suffering from other obstructive lung diseases such as chronic obstructive pulmonary disease (COPD), e.g. bronchitis and emphysema, have residual volume values that are greater than normal. It is important to remember however that that residual volume cannot be measured by spirometry.

AS

Unit 3
Monitoring the activity of
the human body

3.3.5 Measurement of ventilation

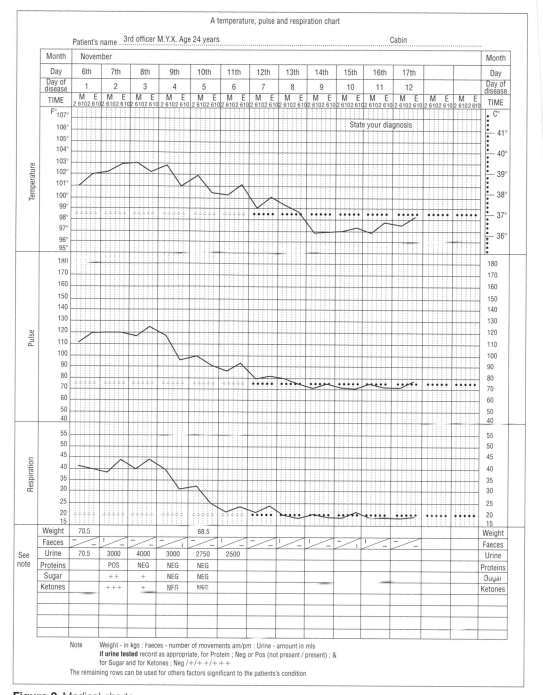

Figure 2 Medical charts

Heat exhaustion is linked to, and can result from, any activity that causes extreme levels of sweating. During sweating the body loses water and sodium and chloride ions. If the water and ions are not replaced this can result in nausea, vomiting, headaches and tachycardia. This is common among long-distance runners who do not drink enough fluids during a race or are exposed to high environmental temperatures.

When the core temperature is greater than 40°C tissue damage is caused. Irreversible damage to tissues can occur and the individual is said to be suffering from heat stroke. This is a particularly dangerous thermal disorder because of its high fatality rate. Once more those at greatest risk are the very young and the elderly.

Also at risk of heat stroke are those who have occupations where high temperatures are the norm. This is of significance to anyone who works strenuously in the heat. Examples might include, among others, athletes, construction workers, steel workers or farmers.

Peak flow meter

A peak flow meter is used to measure the peak expiratory flow rate. This is the maximum flow of air that can be forced out of the lungs.

Table 1 shows the ranges of normal values of peak expiratory flow (PEF) at different ages.

	Range of PEF/dm³ min⁻¹	
Age/years	Men	Women
20	540–600	410–445
30	595–660	425–465
35	600–665	425–465
40	600–660	420–455
60	530–590	375–410

Table 1 Peak expiratory flow for different age groups

Peak flow meters can be used by patients at home to monitor their peak flow rates. This enables patients and their carers to monitor the disease and effectiveness of any medication. Sufferers are encouraged to keep a peak flow diary. Figure 2 shows a page from an 80-year-old lady's peak flow diary.

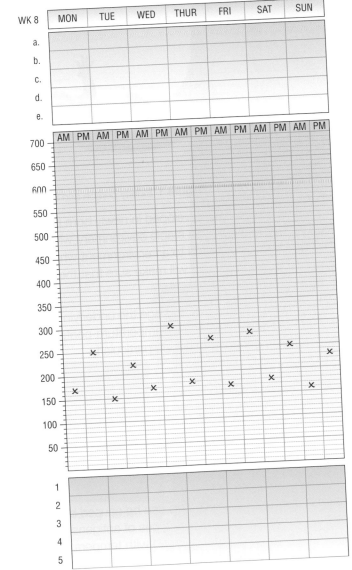

Figure 2 Page from an asthmatic's peak flow diary

Figure steel

⑥ Body temperature

By the end of this spread, you should be able to:

* recognise the normal body temperature for an averag[...]
  body can withstand, and body temperatures that are d[...]
* use graphs to monitor changes in body temperature (fr[...]

Key definitions

The **core temperature** is the temperature of the organs within the skull, thoracic and abdominal cavities i.e. organs such as the brain, heart and lungs, liver and gut.

A **thermal disorder** is one where heat or lack of it is the significant problem for the individual. This is different, for example, to the condition where there is a raised temperature because of an infection or stress or hormones.

As you have seen earlier, as with other vital signs, a[...] for different individuals. There is no absolute standar[...] often used is 37 °C but it is probably more sensible t[...]

The body maintains an internal temperature within th[...] internal and external environment. Changes in metab[...] conditions initiate self regulatory processes within the[...] **core temperature** within the acceptable range.

When the body's core temperature falls below the lo[...] individual is said to be hypothermic or suffering from [...]

Hypothermia occurs below 34.4 °C. The heart rate, re[...] falls. Several factors affect body temperature including[...] of the human life-span are particularly at risk of **therm**[...] consequences.

Fig[...]

The temperature regulating mechanisms are not fully de[...] and consequently they are at risk. The womb provides a[...] appropriate temperature. After birth the baby is exposed[...] temperature can fluctuate widely. Appropriate child care[...] does not suffer.

Old age poses problems with respect to hypothermia. A[...] may include physiological, behavioural or economic facto[...] processes deteriorate as you get older. The control proce[...] vasoconstriction and vasodilation, do not work as effectiv[...]

Elderly people tend to have less body fat just beneath the[...] easily. Reduced mobility and a lowered metabolic rate me[...] Also they may be unable to afford to keep their accommo[...] temperature.

Hyperthermia occurs when the core temperature exceeds[...] 'normal' range.

Fever occurs when the temperature is above 37.2–38 °C. [...] number of factors including bacteria, viruses, fungi and so[...] temperature of a fever patient would be assessed and mo[...] recordings on a chart.

Key definition

Smooth muscle, in the walls of small arteries supplying blood to the skin, contracts. This constricts the blood vessels and less blood reaches the capillaries. This is vasoconstriction. Vasodilation is the converse with extra blood passing through the vessel to the surface capillaries. Vasoconstriction leads to reduced heat loss. Vasodilation leads to increased heat loss.

External assessment

---

① How can you measure physical fitness?

By the end of this spread, you should be able to:

* explain how to take pulse rate and heart rate measurements
* describe how to assess a person's current level of fitness, and whether their performance is improving using pulse rate measurements taken before, during and after exercising

Places to take pulse

Each time the heart beats a wave of pressure passes through the arteries of the body. This causes the elastic walls of the arteries to expand and then recoil. You can register these pulses in any artery that lies close to the surface. You can feel the pulse as it passes along the artery if the artery is lightly compressed against the tissues underneath it. Figure 1 shows the positions of the pulse points of the body. The pulse rate is measured by counting the number of pulses that occur in 60 seconds. Counting the number in 20 seconds or 30 seconds and multiplying up may lead to inaccuracies where the individual has either an irregular or slow pulse rate.

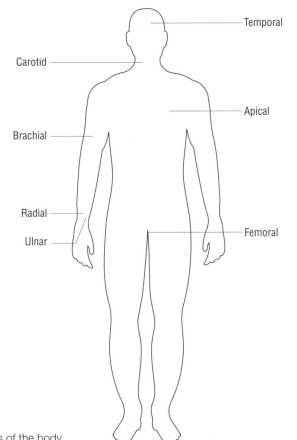

Figure 1 Pulse points of the body

Most of the time for routine assessment a pulse rate is measured using either the radial or the carotid pulse point. These are the easiest points to access. Measuring a peripheral pulse rate is an indirect method of measuring heart rate. The tips of the first two fingers are used to locate the pulsating wall of the artery involved. It is important that only a light pressure is applied or the pulse may be cancelled out. To record the radial pulse the arm and wrist should be extended and relaxed with the palm uppermost. During an investigation into the effect of exercise on cardiovascular fitness the choice of pulse point will be determined by the nature of the activity.

External assessment

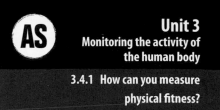

AS

Unit 3
Monitoring the activity of
the human body

**3.4.1 How can you measure
physical fitness?**

Occasionally it may be necessary to use the apical pulse point. This involves the use of a stethoscope. The stethoscope is placed over the fifth intercostal space, roughly in line with the middle of the collar bone on the left side of chest. This should put the diaphragm of the stethoscope over the position of the apex of the heart – the pointed, ventricular end. Here the heart rate is monitored using the sound of the heart beat.

The fact that the heart produces electrical impulses can be used to measure heart rate. You may already have seen evidence of this in spread 3.3.4. The wave of depolarisation passes over the body surface through the skin. Several electrodes are attached at specific places to provide input for the ECG trace. Routine assessment can employ this principle too. A piece of Velcro or a clip can hold a small electrode on the finger tip. The electrical activity of the heart is translated into a digital read out – an electronic pulse record. The equipment used in gyms or fitness centres may have electrodes built into them. A treadmill or a cycle ergometer can have electrodes placed at particular points on the handle bars so that if you hold them during your work out your heart's electrical activity can be monitored continuously during the activity.

How to assess cardiovascular fitness
Three commonly used approaches are:
- step test
- cycle ergometer
- treadmill.

Step test
The individual performs a stepping cycle 'up-up-down-down' onto and off a bench or stool. This is continued for a specified time. The heart rate is monitored before, during and after the period of exercise. The test can be repeated (same procedure) over a period of time to assess the effectiveness of a training programme.

In order to standardise the results and allow comparisons to be made, a specific test may be performed. One example is the Tecumseh step test. The procedure is specific and is employed each time it is used. For example the bench or stool is 8 inches/20.3 cm high. Men and women complete 24 step-ups per minute. A metronome can be used set at 96 beats per minute to ensure timing that gives 1 foot step per beat. The test is started and the individual performs continuously for 3 minutes exactly. After 3 minutes the individual remains standing and 30 seconds after the exercise ended the pulse rate is counted over the next 30 seconds. This gives an indication of the recovery rate. The lower the value, the fitter the individual is.

The value obtained for the 30-second heart rate beginning 30 seconds after exercise stops can be used as a standard measure of cardiovascular fitness. Tables of data exist to indicate how fit you are on a scale from 'poor' to 'outstanding' for men and women according to age group.

Cycle ergometer and treadmill
A similar approach can be adopted using these two machines. Here factors that can be varied or standardised will include e.g. pedal rate or flywheel resistance using a metronome or speedometer to standardise. Treadmill speed or gradient can be varied to change the workload here. However, whichever approach and equipment is used it is important to standardise the activity if you want to be able to make comparisons and establish whether, for example, a training programme has had any effect or not.

Figure 3 Athlete training on a cycle ergometer

How do you use a sphygmomanometer?

By the end of this spread, you should be able to:

* explain how to measure blood pressure data using manual and electronic digital sphygmomanometers

Sphygmomanometers

Blood pressure can be measured using manual or electronic sphygmomanometers.

Manual sphygmomanometers

Manual sphygmomanometers are of two types. These are mercury and aneroid meters.

The mercury version measures pressure changes by means of a vertical column of mercury. Millimetre calibrations mark the height of the mercury. The column is attached to an inflatable rubber bladder. The column of mercury rises as the bladder is inflated. The bladder can be deflated, by using a release valve, and the mercury level falls. The bladder is enclosed in a cloth cuff which is used to encircle the patient's arm over the brachial artery about two inches above the elbow.

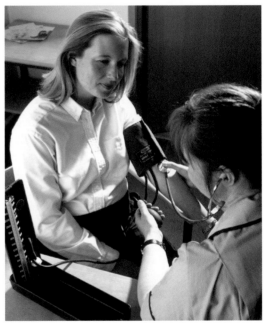

Figure 1 A mercury sphygmomanometer in use

An aneroid sphygmomanometer (see Figure 1, spread 3.3.4) uses a collapsible metal bellows to register pressure change. The inflatable cuff is linked to the bellows which expands as the pressure in the cuff rises and collapses as pressure is allowed to fall. Pressure can be read from a scale in the glass-fronted meter, in mmHg. The meter has to be calibrated against an accurate mercury manometer to ensure reliability. The mercury sphygmomanometer provides the 'gold standard'.

Using a manual sphygmomanometer

Blood pressure can be affected by factors such as anxiety, pain and physical activity. Some people's blood pressure goes up simply because they are about to have their blood pressure read. It is important therefore that you make sure that the individual is relaxed and comfortable to begin with. Eating and smoking can also distort the outcome and should be avoided. Both can temporarily raise blood pressure and cause false high readings to be obtained.

Activity

A young man has arrived late for an appointment to have his blood pressure taken. What questions would you ask before you start the procedure?

The procedure for using mercury and aneroid sphygmomanometers is similar.

- The individual should be in a comfortable position with their arm at 'heart-height'.
- The cuff should be wrapped around the upper-arm, clear of the elbow joint. The cuff should be secured using the Velcro tab with the end tucked in.
- The brachial pulse is registered with two finger tips of one hand and the sphygmomanometer bulb is squeezed, simultaneously, with the other hand. The pressure is increased up to the point where you cannot feel the pulse. This is the systolic pressure.
- With the ear pieces in place the bell of the stethoscope is placed firmly over the brachial pulse point.
- The valve on the bulb is then closed by tightening the screw.
- At this point the pressure in the cuff is increased by a further 30 mmHg to make sure that the brachial artery is compressed.
- At this point no sounds should be audible through the stethoscope.
- The screw valve is opened gradually to slowly release the pressure in the cuff at about 5 mmHg per second. When the pressure in the cuff drops to, or just below, blood pressure the artery allows some blood to flow through. This creates 'tapping' sounds which can be heard through the stethoscope. The reading on the manometer at this point will be systolic blood pressure in mmHg.
- As the pressure is released from the cuff the sounds become muffled and eventually inaudible. At this critical point the manometer reading will be diastolic pressure in mmHg.
- The systolic and diastolic readings should be recorded.

Electronic sphygmomanometers

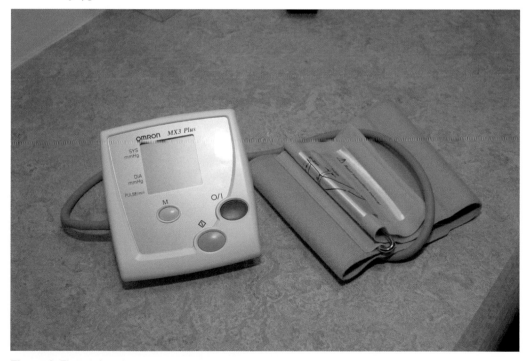

Figure 2 Electronic sphygmomanometer

These devices are battery powered, lighter and more portable than the manual sphygmomanometers described above. They have a cuff which is easy to put on one-handed so individuals can monitor their blood pressure unaided at home if necessary. When the device is switched on it will inflate and deflate automatically. You do not need to use a stethoscope to register the critical pressures. The readings are displayed digitally and some machines can download information for storage and display.

External assessment

By the end of this spread, you should be able to:

* ✱ **explain how to measure breathing rate**
* ✱ **explain how to measure tidal volume and vital capacity using a simple spirometer**
* ✱ **explain how to measure peak expiratory flow rate using a peak flow meter**

Assessment tip

Please note that some pieces of data refer to *minute ventilation* V_E. This is the *volume* of air breathed each minute *not* the *number* of ventilations per minute.

Breathing rate

Breathing rate is usually defined as the number of inhalations and exhalations completed in one minute. The rate can be determined by simple observation or by reading off data from a spirogram.

Measurement of tidal volume and vital capacity

Tidal volume, vital capacity and other lung volumes and capacities can be assessed using a spirometer. You can refer to spread 3.3.5 for definitions of lung volumes and capacities and to spread 3.3.1 for their normal ranges. Figure 1 shows the typical arrangement for carrying out lung assessments using a spirometer.

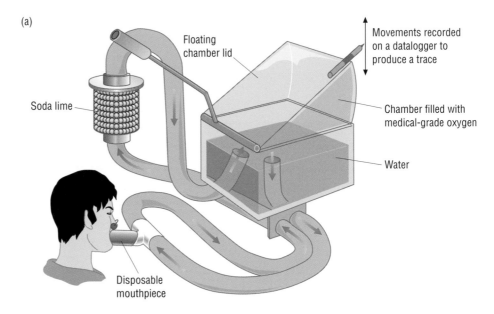

(a)

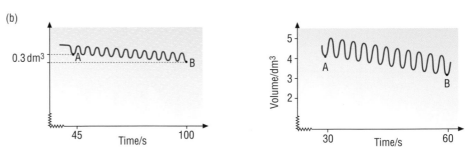

(b)

Figure 1 a Using a spirometer. **b** Spirometer traces of a person at rest and during exercise

Procedure

* The spirometer is pre-filled with medical grade oxygen to ensure the safety of the subject being assessed.
* The spirometer is left full with taps closed.
* The subject is invited to sit down and to try to relax.
* The mouthpiece of the spirometer is rinsed in antiseptic solution or a new mouth piece is used from its sterile pack.
* The mouthpiece is placed in the subject's mouth and a nose clip is put in place.

AS

Unit 3
Monitoring the activity of
the human body

3.4.3 How do you measure ventilation?

Up to this point the valve leading from the patient to the spirometer has been open to the atmosphere and the subject has been breathing a mixture of atmospheric gases.

- The recorder is started.
- At the end of an exhalation the spirometer tap is turned to connect the subject to the spirometer.
- From this point the subject is breathing oxygen from the spirometer bell.
- Normal breathing is recorded for about one minute.
- The subject is asked to breathe in as deeply as possible followed by normal breathing for a few breaths.
- To complete the assessment the subject is asked to breathe out as far as possible followed, once more, by normal breathing for a few minutes.

A spirometer consists of a bell or hinged chamber placed over a container of water. The lower edges of the chamber are always submerged so that gas can be trapped above the water. A tube leads from the gas filled space to the outside. Fitted into this tube is a three-way valve. One way leads to the chamber, a second to the atmosphere and the third via a mouthpiece to the subject under investigation. This means that the subject can breathe air up to the point when the investigator switches to the air or oxygen under the bell. As gas goes into the chamber the chamber rises and as gas is removed, the chamber falls. A pen is attached to the bell so that as it rises and falls a trace is produced on a chart. The paper is moved past the pen at a set speed so that a continuous volume–time trace is produced (see spread 3.3.5).

Peak expiratory flow rate

Peak expiratory flow rate (PEF) is the maximum flow during forced expiration. It is measured in dm^3 per minute and is most commonly measured using a Wright or Mini-Wright flow meter.

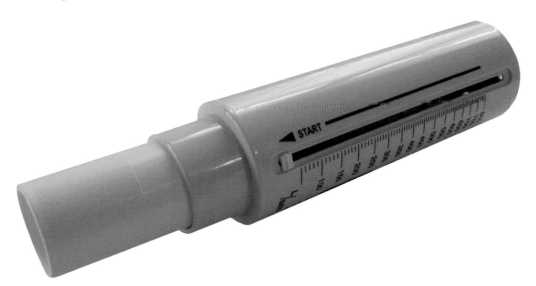

Figure 2 Mini-Wright peak flow meter

Procedure

- Before any reading is taken it is important that the mouthpiece is clean and the meter is zeroed.
- The subject then takes as deep a breath as possible, immediately blowing out as hard as possible.
- The lips should be sealed firmly around the mouthpiece to ensure that none of the air escapes and all the air blown out goes through the meter.
- The process is repeated *three* times and the *highest* value is written down as the recording.

External assessment

By the end of this spread, you should be able to:

* ✳ explain how to measure body temperature accurately

Locations

Body temperature is commonly taken using one of the following sites:
* mouth
* rectum
* axilla (arm pit).

Some techniques involve using:
* forehead
* tympanic membrane (at the inner end of the external ear canal).

Thermometers

Mercury, glass clinical

Figure 1 Clinical thermometer

This thermometer is a glass tube enclosing a column of mercury. The tube is sealed at one end with a bulb filled with mercury at the other end. As the mercury is heated it expands, moving out of the bulb, passing through a constriction into the straight section of the tube. This section is calibrated with marks indicating temperature in °C. To read the thermometer accurately you hold it between finger and thumb, horizontally at eye-level, with the bulb to the left. The thermometer is rotated slowly until the column of mercury appears as a broad band. The temperature is the point on the scale in line with the meniscus of the mercury.

Electronic

An electronic thermometer involves a display unit linked to a temperature sensitive probe by a thin wire. There are separate, different probes for oral and rectal use. The unit can be battery powered. The probes are prepared for use by covering them with a disposable plastic sheath in order to avoid cross-contamination. The probe is inserted into the patient and the temperature is displayed, almost immediately, as a digital read-out. These thermometers are easy to use and read and they provide a result quite quickly. Some digital thermometers are downloadable and their results recorded electronically.

Figure 2 Electronic thermometer

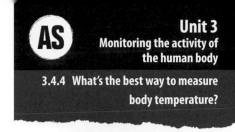

AS **Unit 3**
Monitoring the activity of
the human body

3.4.4 What's the best way to measure
body temperature?

Disposable temperature-sensitive plastic strip

One of the more child-friendly ways to obtain a temperature reading is to use a disposable temperature sensitive strip. A series of dots are deposited along the strip. These contain chemicals that indicate different temperatures by colour. The strips are more commonly used to record oral or axillary temperatures. They are sometimes applied to the forehead. Disposable thermometers work very quickly and are not particularly invasive. They are not that accurate but provide a fast, friendly guide to the temperature range presented.

Tympanic infrared, digital

This type of thermometer is an infrared detecting device. It consists of a battery or mains powered unit with a flex ending in a shaped probe, to fit comfortably into the external ear. The probe has disposable attachments so that, with each use, cleanliness is maintained. The probe is introduced into the external ear and a result appears, almost instantaneously, as a digital read-out on the LCD screen.

Figure 3 Disposable thermometer strip

Factors affecting use, reliability and accuracy

Some methods are more appropriate than others for different situations. For example, it would not be appropriate to use an oral thermometer with someone who, for whatever reason, cannot breathe through their nose. Children might be at risk with a glass thermometer because of its fragility. Tympanic membrane thermometers might be less available because of their cost.

Certain factors need to be monitored to ensure the reliability and accuracy of oral measurement of body temperature. A subject is likely to provide a false reading, for example, if they have eaten or drunk something hot or cold any time up to 30 minutes before the measurement is taken. Also, if they've been smoking or exercising during that time, these activities may also affect the outcome of the temperature measurement.

The reading obtained using an oral thermometer can vary according to its position in the mouth – by anywhere up to 1.7 °C. The oral thermometer should be placed under the tongue and kept there to get it as close as possible to the blood vessels in that position. It needs to stay there for a certain time interval to ensure that a reliable reading is obtained. Once the thermometer is removed from the mouth the mercury column will stay where it is because of the constriction. But the bulb must not be touched. Provided it is below body temperature, air temperature will not affect the reading. However, the mercury must be shaken past the constriction, back into the bulb, before the thermometer is used again.

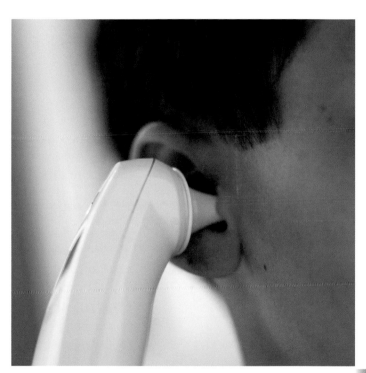

Figure 4 Tympanic membrane thermometer

Axillary temperature is lower than oral temperature and makes the use of that site less accurate.

The tympanic membrane (ear drum) probe measures temperature by registering the amount of infrared radiation coming from the ear drum. The ear drum shares a blood supply with the area of the brain that acts as the body's thermostat. This is the temperature control centre found in the hypothalamus. The temperature control system will be monitoring the temperature of blood arriving from internal organs. This will therefore be, currently, as close as you can get to monitoring core temperature. Also, providing the probe fits the external ear canal 'snugly' it will be less affected by external air temperature.

How do you measure blood-glucose concentration?

By the end of this spread, you should be able to:

* outline the principles for measuring blood-sugar level using clinistixs and blood sugar metering devices

Blood glucose

Glucose absorbed from the gut will enter the bloodstream. The concentration of blood glucose therefore can rise after a meal. Actively respiring cells in the body will remove glucose from the blood supplied to them. Therefore the concentration of blood glucose falls. In order for tissues to function efficiently blood glucose concentration must be kept within controlled limits.

The liver and the pancreas are two organs involved in the control of blood-glucose concentration. When the concentration of blood glucose rises above the limit, liver cells absorb soluble glucose and convert it into insoluble glycogen to be stored. When blood-glucose concentration falls below the acceptable range glycogen is converted into soluble glucose and released into the blood.

Various factors affect the level of glucose in the bloodstream. These include: variations in carbohydrate levels in foods eaten; how active you are; you may need to respire more glucose during cold weather and less during hot weather; and so on. In order that a glucose-balance is achieved, the uptake of glucose by the liver cells and its release must be monitored and controlled.

This is where the pancreas comes in. Two different types of pancreatic cells produce two hormones. The β-cells produce insulin and the α-cells produce glucagon. Insulin promotes the conversion of glucose to **glycogen**. Glucagon promotes the release of glucose from glycogen. These two hormones work to provide a glucose balance required by a healthy individual.

Control of blood-glucose concentration

An increase in blood glucose is registered in the β-cells of the pancreas. This triggers a release of insulin into the bloodstream. Insulin travels in the bloodstream to the liver where glucose is converted to glycogen. The blood-glucose concentration falls. The secretion of insulin stops when the glucose falls below a certain threshold concentration. The α-cells then begin to secrete glucagon. Glucose is released from glycogen and the blood-glucose concentration starts to rise. Together the two hormones establish and maintain a balance. This is an example of homeostasis brought about by negative feedback.

Diabetes

Sometimes people are unable to control their blood-glucose concentration. These people have a disorder called diabetes mellitus. This is caused by the lack of, or ineffectiveness of, insulin. They have raised blood glucose and are described as hyperglycaemic.

There are two types of diabetes mellitus:

Type I: Insulin-dependent diabetes mellitus (10–20% of diabetics approximately). This is a result of the complete inability of the pancreas to produce insulin. The cause for this type of diabetes is complex possibly involving autoimmune, viral and genetic factors. Onset occurs early in childhood or puberty.

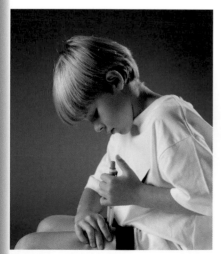

Figure 1 Injecting insulin

Type II: Non-insulin dependent diabetes mellitus (80–90% of diabetics approximately). This results from impaired secretion of insulin, failing to produce enough to manage control and a failure of the tissues to respond to insulin in the normal way. Onset is typically after 35 years of age. Genetic factors are very important.

AS **Unit 3**
Monitoring the activity of
the human body

**3.4.5 How do you measure
blood-glucose concentration?**

Monitoring blood-glucose concentrations

Clinistrip, e.g. Clinistix

Clinistix are strips of plastic with enzymes fixed to them. A blood sample is obtained using a sterile lancet or other suitable, sterile puncturing device. The blood drop is placed over the part of the strip carrying the enzymes. Enzyme controlled reactions then occur. Glucose is converted into products that bring about a colour change in an indicator also fixed to the strip. The colour change is compared to a colour chart and the glucose concentration of the blood estimated. This gives a rapid, semi-quantitative analysis for glucose.

Enzyme reactions:

Stage 1

$$\text{Glucose} \xrightarrow{\text{Glucose oxidase}} \text{Gluconic acid + Hydrogen peroxide}$$

Stage 2

$$\text{Hydrogen peroxide + (reduced) indicator} \xrightarrow{\text{Peroxidase}} \text{Water + (oxidized) indicator}$$

Glucose meters

These are devices, often battery driven, that will accept a clinistrip and 'read' it presenting the data as a blood-glucose concentration. Some of them are downloadable and can be used in conjunction with diabetes management software to monitor the effectiveness of diet, medication and the treatment programme.

Biosensors

A biosensor has three basic components. These are:

* A selectively permeable membrane – allows only the **analysate**, e.g. glucose, through to the recognition layer.
* A recognition layer – has either antibodies or enzymes to bind or interact with the analysate.
* A transducer (possibly a microchip) – a product of the interaction causes the transducer to produce an electrical signal.

A blood-glucose biosensor may use an enzyme to break blood glucose down (see stage 1 above). As a result the gluconic acid produced causes a positive charge to form on the surface of the microchip. This induces an electron flow and this is 'processed' into a measure of blood-glucose concentration. This happens for each glucose molecule 'captured' and will therefore indicate a measure of concentration. This will be presented on an LCD as a number.

By the end of this spread, you should be able to:

* explain the basic principles of medical X-ray radiography
* describe how CT scans are used for diagnosis

Ionising radiation imaging techniques

Medical X-ray radiography

A conventional X-ray machine generates electrons when its cathode, a tungsten filament, is heated. The cathode is positioned inside the head of a tube which is kept under vacuum. The electrons emitted are attracted to an anode by a large potential difference. The anode gives off X-ray photons. Most of the radiation is absorbed by the tube but a window allows some to escape. The X-ray beam is focussed onto the body or structure under investigation. The X-rays pass through the body to impact with a detector. The detector is photographic film sandwiched between two fluorescent screens. X-rays cause light to be emitted from the screens. The light causes blackening of emulsion to occur when the film is developed. As a result an X-ray image is produced on the film. Denser material, such as bone, absorbs more radiation, softer tissue absorbing less. Consequently, different tissues absorb different amounts of X-rays providing an image that can be interpreted by an experienced radiographer (see Table 1). The X-ray photograph can be kept as a record for assessment purposes and for review after treatment.

Image	Tissue/substance
Black	Gas
Dark grey	Fat
Grey	Soft tissue
White	Bone
'Bright' (very) white	Metal

Table 1 Appearance of image on a conventional radiograph

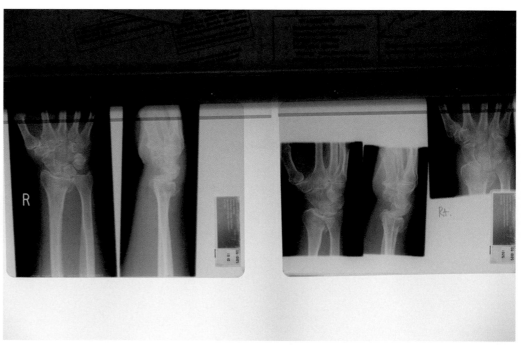

Figure 1 X-ray: bones of the hand and lower arm

External assessment

When an imaging technique involving ionising radiation, e.g. a conventional X-ray, is used the subject is irradiated. We are continuously exposed to natural irradiation. This is called background radiation and in the UK it averages about 2.2 mSV per year. The amount of radiation absorbed by a patient during a scan is called the effective dose (ED). Table 2 includes some examples of procedures and effective dose.

Diagnostic scan	Typical effective dose/mSV
Limb	Less than 0.01
Chest	0.02
Barium meal	2.6

Table 2 Typical effective doses from diagnostic scans

Key definition

Tomography is a process that produces a series of pictures, taken as slices. Axial tomography will be that process along a particular axis of the body being investigated. Computers are necessary to interpret the huge amount of data produced.

Case study

Medical imaging is an important diagnostic tool. The specialists, clinician and radiologist involved in a patient's care have to decide which type of imaging to use. They want to get the maximum information (image quality) with the least risk to the patient (lowest effective dose). During an X-ray investigation and a CT scan the patient is subjected to irradiation. For example, helical CT of the chest requires a radiation dose of about 400 conventional chest X-rays. The question is whether the extra irradiation is justifiable.

Computed tomography (CT) or computed axial tomography (CAT) scans

This method of imaging is similar to conventional X-ray radiography in that it uses X-ray photons to produce the image. However, instead of the single X-ray screen and film arrangement found in conventional X-ray imagery, the CT scanner has many detectors and a fluorescent screen which rotate around the patient. These travel around the ring (gantry) which gives the machine its 'doughnut-like' appearance. As the patient is moved through the scanner the detectors and screen follow a helical path scanning the body as it goes. This provides a large amount of data. Computer software interprets the data providing images of 'slices' through the body. This technique is sometimes referred to as helical or multi-slice computed tomography. Reconstruction of the slices allows the radiographer to build up extremely detailed three-dimensional images.

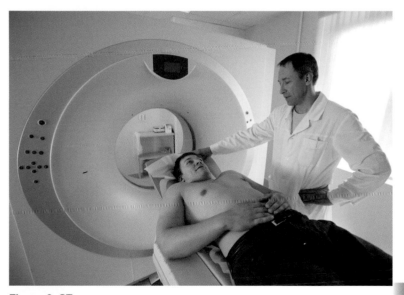

Figure 2 CT scanner

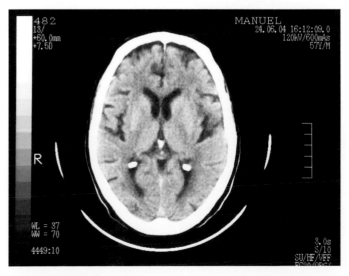

Figure 3 CT axial head scan

External assessment

87

By the end of this spread, you should be able to:

✱ describe how MRI scans are used for diagnosis

✱ explain the basic principles of how ultrasound scans are used in diagnosis

✱ distinguish between different types of medical scanner used in diagnosis to include X-ray, CT, MRI and ultrasound

Non-ionising radiation imaging techniques

Magnetic resonance imaging (MRI)

MRI is based on the principle that the two hydrogen atom nuclei in every water molecule have magnetic properties. The hydrogen nucleus is a proton. Each proton is positively charged and spins about an axis. If an external magnetic field is applied, protons will align with the field. When a second magnetic field is applied in the form of a radiofrequency (RF) pulse, at right angles to the first, the protons gain energy and they all spin the same way **(synchronously)**. In that state the protons are said to be 'in phase'. Once the pulse has ended, the protons do two things. First, they give out energy to the surroundings and, second, they go 'out of phase' and spin asynchronously again. The energy they give out can be recognised and located and the signals interpreted by computer software to produce highly detailed images. This is particularly significant with respect to soft tissue. The contrast produced is superior to CT images and the system does not involve exposing the patient to ionising radiation.

> **Key definition**
>
> Protons spinning **synchronously** will be exactly together and at the same rate.

Figure 1 MRI artic-unit in car park

Ultrasound scan

The sound waves used in an ultrasound examination are beyond the range of human hearing. The diagnostic frequency range is 2–20 MHz. Ultrasound is transmitted and received using a probe. The probe includes a transducer (a **piezo-crystal**) which acts as the 'loudspeaker' sending ultrasound waves out and as the 'microphone' picking them up on the way back. Different probes, emitting different frequency ranges, are used for scanning different structures. A gel is used to fill the gap between the probe and the surface of the area being scanned. This is to prevent reflection at the surface. Those waves that do penetrate are reflected off internal organs, barriers, layers of tissue or interfaces. The echo pattern of the returning waves is picked up by the transducer now acting as the 'microphone'. The ultrasound image is viewed as a real-time picture on a monitor. The images produced can be recorded and presented as either stills or moving images.

> **Key definition**
>
> A **piezo-crystal** changes size when a voltage is applied to it. An AC voltage makes it vibrate at the frequency of the signal. When the crystal is made to vibrate, e.g. when it experiences pressure changes, it generates an alternating voltage.

External assessment

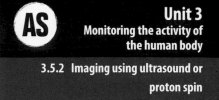

AS

Unit 3
Monitoring the activity of
the human body

3.5.2 Imaging using ultrasound or
proton spin

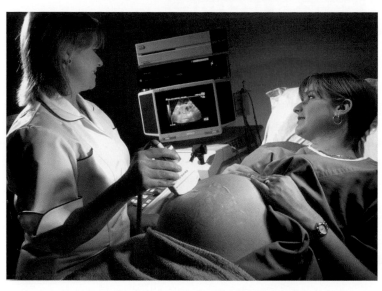

Figure 2 Ultrasound scan in progress (pre-natal)

Differences between different imaging techniques

Table 1 explores the differences between the different types of medical imaging in terms of the advantages and disadvantages of the different techniques.

Type of scanner	Advantages	Disadvantages
X-ray	Relatively cheap and easy	Poor soft tissue resolution
	Good bone resolution	Contrast media can be unpleasant and hazardous
	Can be interpreted by non-radiologist	Ionising radiation harmful/increased cancer risk/dose accumulative
		High-voltage supply hazardous
CT or CAT	More readily available than MRI in UK	Significantly higher radiation doses
	More detailed information (particularly soft tissues)	Very expensive
		Requires cooperative or sedated patient
MRI	Does not involve ionising radiation	Very high cost
		Cannot scan patients with metallic implants
	No known harmful side effects	Unsuitable for claustrophobic or obese patients
	Non-invasive	
	Better soft tissue contrast than CT	
	3D data	
Ultrasound	Does not involve ionising radiation	All ultrasound reflected at the air/tissue interface
	No known harmful side effects	
	Good soft tissue resolution	Nothing can be seen beyond bone
	Non-invasive	
	Images over time/equipment *relatively* cheap	

Table 1

External assessment

By the end of this spread, you should be able to:

＊ describe how to carry out a risk assessment for a blood test, state what the hazards are, what risks arise from these hazards and explain how to minimise the risk to those involved

＊ describe regulations for the disposal of hazardous biological waste, e.g. sharps and hypodermic needles used obtaining blood for testing

＊ describe and explain procedures for the treatment of material that may be contaminated with microbiological hazards, e.g. used Petri dishes, materials from antibody testing

Risk assessment for a blood test

The volume of blood required for different laboratory analyses will differ. For example, the volume of blood for a drug analysis will require a larger volume than one for a **haematocrit**. The details for taking blood for a drug test are described in spread 3.3.2. The blood is removed from a vein using a hypodermic needle attached to a syringe. The blood sample for a haematocrit analysis is drawn from a vein in your arm or by a finger-stick (children and adults) or a heel-stick (newborns). A lancet or some other skin puncturing device is used to release a drop of blood. The techniques for taking the sample in each case will differ but the hazards, risks and precautions will be similar.

The following risk assessment record, shown in Table 1, might be used for a blood test. This is only one example of how the risk assessment might appear.

> **Key definition**
>
> A **haematocrit** is the percentage of a blood sample that consists of red blood cells, measured after the blood has been centrifuged and the cells compacted. This is often carried out as part of a full blood count.

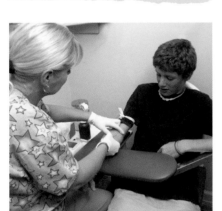

Figure 1 Phlebotomist taking blood sample

SERVICE or TREATMENT Taking a blood sample for testing
Hazards Needle-stick injury, sharps injury, inappropriate disposal of hypodermics, sharps and contaminated dressings, exposure/infection with blood-borne viruses such as HIV, hepatitis B and C.
Who might be harmed and how Clinical staff: phlebotomist, nurse, doctor. Non-clinical staff: porters, drivers, cleaners, caterers. Injury during taking of blood sample and/or possible injury through inappropriate disposal of contaminated hypodermics, sharps or dressings.
Evaluation of risk that someone could be harmed and how serious Low risk for clinical staff because of level of training. Low risk for non-clinical staff if appropriate disposal procedures in place. Otherwise very high risk of blood-borne virus disease.
Precautions/reducing risk Consider using puncturing devices with built-in safety devices to lower risk of needle-stick injury, use disposable equipment to avoid potential cross-contamination, use personal protective gloves, chemical waste wheelie-bins close to activity to reduce handling by non-clinical staff to reduce risk of needle-stick, use of sharps boxes to reduce possible contact, sharps awareness posters and training to encourage awareness and good practice, sharps disposal training, training to make sure staff know what immediate steps need to be followed upon contamination with blood.
Reporting Name and telephone number for emergency reporting of incidents involving contamination with blood.
Review date .... Set a date to look at this risk assessment to see whether anything has changed, anything been learnt by experience, whether there are improvements to be made, whether the assessment is up to date.

Table 1 Risk assessment record

AS   **Unit 3**
Monitoring the activity of
the human body

3.6.1 Health and safety issues

Disposal of sharps and hypodermic needles

Sharps and hypodermic needles are disposed of in special containers to avoid contact. Specialist waste disposal companies provide a service to collect and dispose of waste materials in sharps boxes. Similar services exist for the disposal of other clinical waste that might be contaminated with blood-borne viruses, such as swabs and other soiled waste from the treatment area. The clinical waste can be disposed of finally by incineration.

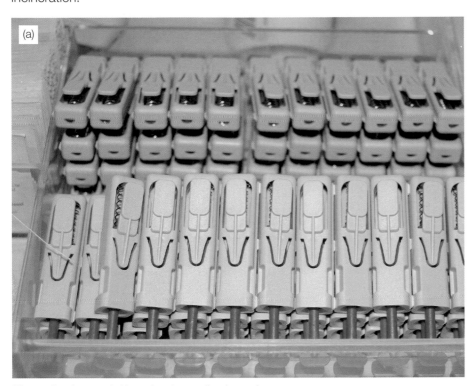
(a)

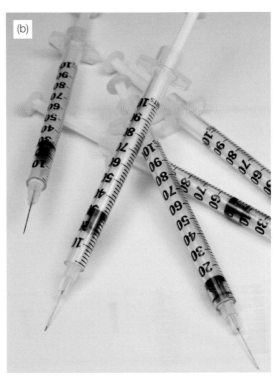
(b)

Figure 2 a Lancet. **b** Hypodermic needle plus syringe

Figure 3 Autoclave

External assessment

Disposal of microbiological hazards

Pathology laboratories produce large quantities of clinical waste. This will include microbiological cultures, antibody testing kits, including ELISA plates, and potentially infected waste. Many of the systems used are disposable and are collected and disposed of in the way already described above.

On a smaller scale some non-disposable apparatus may be sterilised in alternative ways. One way that instruments and glassware may be sterilised is by using an **autoclave**.

By the end of this spread, you should be able to:

* discuss the risks, benefits and ethical issues involved in using imaging methods
* identify the risks and benefits arising from the diagnosis and or treatment of patients with circulatory or respiratory disorders
* identify situations where it may be considered inappropriate to diagnose and/or treat patients

Risks, benefits and ethical issues involved in using imaging methods

Two of the main benefits in using imaging methods are fast application and rapid feedback. These are features which enable diagnostic information to be obtained very quickly. Consequently it is possible to start appropriate treatment sooner.

Some of the risks have already been highlighted in earlier spreads (3.5.1 and 3.5.2). Others might include:

* potential for misinterpretation of images
* some aspects of imaging techniques are invasive, e.g. MRI scan noise-level, claustrophobic, X-ray procedures involving e.g. ingestion of barium salts or radioactive material
* confidentiality issues – who should have access to the information obtained by imaging techniques?

Conventional X-ray and ultrasound scanning machines are relatively inexpensive pieces of equipment as compared to MRI scanners and CT scanners. These are very expensive and organisations that employ them obviously have to balance their budgets. Purchasing an MRI scanner means less money is available for other equipment and staffing costs. Equipment and staffing costs have to be taken into account in terms of allocation of resources. This inevitably means that decisions taken by different health authorities will lead to differences in availability of services in different localities. Where you live may affect how quickly you can get access to highly sophisticated, expensive scanning machines. You may have been aware of 'post code' issues related to health care provision in the media.

Limited availability will also mean that those who could benefit from a scan will be subject to a prioritising process. This automatically raises ethical issues in terms of who does and who does not get priority.

As with any situation involving benefits and risks it is important to establish a sensible balance. The questions to be asked are: 'Do the benefits outweigh the risks?' What is the benefit-risk ratio? To illustrate the point consider the following points concerning the use of radiographic investigation of potential breast cancer.

* Risk of radiation damage associated with having a **mammogram** is approximately 1 in 20 000 per visit.
* 154 **tumours** detected for every 1 induced by imaging technique.

Patients and consultants are always likely to have to decide whether to proceed on any course of action on the basis of their answer to this question.

Key definitions

A **mammogram** is a particular type of X-ray investigation used to screen for breast cancer.

A **tumour** is a mass of cells that keep on dividing. Malignant tumours are cancerous.

AS

Unit 3
Monitoring the activity of
the human body

3.7.1 Ethical issues

Risks and benefits arising from the diagnosis and/or treatment of patients with circulatory or respiratory disorders

Imaging techniques are often used to assess the condition of patients suffering from circulatory or respiratory disorders. Ultrasound examination and chest X-rays may be used in the initial investigation of patients with suspected heart or lung problems. Diagnosis might suggest the need for surgical intervention. The medical and ethical issues raised above are as significant here as elsewhere. Risks and benefits might include:

- the medical procedures could be dangerous – the patient might be too unwell already
- quality of life issues – the patient might not benefit long-term, they may stay alive but have a very poor quality of life after the surgery
- increase life expectancy – the five-year survival rate may be high enough to help a patient to decide to ignore any risks.

Identify situations where it may be considered inappropriate to diagnose and/or treat patients

Is there ever a situation where it is inappropriate to diagnose and treat a patient? This would be viewed as extremely discriminatory. Should a patient have the choice?

Factors that might affect decisions could include:
- pre-existing medical condition
- obtaining informed consent may be difficult with people with learning disabilities or elderly people may not have the understanding to give it
- lack of understanding in patients with dementia, the individual might not understand what the treatment involves
- vulnerability to invasive procedures.

The provision of health care service is extremely expensive. This raises medical-ethical questions that need to be addressed. Examples might include:

Figure 1 Care-home dining room

- use of radiological investigations of conditions already diagnosed on clinical grounds where doctors are put under pressure to request radiological investigation invoking fear of litigation – a 'back-covering' job
- the question as to whether you deny smokers and obese individuals diagnosis and treatment for what might be argued by some people as self-inflicted damage.

CT scanning is usually used to identify a cause for symptoms that have been recorded. This is targeted scanning. In the recent past the advertising and commercialisation of medical techniques has increased. Magazines frequently carry advertisements for cosmetic surgery and for ophthalmology. This is generally deemed to be acceptable practice. However some encourage the self-referral of people who are apparently healthy (asymptomatic), for whole-body CT scanning. Non-targeted scanning is deemed by some to be unacceptable practice. This raises medical-ethical issues too. Examples include:
- exposure to potentially unnecessary extra radiation
- using low-dose CT, the image quality can be degraded leading to misinterpretation
- discovery of incidental findings that might warrant follow up or invasive treatment – overload NHS funding
- counselling issues arising from discovery
- the fact that nothing is found might not mean a clean bill of health; some problems do not show up using imaging techniques – leads to a sense of false security
- young people are more at risk of extra radiation from potentially unnecessary scanning because the under-40 age group is likely to have fewer problems so the risk-benefit issue is raised.

Planning an investigation

By the end of this spread, you should be able to:

✳ understand what is involved in producing a plan for an investigation
✳ understand how your work will be assessed
✳ work in a way that is more likely to bring success

Structure of the planning exercise

In G623/PLAN you will find an 'EXAMINATION PRE-TASK' which instructs you to read an article in G623/INSERT. It also sets the task: 'Your task is to ...' You will find the marking criteria here too.

The article is to give you some background information that you might find helpful in planning for the task you are given. It's important to note that not all the information will be directly relevant and you are expected to select information which is relevant to the task.

Timing and guidance

The earliest that you can start work on this part of your assessment is six weeks before the written paper is taken.

You will be given an examination paper that includes a set of instructions for the completion of your planning task. A set of notes are issued to you, giving guidance on how you should approach your work. It is important that you follow these instructions if you are to produce the evidence in the required way.

How will you be assessed?

Inside the examination paper you will find a table including the assessment and marking criteria. This information summarises what you have to do and what evidence the person marking your plan will be looking for to show that you have done it.

In addition your teacher may give you a copy of the marking schemes actually used for previous papers.

So you should now know:
• what you have to do
• what evidence you have to produce
• how the marks are awarded.

If you use these three pieces of information when working in the context or setting of the particular planning task, on your particular year's examination paper, you should be successful.

What can you do to make more success likely?

• Use Table 1 below to guide the way you work – read the additional notes. These are the things the examiners have been asked to look for.
• Structure the report that you write up following the order of Table 1.
• Use headings and sub-headings to identify the areas of work listed under 'marking criteria'.
• Make sure that you do actually include information on preliminary work and it's essential that you *make clear* what the 'preliminary' is and what the 'main' work is in your report.

Assessment tip

As far as this planning exercise is concerned you should be aware of three types of variables. These are: independent (input), dependent (outcome) and control variables. Independent variable: *you* change this factor deliberately – input. Dependent variable: change that happens because of what you did – the outcome. Control variables: anything else that might affect the outcome – all of these must be kept constant throughout the investigation.

Marking criteria	Mark	Additional notes
1 Easily recognised safety procedures highlighted.	1	Give evidence of something that is going to make doing the investigation safer – an active document, a working document related to the plan. Not just general safety info. Make it fit the task.
2 Prediction made;	1	You have to suggest what the outcome will be. Make a statement related to the task.
3 with justification.	1	Refer to information you have, that made you make the prediction you did. Give some evidence that supports your suggestion.
4 Description of preliminary work;	1	In your report you have to give at least one example of preliminary work. INCLUDE a heading in your report: 'PRELIMINARY WORK'. Examples of the kind of thing you might include are given in the exam question section of this book.
5 clear and in detail.	1	Explain how to do the preliminary work.
6 Reason (for doing it) explained;	1	If you briefly explain why the preliminary work was necessary and or useful for completion of the whole investigation you get this mark.
7 clear and in detail.	1	If you give a full explanation with extra information or suitable extension you may get this mark too.
8 At least two secondary sources of information identified;	1	At least two references stated. You can use the pre-release information as one of these if you want to. Full website address needed. Full description of named text (Title, Author, Publisher).
9 relevance explained.	1	Brief explanation as to how references helped in the planning.
10 Basic practical skills and accuracy;	1	INCLUDE a heading in your written report: 'MAIN INVESTIGATION'. Make it clear to the reader where your main practical investigation starts and the preliminary work ends. A simple method. A list of instructions. A basic method. If you are not going to carry out your plan ask yourself the questions: 'Is it a feasible approach?' 'Would it work?'
11 sound practical skills and accuracy (may also look for evidence of '16' here).	1	If you can say yes to the questions here you might pick up an extra mark. Could someone follow the instructions unaided? Are quantities shown? Is it repeatable to an appropriate degree of accuracy?
12 Range of appropriate equipment listed.	1	Imagine that you were asking a technician for the equipment to do the practical. List the names of main items of equipment and materials needed for the investigation. If you only use general terms e.g. beakers, flasks etc. you may get this mark.
13 Full range of appropriate equipment listed.	1	Qualifications are required here. If you indicate the number of each type of apparatus you would need, specific sizes, e.g. 250 cm³ beaker, 1dm³ flask, you could pick up another mark here. But if any major, essential, item is missing this mark is not awarded.
14 Appropriate number of measurements stated;	1	Make sure that you refer to replicates/repeats.
15 need for range of measurements stated;	1	Make a statement explaining why the stated range was chosen.
16 appropriate range stated.	1	At least five values should be used to provide a sensible range.
17 Relevant variables are identified (stated); controlled variables:	1	State at least two variables. These will be specific to the task set.
18 how variables to be controlled explained.	1	Explain how you would control the variables affecting your investigation. You must refer to at least two stated variables.
19 One suitable method to display data;	1	If you use one method to display your results e.g. a table with appropriate column headings, you should get this mark. However make sure that you include appropriate units. (See spread P.1.10.)
20 additional method to display data.	1	Display your data as e.g. graph to gain an additional mark. Any *different* form is acceptable. (See spread P.1.11.)
21 Simple data handling.	1	To be awarded this mark you must provide evidence of having done some calculations, used your data e.g. mean or use of graph data.
22 Possible conclusions.	1	Make a statement of expectations or observations to confirm or reject the prediction you made in mark criteria 2 above. 'What would the results need to show to confirm or reject the prediction?'
23 Recognises sources of error.	1	State at least two examples: • equipment/materials/specific • human error. (See spread P.1.11.)
24 Suggests methods for improving accuracy and or validity.	1	Suggest ways to improve accuracy: the suggestions should be related to mark criteria 23 above or use of alternative technique(s). and/or Validity. Compare aspects of the collected data to data from secondary sources.
Maximum for plan = 25		24 + 1 *(appropriate use of scientific terminology)*

Table 1 Guide for the way you work

By the end of this spread, you should be able to:

* describe how to produce a slide of a cellular tissue
* describe the structures observed within a cell using a light microscope
* describe the additional structures observed using an electron microscope
* explain the functional differences between a light microscope and an electron microscope

How do you prepare a slide for light microscopy?

There are two ways in which slides are produced for use with a light microscope. Which you use depends on how long you want to keep it. A temporary slide preparation involves placing the tissue in water or a liquid such as glycerine. A stain may have been added to make different types of cells to show up. This approach will keep the tissue in a state that allows you to study it but will dry out and become useless after a relatively short time. You could of course take a photograph of it, through the microscope, before that happens if you want a permanent record. The other method involves the following actions:

* Carefully dry out the tissue using a series of alcohols.
* Stain the tissue to make different cell types show up.
* Place the tissue, under a cover slip, in a mounting fluid that sets hard, excluding the air and preventing any further change in the tissue.

This is called a permanent mount or preparation.

A temporary preparation will be adequate for most of the work you are likely to carry out in this course.

The tissue has to be very thin in order to let light through it. Single cells or groups of cells such as freshwater algae are viewable as they are. However most plant and animal tissue has to presented as a thin 'slice' or section, cut from a larger piece of material such as a plant stem or leaf. This can be done by hand using a razor blade or by a machine called a microtome. Both require skilled techniques. Starting with tissue that is transparent, the slide can be prepared as follows:

* A drop of water is placed on the centre of a clean microscope slide using a pipette.
* The tissue is transferred to the slide using a fine-haired watercolour paint brush.
* A coverslip is carefully lowered over the specimen so that any air is pushed out from under the coverslip as it is lowered onto the surface of the water (see Figure 1).
* Make sure that you do not trap any air bubbles under the coverslip because they will show up as **artefacts**.
* Any excess water can be removed by dipping the edge of a filter paper into it.
* A drop of staining solution such as iodine or methylene blue can be placed touching, but not on, one edge of the coverslip.
* The stain can be drawn under the coverslip using a piece of filter paper applied to the opposite edge of the coverslip.

Key definition

An **artefact** is something that has appeared in a preparation as a result of the preparation technique itself. For example air bubbles appear in a temporary mount because they are easily trapped when the cover slip is lowered over the tissue and water.

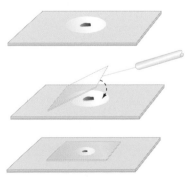

Figure 1 Lowering a coverslip onto a slide

External assessment

What can you see in a cell using a light microscope?

Figure 2 shows the structures that can be seen inside a typical plant cell using a light microscope.

What extra structures within a cell can you see using an electron microscope?

Figure 3 shows the extra structures inside a typical plant cell that become visible using an electron microscope.

How do light and electron microscopes differ?

When you compare the two types of microscope start by imagining the electron microscope as a light microscope placed upside down. The light beam passes up the light microscope, through the specimen to enter your eye at the top. In an electron microscope the electron beam passes down the tube, from a high voltage source, through the specimen to produce an image on a screen that you look at, at the base of the microscope. Both systems have focussing devices and other properties that affect the beams as they pass from their sources to your eyes. This is where the differences lie. Table 1 summarises the differences.

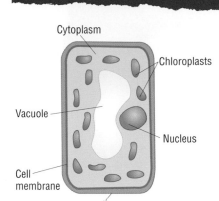

Figure 2 A typical plant cell as viewed using a light microscope

Feature	Student microscope	Electron microscope
Beam	Light	Electron
Body of microscope	Air-filled	Under vacuum
Lenses	Glass or plastic	Electromagnets
State of specimen	Dead or alive	Dead
Maximum magnification	100–400× 1500× using oil immersion lens technique	500 000
Approximate resolution/nm	200	0.5

Table 1 Comparison of student (light) microscope with an electron microscope

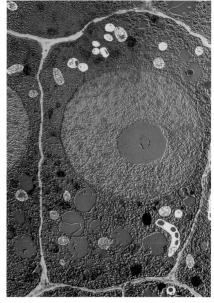

Figure 3 Electron micrograph of a plant cell (the root tip of a maize plant). The cell wall is the thin layer between the cells. The prominent, round organelle in the cell is the nucleus, which contains a smaller, red nucleolus. The yellow areas in the cytoplasm are vacuoles

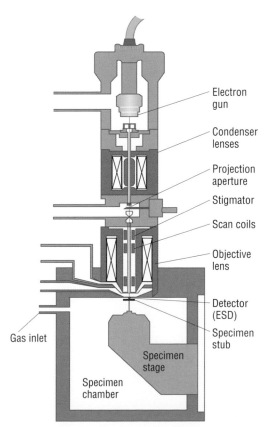

- Electron gun
- Condenser lenses
- Projection aperture
- Stigmator
- Scan coils
- Objective lens
- Detector (ESD)
- Specimen stub
- Specimen stage
- Specimen chamber
- Gas inlet

Figure 4 The essential structures involved in an electron microscope

By the end of this spread, you should be able to:

✻ **explain the role of the cellular organelles found in animal and plant cells**

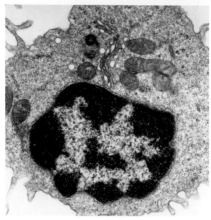

Figure 1 Electron micrograph of a typical animal cell

What are cell organelles for?

Cell organelles found in both plant and animal cells

You will already know that complex organisms have organ systems each structured to carry out major functions in the animal or plant. The human digestive system for example is composed of the mouth, oesophagus, stomach, intestine and anus. Each of these parts has a specialised structure that enables it to do a particular job in the processing of food. The mouth is equipped with teeth to chew food. Salivary glands release saliva containing an enzyme to start digestion. The same sort of idea can be applied to all cells. They too have specialised parts or regions that carry out particular functions within the cell. These structures are called **organelles**. You will have met the names of these in spread 4.2.1 when you looked at the structure of a plant cell using a light microscope. The **nucleus** and **chloroplast** are two examples.

There are exceptions but most cells show two defined areas. These are the nucleus and the cytoplasm in which it is suspended. The cytoplasm is composed of an aqueous solution in which large insoluble molecules are suspended. The solution contains solutes such as sugars, amino acids and a variety of ions. The cytoplasm contains globular proteins that function as enzymes. The cytoplasm is the site of many reactions. For example those reactions which go on when a cell respires without oxygen (glycolysis) take place in the cytoplasm. A complex system of protein fibres within the cytoplasm provides a framework that gives a cell its shape and a place within which the organelles are arranged.

Table 1 includes those cell organelles that are found in both plant and animal cells. You will find it helpful to refer to the figures in this double page spread and those in 4.2.1 when you are reading this table.

Organelle	Function/role of the organelle
Golgi	A membranous structure that processes molecules before they are exported out of a cell. Golgi produces vesicles in which molecules are transported out of a cell. They are an important feature in secretary cells and are involved e.g. in the release of mucilage or enzymes.
Mitochondria	They are sometimes described as the 'power-house' of the cell. This comes from their involvement in aerobic respiration. This organelle is formed from a pair of membranes arranged so that the inner surface of the double-membrane boundary forms projections called cristae (see Figure 2). The cristae provide the location for enzymes involved in the production of ATP. Cells requiring a high turn-over of ATP have more mitochondria to meet the demand e.g. muscle cells and sperm cells.
Nucleus	This is often referred to as the 'control centre' of the cell. It is a membrane-bound organelle. The nuclear membrane separates the nucleoplasm from the cytoplasm. There are pores in the membrane that enable molecules to pass from one zone to the other (see Figure 3). This is very important e.g. in protein synthesis. The nucleus contains the chromosomes. These have discrete areas called genes. A chromosome is composed of a tightly coiled strand of DNA and some special proteins. The genes are specific lengths of DNA each carrying specific genetic code, coding for a specific protein.
Plasmalemma	The plasmalemma is found at the external surface of the cytoplasm of a cell. It is sometimes called the surface membrane. Its function is to control the movement of ions and molecules into and out of a cell. It is an example of a selectively permeable membrane.
Rough Endoplasmic Reticulum (RER)	The RER is a complex system of paired membranes. They provide fluid-filled spaces that are isolated from other areas enabling conflicting chemistry to take place within the same cell. The RER gets its name from the fact that the surface of the membrane carries large numbers of ribosomes giving it a 'rough' appearance. The RER is involved in the synthesis and export of proteins.
Ribosomes	A ribosome makes proteins. Ribosomes attached to the endoplasmic reticulum are involved in the synthesis of proteins for export. Those free in the cytoplasm of a cell produce proteins for use within that cell.
Smooth Endoplasmic Reticulum (SER)	This paired membrane structure forms fluid-filled spaces involved in lipid synthesis and transport.

Table 1 Cell organelles common to plant and animal cells

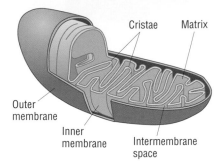

Figure 2 Internal structure of a mitochondrion

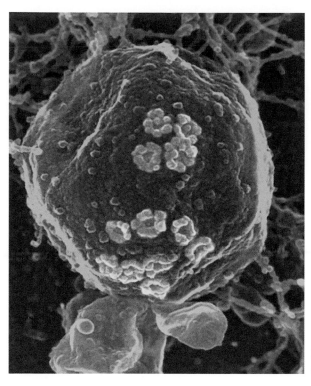

Figure 3 Electron micrograph of nucleus showing nuclear pore

Cell organelles found only in plant cells

When you compare a plant cell with an animal cell you will notice three structures are present in a plant cell that are absent from an animal cell. These are the chloroplast, a large (permanent) vacuole and the outer boundary – the cell wall.

Chloroplast

A chloroplast has two membranes forming its outer surface. Within the organelle are other membranes. In some places these form disc-like structures, stacked up like a pile of coins. These membranes contain chlorophyll molecules and are essential to the process of photosynthesis. They absorb light energy and make it available to the cell to reduce carbon dioxide to form carbohydrates.

Central cell vacuole

A large, permanent central vacuole is a characteristic feature of a typical plant cell. Animal cells possess vacuoles too but they tend to be temporary features. This organelle functions as:

* a place for water storage
* a waste disposal sink
* a structural support system provided by hydrostatic pressure.

The vacuole is enclosed within the cytoplasm by a membrane called the tonoplast. This is a selectively permeable membrane playing an important part in the osmotic, water balance of individual cells and the plant as a whole.

Cell wall

Unlike animal cells, plant cells have another boundary, external to the plasmalemma (see above). This is the cellulose cell wall. This is made from cellulose fibres. Cellulose is a complex carbohydrate. In young cells the fibres are laid down in such a way that the wall can 'grow' to accommodate the increase in cytoplasm within the cell. At this stage the wall is totally permeable – quite large molecules being able to get through it in either direction. Movement of water into the cell through the wall and the plasmalemma makes the cell vacuole 'inflate' with water pushing the cytoplasm out against the inner surface of the cell wall. When the cell is fully 'blown-up' with water it works well as a supporting structure. As the cell matures materials are laid down in the wall that makes it impermeable – waterproof. This effectively kills the cell but the wall is much stronger.

External assessment

Case study

Plant cell walls have been put to use as valuable resources for centuries. Examples include the use of flax, cotton, hemp and of course wood.

By the end of this spread, you should be able to:

✳ **describe and explain the function and importance of water as a biological molecule**

✳ **describe the process of osmosis and explain how cells maintain their correct water balance**

Why is water so important to living things?

The following paragraphs describe a few examples of why water is such an important biological molecule. You may be able to suggest others.

Protoplasm

Water is a major component of protoplasm. The amount of water in protoplasm varies but on average provides about 85% to 90% of its mass.

Habitat

Water covers a very large proportion of the surface of the Earth. This large volume of water provides a habitat for an enormous number of plants and animals. Not only those who have to be there all the time because they are truly aquatic, such as plankton, marine algae, fish and whales but also those who are dependent upon the aquatic environment in other ways. Many terrestrial animals e.g. polar bear are part of an aquatic food web.

Figure 1 Shark – top carnivore in the aquatic world

Sexual reproduction

Many species of animals and plants rely on an aquatic environment to enable them to reproduce sexually. Sexual reproduction for many organisms involves external fertilisation. Many aquatic organisms simply release gametes into their environment relying on chance meetings resulting in fertilisation. The same is true, for example, for marine plants such as brown algae. They too release vast numbers of gametes into the water to reproduce sexually. Many terrestrial animal species e.g. frog have to return to the water to reproduce. Even those terrestrial animals where fertilisation is internal rely on water to get the male and female gametes together. As an example male human sperms swim to meet the egg in the oviduct of a woman. They swim in water-based fluids secreted within her body.

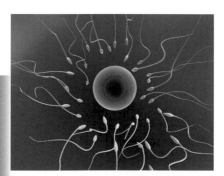

Figure 2 Sperm swimming to egg

Solvent and medium for chemical reaction

Water acts as a solvent and a medium for chemical change. All the chemical reactions that go on in the cytoplasm of living things go on in aqueous solution. The reactants and enzymes that promote the reactions are all in solution in the cytoplasm.

Metabolite

Photosynthesis fixes carbon from carbon dioxide reducing it to form carbohydrate. Water is used to provide the reducing power to do this. Many of the reactions that go on during digestion in the human gut involve water as a reactant. Complex food molecules are broken down to simpler ones by a process of hydrolysis.

Transport

Plants and animals use water as a transport medium. Water passes up the xylem cells in the stems of plants carrying dissolved mineral salts from the soil. Sugars produced in the leaves are translocated in solution in sap. Water is the solvent used to transport solutes in blood.

Blood pressure

Water is not compressible and therefore when put under pressure can be moved from one place to another. Blood put under pressure by a contracting heart will cause the mass of blood to be moved through the vascular system.

Cell volume

Water provides support within cells. Hydrostatic pressure maintains cells in a more rigid state.

Osmosis – diffusion with a difference

Molecules and ions are particles that have energy associated with them. This, kinetic energy, keeps them in a state of constant movement. Particles in solids vibrate only but those in liquids and gases move freely within any space available to them. This continuous movement is described by the term diffusion. Diffusion continues until equilibrium is achieved. At equilibrium all the molecules of a gas or water, for example, will be uniformly distributed throughout the available space.

In a biological context, osmosis is the process of diffusion of water molecules involving a selectively permeable membrane.

The plasmalemma is selectively permeable. Water can pass through the plasmalemma in either direction. Larger solute molecules may not.

The tendency for water to diffuse in a particular direction through a selectively permeable membrane is defined as its water potential. Solute molecules, such as sugars for example, 'get in the way' lowering the potential of the water. Pure water therefore has the maximum water potential possible. Aqueous solutions must have lower water potentials. If the concentration of solute is increased, the water potential of the solution decreases. Concentrated solutions have relatively low water potentials, when compared to pure water. Dilute solutions have relatively high water potentials.

Imagine two solutions, separated by a selectively permeable membrane. The direction in which net diffusion of water will take place depends on their relative concentrations. If the water potential on one side is greater than on the other a water potential gradient exists. Water will move in both directions but at a faster rate from high to low. As this happens there will be a lowered potential on the high side and a rise in potential on the low side. This will continue until the water potentials are the same on either side of the membrane and the gradient will be 'flat'. From then on the tendency for water to move in both directions will be the same and there will be no apparent change. Just remember however that diffusion will continue but it will be at the same rate in each direction. This is equilibrium. When two solutions have the same solute concentrations and therefore the same water potentials, they are said to be **isotonic** solutions.

Osmoregulation – water in balance

Water gain and loss occurs in humans as a result of processes such as eating, drinking, urinating, sweating and breathing. There is therefore a need for water balance to enable normal chemical activity, maintain cell structure, avoid pH shifts, maintain blood pressure and so on. The activities which work to keep the concentration of water in the human body in balance, together, provide a process known as osmoregulation. In human osmoregulation, kidney function provides the fine tuning.

Key definition

When two solutions have the same concentration of solutes they will have the same water potential. These are isotonic. Where two solutions differ, e.g. A has a higher water potential than B, A is said to be *hypotonic* and B *hypertonic*.

External assessment

Case study

A patient in hospital suffering from severe burns or blood loss is likely to need fluid replacement. This is supplied as isotonic saline via a drip feed. It's very important that it is isotonic.

By the end of this spread, you should be able to:

＊ **describe and explain the importance of carbon in biological molecules**
＊ **describe and explain the structure of carbohydrates to include the glycosidic bond, condensation and hydrolysis reactions**
＊ **describe how to carry out tests for reducing sugars, non-reducing sugars and starch**

Carbon – the major element in biomolecules

When you consider the carbon cycle you should start to realise how important carbon is as an element in biological molecules. This explains the way in which carbon atoms circulate within the ecosystem. The processes of photosynthesis, animal nutrition, respiration, decomposition are all involved in this movement of carbon compounds – organic compounds. Atoms of carbon form the basic building blocks for all organic molecules including carbohydrates, lipids and proteins. These are the molecules that make up protoplasm and therefore all living things.

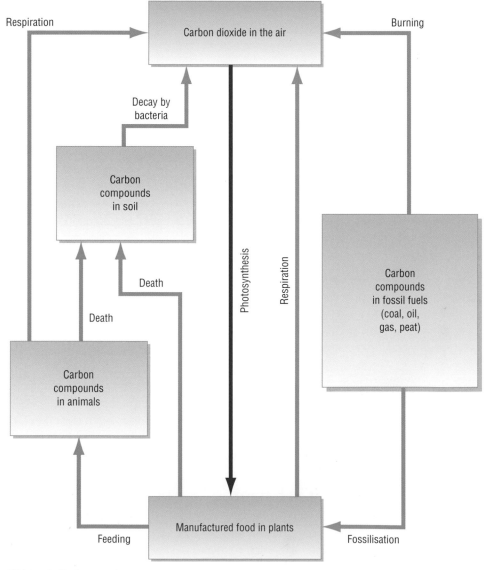

Figure 1 Carbon cycle

Carbohydrates

Classification and structure

Type of saccharide

Carbohydrates are organic molecules containing the elements carbon, hydrogen and oxygen. The name suggests 'hydrated carbon'. The proportions of the three elements are $C_x H_{2x} O_x$. Carbohydrates function as nutrients, storage compounds or structural compounds. **Monosaccharides** and **disaccharides** include the sugars. Starch, glycogen and cellulose are examples of **polysaccharides**.

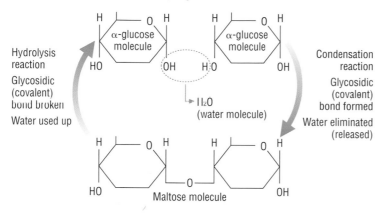

Maltose is a disaccharide sugar. It is sweet and soluble.

Figure 2 Structure of glucose

Monosaccharides are simple sugars. Disaccharides are produced when two monosaccharides are joined together. This occurs during a condensation reaction. It is reversed by hydrolysis. The bond being made and broken during these two reactions is called a glycosidic bond.

Number of carbon atoms

You may see carbohydrate molecules referred to as triose, pentose, or hexose sugars. This simply refers to the number of carbon atoms in their molecules. Glyceraldehyde is a triose sugar because it has three carbon atoms in its molecule. Ribose is a pentose sugar having five carbon atoms per molecule. Glucose, with six carbons, is called a hexose.

Tests for carbohydrates

Test for a reducing sugar (all monosaccharides and maltose):
- Warm a solution with Benedict's reagent.
- A green, yellow, orange, brown or deep red colour indicates the presence of a reducing sugar.
- If the reagent stays blue reducing sugars are absent.

Test for a non-reducing sugar e.g. sucrose:
- First confirm absence of reducing sugar by carrying out the above test on a sample.
- Boil another sample with dilute hydrochloric acid to hydrolyse the sugar (if present).
- Cool the mixture.
- Neutralise the acid using sodium hydrogen carbonate.
- Test for reducing sugars in a sample of the neutralised hydrolysate using Benedict's reagent as above.
- A green, yellow, orange, brown or deep red colour indicates the presence of a reducing sugar.
- The appearance of a reducing sugar at this stage indicates, indirectly, that a non-reducing sugar was present in the original sample.

Test for starch:
- Starch turns iodine in potassium iodide solution from yellow to blue-black.

Case study

Carbohydrates are a valuable human resource:
- food industry – sugars and starches
- paper – cellulose
- cotton – cellulose
- complex organic molecules linked to sugars from plants yield pharmaceuticals.

Assessment tip

Remember that the colours green, yellow, orange, brown and deep red with Benedict's all indicate the presence of reducing sugar. The colour shift indicating increase in concentration from green to deep red.

External assessment

By the end of this spread, you should be able to:

* describe and explain the structure of lipids and phospholipids to include the ester bond, saturated and unsaturated fats
* describe the role of phospholipids in the structure of the cell membrane to include the fluid mosaic model
* describe how to carry out a test for lipids

Lipids

Lipids are a complex group of organic compounds. Most people are familiar with fats and oils but this group also includes phospholipids, waxes, **cholesterol**, lecithin and steroids. They contain carbon, hydrogen and oxygen but the proportion of oxygen to carbon and hydrogen is much lower than it is in carbohydrates.

Fats and oils

Fats and oils essentially have the same chemistry. The two groups are separated mainly on the basis that fats are solid at room temperature and oils are liquid.

Fats are formed by condensation reaction (see Figure 1 below) between glycerol (three hydroxyl groups) and one, two or three molecules of fatty acid. All fatty acids have a long hydrocarbon chain and an acid group at its end. Some fatty acids have hydrocarbon chains that are saturated i.e. no double bonds, e.g. palmitic acid. Others have one or more double bonds in their hydrocarbon chain e.g. oleic acid has one. Fatty acids with double bonds are called unsaturated fatty acids. Fatty acids with one double bond are called monounsaturated fatty acids. Linoleic acid has two double bonds. Fatty acids having two or more double bonds are called **polyunsaturated** fatty acids.

> **Key definition**
>
> **Cholesterol** is an important lipid. It is taken in as part of our diet and is manufactured in the liver. High concentration in the blood may be indicative of arterial disease and is monitored in older individuals. It is a natural component of cell membranes

> **Key definition**
>
>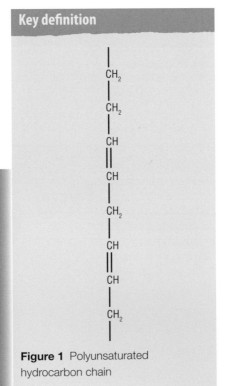
>
> **Figure 1** Polyunsaturated hydrocarbon chain

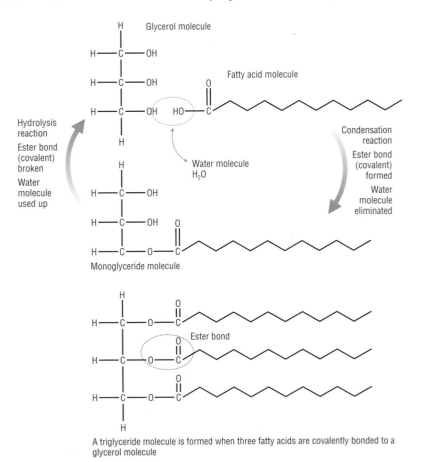

A triglyceride molecule is formed when three fatty acids are covalently bonded to a glycerol molecule

Figure 2 Formation of a triglyceride by condensation reaction

Each condensation reaction between a fatty acid molecule and one of the hydroxyl groups on the glycerol molecule results in the formation of a monoglyceride molecule, with one glyceride bond (ester bond), and one molecule of water. A second condensation will produce a diglyceride and the third a triglyceride.

Complete hydrolysis of a triglyceride (fat molecule) will yield one molecule of glycerol and three molecules of fatty acids.

The glycerol molecule is the same on every occasion therefore any differences shown by triglycerides must be due to the combination of fatty acids involved in the condensation reactions.

Phospholipids

Some condensation reactions produce phosphoglycerides, commonly called phospholipids. Here two of the condensation reactions involve fatty acids and the third glyceride bond is formed with phosphoric acid. Phospholipids are a major component of cell membranes, only very small quantities appear anywhere else in the cell.

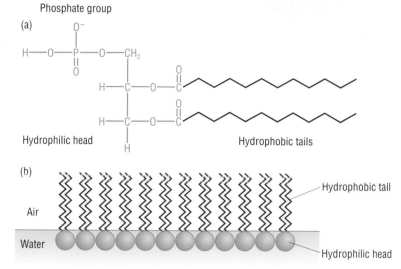

Figure 3 Phospholipid molecule

Cell membrane structure

Phospholipids have polar heads. In other words they carry an electric charge and will attract water (hydrophilic). The 'tail-end' is composed of the hydrocarbon chains of the fatty acids. These repel water (hydrophobic). Protoplasm is anything up to 90% water.

Fats are insoluble in water. The phospholipid molecule enables heavily fat-based membranes to exist in this aqueous system. The polar ends always point towards the watery interior or the watery exterior, the fatty acid chains towards each other. Suspended in and on this bilayer are two types of protein. One type of protein (intrinsic) crosses or 'bridges' the membrane. The second type of protein (extrinsic) 'floats on the surface' or is partly embedded in it (and may act as enzymes). This arrangement allows fat soluble materials to dissolve in the membrane and pass across. It also provides protein lined pores allowing water soluble materials to pass through (carrier proteins). The whole system can be broken down and reformed easily, an essential feature during cell division for example. The arrangement of proteins and phospholipids in this form and the fluid nature of it has led to its being described as a 'fluid-mosaic' model.

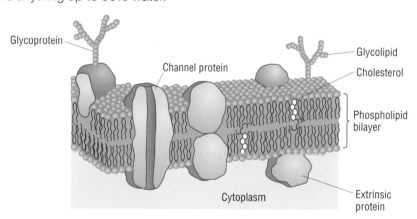

Figure 4 Phospholipid bilayer in the cell membrane

Test for lipids

One simple test for a lipid is the emulsion test:

- Place approximately 2 cm^3 of the unknown sample into a clean and dry test tube.
- Add approximately 5 cm^3 of ethanol to the sample.
- Shake the tube vigorously to dissolve any lipid present.
- Add approximately 5 cm^3 of distilled water.
- Shake the mixture gently.
- A cloudy-white colour is seen if the sample contains any lipid (caused by the formation of an emulsion).

(4) Amino acids, peptides and proteins

By the end of this spread, you should be able to:

✱ describe and explain the structure of proteins to include the peptide bond, α-helix and β-pleated sheets; primary, secondary and tertiary structures and the formation of globular proteins

✱ describe how to carry out a test for proteins

Structure of proteins

The peptide bond

You may recall that when meat is digested, in your gut, the digestion products are **amino acids**. Digestion of protein by enzymes (or acids) is a process of hydrolysis. Proteins are large, complex molecules. They are polymers made from monomers called amino acids. They are linked together by a chemical change called condensation. The bonding which links two amino acids together during condensation reaction is called a **peptide bond**. The products are a **dipeptide** molecule and a molecule of water (see Figure 2). Adding another amino acid produces a tripeptide and another molecule of water. Adding a few more amino acids to the chain produces a short-chain polypeptide. Adding more creates a long-chain polypeptide.

All amino acids have the same basic structure. They all contain atoms of carbon, hydrogen, oxygen and nitrogen. A few of them have sulfur too. The atoms are arranged to form three basic groups within the molecule. These are the amino group (–NH_2) which is basic, the carboxylic group (–COOH) which is acidic and a side chain (R). The atoms which make up the R group determine the particular nature of the specific amino acid containing it. The simplest R group is one formed by a single H atom. This amino acid is called glycine. Alanine has an R group, –CH_3.

There are about 20 different amino acids commonly found in the proteins of the human body. Each has its own characteristic R group, approximately the same number of R groups as there are letters in our alphabet.

Assessment tip

Remember for carbohydrates, lipids and proteins:
• 'simple to complex' CONDENSATION
• 'complex to simple' HYDROLYSIS.

General formula of any amino acid   RCH NH_2 COOH

Structural formula

Figure 1 General formula of an amino acid and the formulae for glycine and alanine

Glycine R is H–   HCH NH_2COOH
Alanine R is CH_3– CH_3CHNH_2COOH

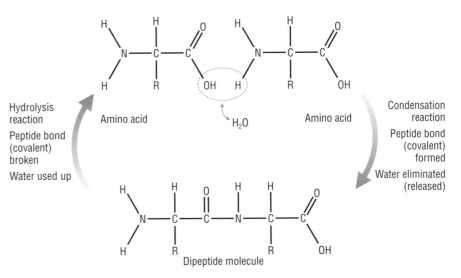

Figure 2 Formation and breakdown of a peptide bond

An amino acid molecule has a basic group and an acidic group. This makes the molecule polar. It is relatively 'positive' (H^+) at the amino end and relatively 'negative' (O^-) at the carboxylic end. This has important consequences in terms of the structure and arrangement in space of a polypeptide chain and the protein formed from it. These charges allow the formation of hydrogen bonds between different parts of a polypeptide chain. This results in the chain being held in a particular position.

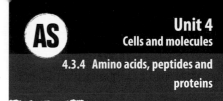

The α-helix and β-pleated sheets

Hydrogen bonds cause a polypeptide chain to show a regular coiled or zigzag arrangement along one dimension. This produces long fibres or sheets. These arrangements are referred to as an α-helix or a β-pleated sheet.

(a)

(b)

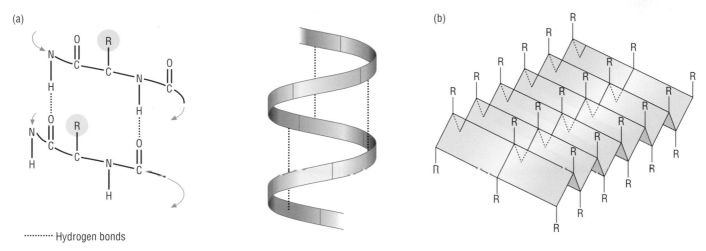

············ Hydrogen bonds

An α-helix has 36 amino acids per 10 turns of the coil. H-bonds form between one amino acid and the one 'four places' along the chain.

Figure 3 a α-helix and **b** a β-pleated sheet

These are features shown by fibrous proteins. These are physically tough proteins, insoluble in water, found in tendons, bone, skin, nails and hair.

Primary, secondary, tertiary and quaternary structure and globular proteins

Primary structure

This describes the backbone of the polypeptide chain and the order of the amino acids in it.

Secondary structure

This is the regular, repetitive arrangement shown by polypeptide chains. This is particularly obvious in fibrous proteins.

Tertiary structure

Each protein shows its own characteristic shape in 3D. The tertiary structure is the way that a polypeptide chain is bent and folded to take up a particular arrangement in space. This is particularly obvious in globular proteins. These proteins are compact, rounded, soluble in water and usually physiologically active. Globular proteins include nearly all of the known enzymes, antibodies, many hormones and transport proteins such as **haemoglobin** and serum albumin.

Many proteins are composed of more than one polypeptide chain held together in a particular way in space. This aspect of structure is called the quaternary structure of the protein in question.

Test for proteins

Biuret test:

• Place the sample in a test tube.
• Add Biuret reagent (blue).
• If protein is present the solution turns lilac.

External assessment

By the end of this spread, you should be able to:

✳ describe and explain the role of enzymes within the cell – how they work

How do enzymes work?

Biological catalysts

Enzymes are a group of very special proteins. These are the molecules, sometimes described as 'biological catalysts', which effectively control the biochemistry of living cells. They do this by affecting the rate of chemical change. They speed the reactions up. They are very active in very small quantities and are recycled at the end of the reaction.

It's important to remember that enzymes only affect the rate of chemical change. They are not 'miracle' molecules. They only affect a change that would go without them, albeit very, very slowly.

Activation energy

In order to react, the molecules involved have to have a certain amount of energy associated with them. This is called the **activation energy**. As an example, think of a fuel such as ethanol (alcohol). This will react with oxygen, when burning, to produce carbon dioxide, water and a lot of energy as heat and light. The energy associated with the products carbon dioxide and water is less than the amount that the ethanol and oxygen had before combustion. The difference provides the heat and light. But, fortunately, you can keep ethanol in a glass exposed to the air without it bursting into flames. To do that it needs a little extra energy to get the process going – the energy from a lighter or a lighted match. This raises the alcohol–air mix to, or above, the activation energy level and the burning begins. What enzymes do is to lower the activation energy threshold so that the substrates react and the reaction proceeds under the conditions found in living cells.

> ### Activity
>
> The athlete's friend.
> In spread 3.2.5 you may have met the enzyme carbonic anhydrase. This speeds up the removal of carbon dioxide from respiring cells by getting it to dissolve in water to form carbonic acid. This means the muscle will work much more efficiently. Each molecule of the enzyme hydrates 100 000 molecules of carbon dioxide per second. That's about 10^6 times faster than it would be if the enzyme wasn't there.

Adding the enzyme maltase reduces the amount of activation energy required for the reaction to take place

Figure 1 Activation energy and enzyme action

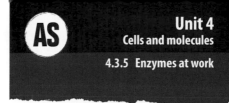

What's an enzyme–substrate complex?

One of the most important features shown by enzymes is their specificity. Enzymes will only work with one type of molecule – the one known as its substrate. As you have seen in spread 4.3.4 specific proteins are built from specific amino acids with the polypeptide chain or chains arranged in space in a way peculiar to that protein. This means that certain places within the enzyme molecule will have their own special shape, a shape that allows another molecule, a substrate molecule perhaps, to fit perfectly. These 'special-fit' places are called active sites. Put the appropriate substrate into its **active site** and you have an enzyme–substrate complex.

Lock and key, or induced fit?

There are two commonly described models to explain how enzyme–substrate complexes are formed. The one explained above is described as the 'lock and key' model. The enzyme is the 'lock' and the substrate the 'key'. To work the one has to fit perfectly In the other. Both are of a fixed size and shape. The second model assumes that the substrate molecule can produce a change in the active site that enables the substrate to fit. This is the 'induced fit' model.

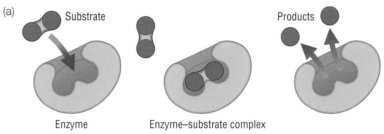

Lock and key mechanism of enzyme action. In this case, the enzyme splits the substrate molecule into two smaller products. It is worth noting that, given the right circumstances, the enzyme can catalyse the reverse reaction.

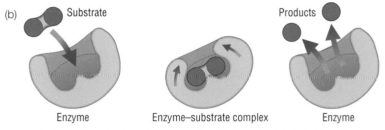

Induced fit mechanism of enzyme action. Binding of substrate to the active site results in a change of shape in the enzyme so that it fits around the substrate more closely to give the enzyme–substrate complex.

Figure 3 Enzyme–substrate complex: **a** lock and key, **b** induced fit

Naming enzymes

Some enzymes have chemically uninformative names e.g. trypsin and catalase. However, usually you can learn something about what substrate an enzyme works with or what type of reaction it catalyses from its name. Many enzymes have been named by adding –ase to the substrate. For example, maltase catalyses the hydrolysis of maltose to glucose. Sucrase catalyses the hydrolysis of sucrose to glucose and fructose. Since both these enzymes catalyse the hydrolysis of their substrates both enzymes are hydrolases. Members of this group of enzymes will work on glyceride (ester), glycoside and peptide bonds.

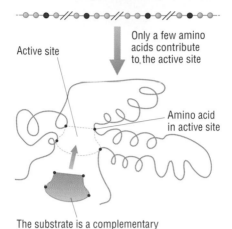

Figure 2 Active site

Activity

What type of reaction do you think the following enzymes catalyse? What do you think happens?

1 oxidase
2 dehydrogenase
3 peptidase
4 endopeptidase
5 exopeptidase
6 transferase.

1 adds oxygen/oxidation
2 removes hydrogen/oxidises
3 works on peptide bond/ hydrolysis
4 same as 3 but somewhere 'inside' the polypeptide chain
5 same as 4 but on the outside of the polypeptide chain i.e. at the end, the last peptide bond, 'cuts' one amino acid off' at a time
6 transfers a chemical group from one molecule to another

4.3 ⑥ Enzymes work best under certain conditions

By the end of this spread, you should be able to:

✷ describe and explain the role of enzymes within the cell – factors affecting the rate of enzyme-controlled reactions

Factors affecting enzymes

Measuring enzyme-controlled reactions

Enzyme-controlled reactions are commonly measured in one of two ways. These are by time-course and by rate of reaction. A time-course graph will have time on the horizontal axis and either appearance of product or disappearance of substrate on the vertical axis. Rate of reaction is measured by recording the amount of substrate that is converted into product in a set period of time. Another way could be the inverse of the time taken to bring about a set change.

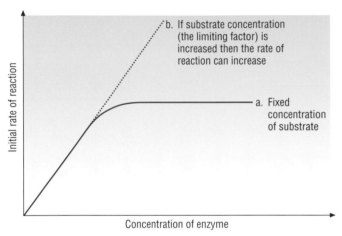

Figure 1 Effect of enzyme concentration on an enzyme-controlled reaction

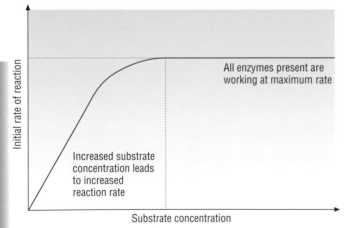

Figure 2 Effect of substrate concentration on an enzyme-controlled reaction

Concentration

Enzyme concentration

Enzyme action depends on the formation of an enzyme–substrate complex. Enzymes work very quickly and are usually not affected by the products of the reaction. They are 'available for work' as soon as they have finished the previous one. Therefore a small amount is adequate and can bring about a huge turnover of substrate molecules in a very short time. If there are a fixed, finite number of enzyme molecules and an excess of substrate molecules then the rate of reaction will increase; also every time you increase the number of enzyme molecules available, i.e. increase the enzyme concentration, the same happens. However once you increase the enzyme concentration to the point where some of them are redundant – too many enzyme or too few substrate molecules – the rate will no longer increase with increase in enzyme concentration. At that point the substrate concentration is limiting the rate of reaction.

Substrate concentration

If there is a fixed concentration of enzyme, then the rate of the reaction will increase as the substrate concentration is increased. But, only up to the point where all the enzyme molecules are in enzyme–substrate complexes. Increasing substrate concentration beyond that point will have no effect because the rate is then limited by enzyme availability i.e. concentration. All the enzyme molecules are working as fast as they can.

Temperature

Temperature affects enzyme action in two ways. Firstly all the molecules in the reaction mixture will have kinetic energy associated with them. This causes them to move around and as a result collide with each other. Some of these collisions will result in the formation of enzyme–substrate complexes. Consequently, if the temperature is increased the reactants and the enzymes will have more kinetic energy, move more quickly and experience more collisions. Therefore the rate will increase. However enzymes are proteins and this is where the second temperature effect comes in. Enzyme activity depends on the special spatial features of enzyme molecules. The shape of the active site is critical. The active site is maintained by hydrogen bonding within the polypeptide chains of the enzyme. Increasing the temperature above an optimum (best) level disrupts the hydrogen bonding. The **active site** loses its special shape and the molecule ceases to function as an enzyme. The protein has been denatured. Most are denatured at around 60 °C and stop working.

Because of the peculiar, individual properties of individual enzymes – they are all unique proteins – different enzymes each have a different optimum temperature. Many human enzymes have an optimum around 40 °C.

pH

The hydrogen bonding described above in the paragraph on temperature is also affected by pH. A shift in pH either way, with increasing or decreasing hydrogen ion concentration, will cause positional change and loss of 'shape' in the active site formed by the polypeptide chain or chains. Consequently the rate of an enzyme-controlled reaction is very sensitive to change in pH. Each enzyme will have its optimum pH and the rate of reaction will increase up to that peak and fall after it. Different enzymes can occupy and function optimally in different environments as a result. Examples in the human gut include those enzymes that operate in an acidic medium such as the stomach and other that are optimal in the alkaline environment of the small intestine.

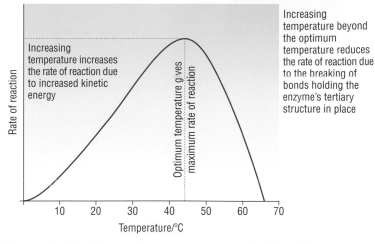

Increasing temperature increases the rate of reaction due to increased kinetic energy

Optimum temperature gives maximum rate of reaction

Increasing temperature beyond the optimum temperature reduces the rate of reaction due to the breaking of bonds holding the enzyme's tertiary structure in place

Figure 3 Effect of temperature on an enzyme-controlled reaction

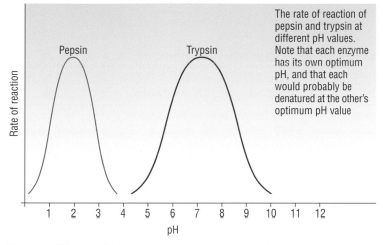

The rate of reaction of pepsin and trypsin at different pH values. Note that each enzyme has its own optimum pH, and that each would probably be denatured at the other's optimum pH value

Figure 4 Effect of pH on an enzyme-controlled reaction

Inhibitors

Non-reversible inhibitors
Heavy metals including mercury and silver attach to the active site of an enzyme and stay there. This irreversible change means that the enzyme molecule is useless. Cyanide binds to respiratory enzymes. This makes it a pretty effective poison.

Reversible inhibitors
Some types of inhibitor molecule are very similar in shape to the normal substrate and occupy the active sites when they collide with the enzyme. They can be displaced as easily as they are formed. Provided there are more substrate molecules around than inhibitors the reaction will continue but at a reduced rate. If the proportion of substrate molecules is increased then the inhibition may well be masked because the competition for active sites will be in the favour of the proper substrate. This is why this type of inhibition is called competitive inhibition.

Non-competitive inhibitors exist. These affect an enzyme's active site indirectly. They attach to part of the polypeptide chain at another place, possibly distant, relatively, from the active site. This distorts the shape of the polypeptide chain as a whole and the active site's special shape is lost. The substrate can no longer combine accurately to form the essential enzyme–substrate complex.

Case study

There is a forensic link here. Murderers both real and fictional use potassium cyanide as their poison of choice. Because this poison acts as an inhibitor of a vital respiratory enzyme it works very effectively. 100–200 mg of KCN is sufficient to cause unconsciousness after 10 seconds, coma after 45 minutes and death if not treated within two hours maximum.

Case study

Leeches feed on blood. The animals they feed on have systems that prevent excessive blood loss. Factors present in their blood cause clots to form and stop the bleeding. This would make it difficult for the leech to get any blood. Leeches produce a substance called hirudin which they release into the wound they make when feeding. This enzyme inhibitor stops the action of thrombin and prevents clotting. The blood keeps flowing until the leech is full!

External assessment

Putting enzymes to work

By the end of this spread, you should be able to:

✳ **describe and explain the role of enzymes within the cell – application potential**

As you have seen in the previous two spreads, enzymes are very special molecules. Think about the way in which living protoplasm works as a chemical system. All life's chemistry goes on in every cell. We sometimes have enough trouble getting one chemical reaction to take place in a test tube let alone hundreds at once. The least we usually have to apply is a lot of heat to get things going. Enzyme reactions seem to be so much easier to bring about. Perhaps it's because the enzymes are in control.

What's so special about enzymes – why are they potentially so useful?

Enzymes are:

- a very diverse group – there are a large number of different enzymes (most biochemical reactions are controlled by an enzyme of some description) – numerous potential applications
- very specific as to what chemical change they bring about – no complicated mixtures of products and byproducts to sort out
- able to work successfully at relatively low temperatures and pressures – cheaper and more manageable
- able to work in very small quantities – lower costs
- recyclable – lower costs
- able to work very quickly (reaction rates are very high) – fast turnover.

So if you want to create a new product or perhaps make the same product but in a different way – think 'enzymes'. Is there an enzyme available to do the job?

Humans have been employing enzymes for a very long time. Perhaps for most of that time, however, an understanding of the processes involved was not there. Brewing, wine making, cheese manufacture and baking are examples of these processes. More recently, with the expansion in knowledge and understanding of the nature of enzymes and biochemistry in general, more and more enzyme applications have been developed. Table 1 summarises some of the applications available now.

Industrial application	Product/service	Enzymes involved
Biofuel	Biodiesel	Transesterases
	Fuel ethanol	Amylase, zymase
Detergent	Laundry and dishwasher detergents	Hydrolases
Food	Baking, brewing, cheese manufacture, fruit juice extraction, meat extract products, sweetener production, tenderisers for meat products, winemaking	Amylase, chymosin, glucoamylase, glucose oxidase, lactase, lipase, pectinase, peptidase, phospholipase, protease
Forestry	Paper	Xylanase, lipase
Personal care	Contact lens cleaner	Proteases
	Toothpaste	Glucoamylase, glucose oxidase
Textiles	Cotton fabric cleaning	Amylase
	Denim finishing (stonewash)	Cellulase
	Silk finishing	Protease
	Wool	Protease

Table 1 Examples of enzyme applications

Figure 1 Biofuel pump on forecourt

Figure 2 Cheese manufacture

Figure 3 Paper mill

External assessment

By the end of this spread, you should be able to:

✱ **describe and explain the structure and function of DNA – structure and replication**

The **nucleus** is often described as the control centre of the cell. This is where the **chromosomes** are. These are structures that are passed from generation to generation. They carry information, genetic information, which determines the characteristics of the organism. Each generation looks pretty much like the previous generation. Each generation of humans 'looks human' but not all humans look the same. This difference is what we recognise as variation. The chromosomes have discrete units of information called **genes**. These genes, working together, control this continuity yet at the same time allow variation to occur.

How does it all work?

As we have seen earlier (see spreads 4.3.5, 4.3.6 and 4.3.7), living cells are chemical systems. If a specific enzyme is present and active a particular reaction goes on. If it's not, that reaction doesn't go on. The overall pattern of chemical change makes the cell what it is and what it can do. So it looks like your enzymes make you who you are.

All enzymes are proteins. So if we can come up with an explanation for the controlled production of a specific set of proteins we may have part of the answer.

Chromosomes are made of a substance called **chromatin**. This is a combination of a **nucleic acid** and some proteins. There are two types of nucleic acid found in a cell. They are deoxyribonucleic acid (DNA) and ribonucleic acid (RNA). **DNA** is found in the chromosomes in the nucleus. **RNA** occurs in the both the nucleus and cytoplasm. The DNA stores the genetic information and RNA makes use of it. Both types of nucleic acid are polymers.

Structure of nucleic acids

DNA and RNA

Both DNA and RNA polymers are built up from monomers called nucleotides. A **nucleotide** has three basic parts. In order of decreasing molecular size these are a:

- nitrogenous base
- molecule of a pentose (5-carbon) sugar
- phosphate group.

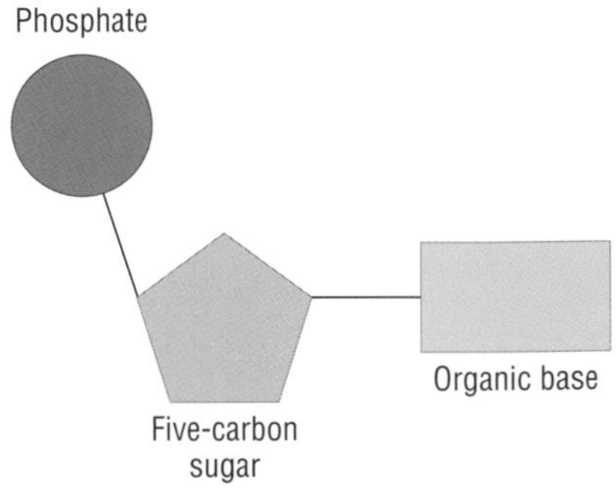

Figure 1 A nucleotide

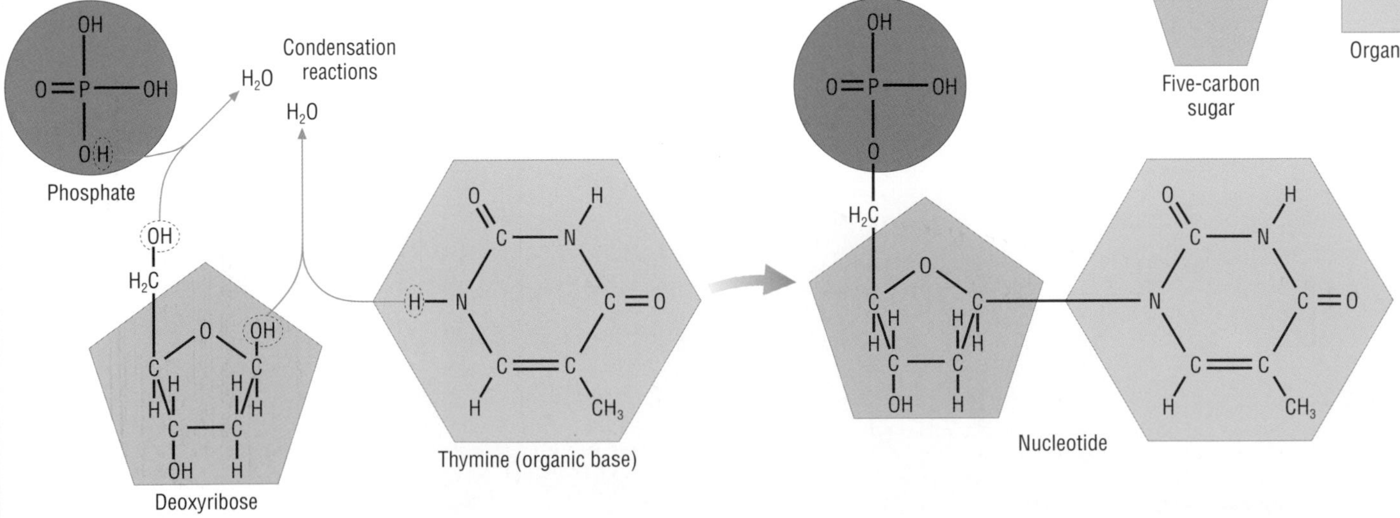

A phosphate, sugar and base are joined by condensation reactions to form a single nucleotide. In this case the sugar is deoxyribose and the base is thymine

Two sugars are involved in the nucleotides of nucleic acids and it is this that provides the difference in their names. RNA has the sugar ribose and DNA has the sugar deoxyribose.

Both RNA and DNA have two types of nitrogenous base in their nucleotides. They are purines and pyrimidines. There is a slight but important difference here between the two acids (see Table 1).

Both RNA and DNA nucleotides have an inorganic phosphate group attached to their sugar molecule.

The sugar-to-base and sugar-to-phosphate bonds within each nucleotide are formed by condensation reactions.

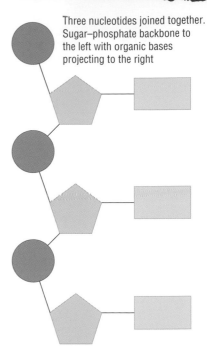

Three nucleotides joined together. Sugar–phosphate backbone to the left with organic bases projecting to the right

Component	DNA	RNA
Sugar	Dexyribose	Ribose
Purine	Adenine (A), guanine (G)	Adenine (A), guanine (G)
Pyrimidine	Cytosine (C), thymine (T)	Cytosine (C), uracil (U)
Inorganic group	Phosphate	Phosphate

Table 1 Comparison of DNA and RNA nucleotide components – differences are shown in red

DNA and RNA polymers are therefore essentially polynucleotide strands or chains with nucleotides as links in the chain. They come together with an alternating backbone of sugar–phosphate units (see Figure 2).

It is at the next level of nucleic acid structure that a major difference exists.

Figure 2 A nucleotide chain

DNA is made up of two nucleic acid strands and RNA just one. RNA polymers are much smaller chains and have a less complicated 3D structure. The two strands of DNA are held in space as a double helix. The two helices are kept together by hydrogen bonds between nitrogenous bases positioned opposite each other in adjacent strands. There are always 10 base pairs for each complete turn of the helix.

The base pairing shown by nucleic acids is the crucial factor which enables the control shown by a nucleus. Base-pairing in DNA always follows a predictable pattern. The pattern in DNA is:
- a purine always pairs with a pyrimidine
- adenine always pairs with thymine bridged by two hydrogen bonds
- guanine always pairs with cytosine bridged by three hydrogen bonds.

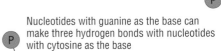

Nucleotides with adenine as the base can make two hydrogen bonds with nucleotides with thymine as the base

Bases which pair with each other are called complementary bases and the process is called complementary base-pairing. To reinforce the idea you might add compulsory, complementary base-pairing. There appears to be no choice. This opens up the possibility of a beautifully simple mechanism for the accurate copying of genetic information. This is the process called replication.

Nucleotides with guanine as the base can make three hydrogen bonds with nucleotides with cytosine as the base

Figure 3 Complementary base-pairing in a section of DNA

Replication

The DNA double helix unwinds. Each exposed strand then acts as a template to make a new strand. Nucleotides line up according to the **base-pairing rules**. The two double helices being formed each have one old strand and one new strand. This process is called semi-conservative replication – half of the old has been 'conserved'. This process is controlled by two enzymes:
- DNA polymerase joins the new strand nucleotides together in short chains
- DNA ligase joins the short chains together.

External assessment

4.3 ⑨ How the genetic code works

By the end of this spread, you should be able to:

✳ **describe and explain the structure and function of DNA – the genetic code and transcription**

In spread 4.3.8 it was suggested that if we could account for the production of specific proteins we might be somewhere near explaining how genetic material exercises control. What is needed at this stage in the argument is a link between the gene and the protein. All proteins are amino acid polymers. The feature that provides the specificity in proteins is the specific order of a specific set of amino acids. There has to be a way of linking DNA base order to amino acid order. This is the genetic code.

Genetic code

There are four bases in any DNA sequence. One base coding for one amino acid would allow you to make a specific polypeptide with four different amino acids in it. Since proteins in cells use around 20 different amino acids this is obviously not a useable code. Taking two bases for each amino acid e.g. AA, AG etc. would give 16 different pairings – not enough to account for the 20 amino acids. Three bases provide 64 options, enough for at least one triplet code per amino acid, possibly more than one. The three-base coding for an amino acid is called its codon. Some of the codons are nonsense codes – coding for nothing. Some act as 'punctuation marks' in the code informing the process where to start reading and where to stop reading. The genetic code is located on the chromosomes inside the nucleus separated from the cytoplasm by the nuclear membrane. Protein synthesis takes place in organelles called ribosomes found in the cytoplasm. The double helix cannot escape from the nucleus, it is too large. Smaller, single strands of **messenger RNA** (mRNA) carry the code to the site of protein synthesis.

Messenger RNA

An enzyme called RNA polymerase attaches to the DNA at a short section of bases that indicates a 'start point'. The RNA polymerase moves away from the start point towards the 'stop point'. The double helix unwinds exposing its base order. This stretch of DNA is what may be referred to as a gene. A large pool of the different types of mRNA nucleotides are available, free in the nucleoplasm. The appropriate nucleotides take up a complementary order according to the base sequence on the coding strand of DNA. The nucleotides link together to form short chain mRNA with the complementary coding of the DNA.

The process of copying the DNA coding into mRNA coding involves a 'rewriting' of the message. It is transcribed, taken from one place and written in another. You may have heard the term 'transcript' used to describe a written record of something said in a business meeting or in court. This part of the 'protein story' is called transcription. What has been transcribed is the DNA message from one gene asking for one polypeptide – the gene product.

The mRNA strand is short enough and small enough to leave the nucleus via a nuclear pore to pass to the place where the information is needed – a ribosome.

Codon	Amino acid
AGA	Arginine
AGU	Serine
CAU	Histidine
CGA	Arginine
GAC	Aspartic
GAG	Glutamic
GUG	Valine
UUU	Phenylalanine

Table 1 mRNA codons and the amino acids they code for

External assessment

Activity

Use Table 1 to work out the amino acid sequence that would result from the following mRNA coding:

AGUCAUCGAAGAGUG.

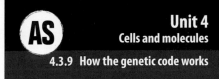
Transfer RNA

Having got the coded message to the ribosome what is needed now is:

- a means to get the required amino acids to the ribosome
- amino acids positioned in the correct sequence for the specific protein being made.

As its name suggests, transfer RNA (tRNA) does this job. tRNA is a short, soluble, single-stranded polynucleotide chain. There will be a population of each type of tRNA molecule in the cytoplasm for each functional codon in the cell's nuclear information.

The tRNA chain has a specialised base order which achieves three things:

- complementary bases are positioned along the chain in such a way that it folds and takes up a particular position in space maintained by hydrogen bonding, two specialised areas are then created as a result; these are
- three unpaired bases, a triplet called an anticodon, which can be used to locate a specific codon on the mRNA at the ribosome and determine which amino acid it can transfer; and
- a set of unpaired bases at the end of the strand that provides a point of attachment for the amino acid carried.

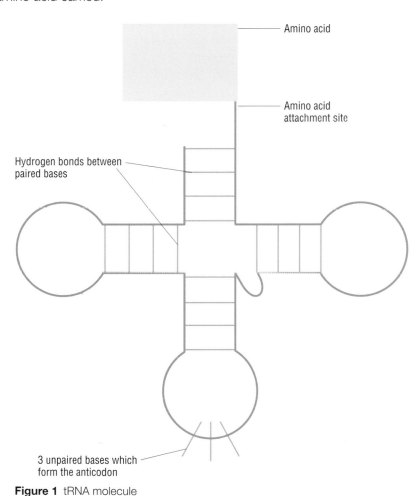

Figure 1 tRNA molecule

By the end of this spread, you should be able to:

✱ **describe and explain the structure and function of DNA – translation and protein synthesis**

Nuclear DNA carries the coding for specific amino acid sequence written in base order. A codon of three bases acts as the code for an amino acid. mRNA is manufactured using the DNA as a template. This leaves the nucleus via a nuclear pore and moves to a ribosome. A population of tRNA molecules exists for each codon. The specific amino acid molecule for that tRNA molecule attaches to part of it. tRNA molecules have three unpaired bases acting as the anticodon for their specific amino acid.

What happens next is called translation.

Translation

Translation, as the word suggests, involves changing language. At the moment the coded message is written in base order, codon order, on the mRNA. This is translated into amino acid order by the ribosome. Codon 'words' translated into 'amino acid' words. The ribosome reads codon order and translates it into amino acid order, in other words polypeptide order, and makes the protein.

One-off polypeptide production
- The mRNA leaves the nucleus via a nuclear pore.
- In the cytoplasm a ribosome attaches to the mRNA.
- The ribosome attaches in such a way that two codons are enclosed within the ribosome. tRNA units with the appropriate, complementary anticodons approach the ribosome each with their amino acid attached.
- They enter the ribosome and locate their codon, delivering each amino acid to its precise designated location.
- A peptide bond is formed between the amino acids to produce a dipeptide.
- The first tRNA unit leaves the ribosome and the ribosome moves along the mRNA as another tRNA enters and delivers its amino acid to form a tripeptide.
- The ribosome continues to read the message, a polypeptide chain and 'empty' tRNA leaving the ribosome at one side, with tRNA units entering the other with their amino acids.
- The 'empty' tRNA units leaving the ribosome return to the cytoplasm to locate and pick up another of their specific amino acid molecules.
- This continues until the ribosome reaches a 'stop' codon when the polypeptide chain is released.

Mass production of polypeptide
Enzyme-controlled reactions operate at a very high rate in cellular processes. Proteins are extremely important in cell structure, as nutrients and as physiologically active molecules. The latter include hormones, enzymes and transport proteins such as haemoglobin. The life expectancy of these molecules may be quite short. There will be a high turnover and as far as protein synthesis is concerned polysome activity may be used to speed up the process.

Polysomes are groups of ribosomes all taking it in turn to read the same mRNA. As one ribosome moves along the mRNA strand a second will attach behind it. Several ribosomes can be reading the same mRNA strand at the same time greatly increasing the rate and efficiency of the protein synthesis.

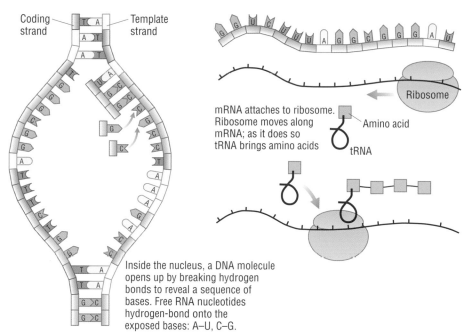

Inside the nucleus, a DNA molecule opens up by breaking hydrogen bonds to reveal a sequence of bases. Free RNA nucleotides hydrogen-bond onto the exposed bases: A–U, C–G.

mRNA attaches to ribosome. Ribosome moves along mRNA; as it does so tRNA brings amino acids

Figure 1 Polysome activity

DNA synthesis

Think of the potential of understanding the way DNA works:

* making genes work in genetic applications
* synthesis of pharmaceuticals, foods, and so on
* gene therapy
* genetic markers.

Once you have identified a need and the possible means to achieve it, the next step would be to make the DNA necessary to do so. The technology does exist to make artificial DNA. Machines that synthesise DNA already exist. Starting with short pieces of the double-stranded DNA to be replicated and the enzyme DNA polymerase it is theoretically possible to make large numbers of copies. This is achieved by a machine operating under the control of a computer. The laboratory process is called polymerase chain reaction (PCR) and has many applications including uses in forensic pathology.

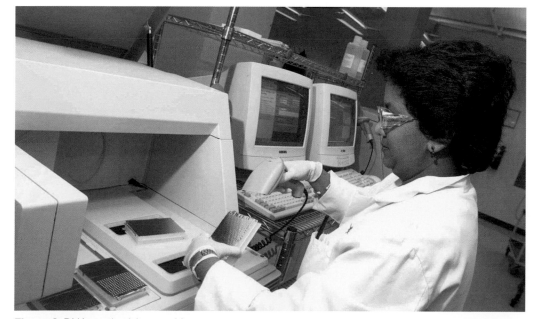

Figure 2 DNA-synthesising machine

External assessment

By the end of this spread, you should be able to:

* describe and explain how to use an eyepiece graticule to determine the relative sizes of different cells, tissues or cell structures
* describe and explain how to use a stage micrometer to determine actual dimensions of cells

In many cases when you are investigating cells and tissues it is sufficient to find out the relative size of a cell or the approximate extent of a particular tissue in an organ. You can make an estimate. Actual, absolute dimension is not always necessary but when it is there is a simple procedure that you can follow.

Eyepiece graticule

Field diameter

The simplest approach to estimate the linear dimension of an object under the microscope is to compare it to the diameter of the field of view. You can place a transparent plastic rule or grid on the stage of the microscope and then position it so that you can read off the diameter of the field of view. An estimate of the linear dimension of a cell or region of tissue can then be found as a fraction of a whole diameter. It is important to remember that you will have to work out the field diameters for lenses of different magnification.

Eyepiece graticule

Greater accuracy can be achieved by using an eyepiece graticule. This is a circular piece of transparent plastic or glass with a fine, linear scale drawn on it. The scale is a simple, graduated, numbered line. The graticule is designed to be used inside the eyepiece lens. As you look at an object on a slide, superimposed on the image, will be the scaled line. It may be sufficient to make simple estimations to make comparisons of the different types of cells under investigation. A white blood cell is 'x times' smaller or larger than whatever, or the medulla region of the kidney was 'x eyepiece units (e.p.u.)' wide, the cortex region was 'y e.p.u.' wide.

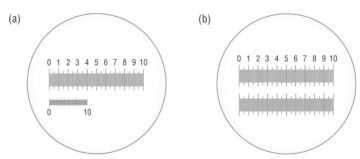

(a) (b)

Figure 1 Use of micrometer and graticule to show cell measurements

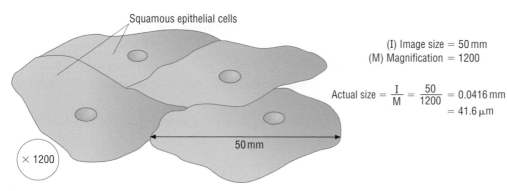

Squamous epithelial cells

(I) Image size = 50 mm
(M) Magnification = 1200

$$\text{Actual size} = \frac{I}{M} = \frac{50}{1200} = 0.0416\,\text{mm}$$
$$= 41.6\,\mu\text{m}$$

50 mm

× 1200

Figure 2 Calculation of actual size from magnification given

An even better estimate can be achieved if you calibrate the eyepiece graticule with a stage micrometer.

Stage micrometer

A stage micrometer is a glass slide with a fine scale drawn or etched onto its surface:
- The scale is 1 mm long.
- The line is divided into 100 divisions.
- 1 mm is 1000 μm.
- 1 division on the micrometer scale is therefore 10 μm.

This simple piece of equipment can be used to calibrate the eyepiece graticule and enable you to make accurate determination of dimensions of microscopic structures.

Calibration of an eyepiece graticule
- The graticule is inserted into the eyepiece lens.
- The stage micrometer is placed onto the microscope stage.
- Move the micrometer slide into position and focus the objective lens so that you can see the micrometer scale clearly.
- Rotate the lens and move the slide so that the two scales are parallel with each other.
- Move the slide on the stage so that the two origins of the scales are in line with each other.
- Determine the value of each eyepiece unit from the fact that 10 divisions on the stage micrometer are equivalent to 100 μm.
- Make a note of the objective magnification and the eyepiece unit value.
- This value will be accurate for the specified objective lens. If you change the objective lens you will need to repeat the process outlined above.
- Draw a table and note the graticule unit value for each objective lens on the microscope.
- It makes sense to use the same graticule each time you use a particular microscope. Keep the graticule and its 'e.p.u. value table' with the microscope so that you don't have to go through this procedure every time.

External assessment

By the end of this spread, you should be able to:

* describe and explain how to use a haemocytometer to determine the number of cells in a specific volume of liquid
* describe and explain how and why the brewing industry and pathology laboratories use Coulter counters

Technicians working in industrial and pathology laboratories sometimes need to estimate the size and nature of cell populations. There are two commonly used pieces of equipment and techniques available to them. These are the haemocytometer and the Coulter counter.

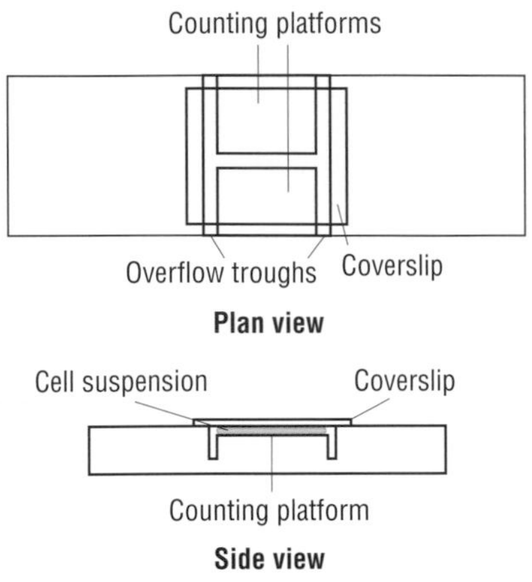

Haemocytometer

The name gives away the original use for this apparatus. It's used as a counting chamber to count the number of cells in a known volume of blood.

The haemocytometer is a plastic or glass microscope slide that has been designed and precisely manufactured to have a chamber of uniform depth on one of its surfaces. When it is enclosed, using a flat cover slip, the chamber will have a fixed, known volume. A grid is precisely etched onto the lower surface of the chamber. This is clearly visible when viewed with an optical microscope. The central square millimetre of the grid is divided into 25 groups of 16 small squares. The central 25 squares are formed by triple lines. The middle line acts as the 'limit' for each cell. Figure 1 shows a haemocytometer assembled, ready for use. Figure 2 shows the ruling for one of the 25 central, 'four by four' squares with some cells in it.

Figure 1 Haemocytometer grid

Counting platforms

Overflow troughs　Coverslip

Plan view

Cell suspension　Coverslip

Counting platform

Side view

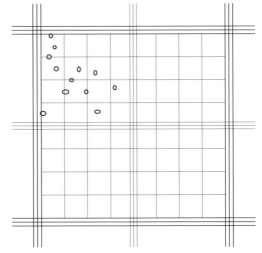

Figure 2 'Four by four' grid

The depth of the chamber is not the same for all types of haemocytometer. One manufacturer may consistently use a different depth to another manufacturer in their manufacturing process. It is important that you check this detail when using the slide.

A haemocytometer is used as follows:
* The cover slip is pressed firmly down to make good contact with the slide. Interference rings can be seen at the margin of the cover slip when it is correctly in position.
* The suspension should be shaken to distribute the cells throughout the medium.
* The chamber is filled with cell suspension using a pipette.
* The slide is left on the microscope stage for two to three minutes to allow the cells to settle in the slide.
* Observe the cells using the ×10 low power objective to locate the central area of the grid.

- Use the ×40 objective to count at least 600 cells. Count the cells within a square including those in contact with the upper and right-hand boundary lines. Those contacting the lower and left-hand lines will be included in adjacent cells if they are counted.
- Record the number of cells and the number of squares counted.

Calculations using cell counts obtained using a haemocytometer.

First, check the specification of your particular haemocytometer to find out what the depth of the chamber is.

For this example assume that the depth is 0.10 mm. Each of the central 25 squares is 0.25 × 0.25 mm. Each of the individual 16 squares is 0.05 × 0.05 mm. The volume over each of the 16 small squares is 0.10 × 0.05 × 0.05 mm³ (2.5 × 10⁻⁴ mm³). There are 1000 mm³ in 1 cm³. Therefore the volume over one small square is 2.5 × 10⁻⁷ cm³. To determine the mean cell count per small square, divide the total number of cells counted by the number of small squares used in the count. Calculate the total cell count per cm³ by dividing the mean cell count per small square by the volume of a small square.

Coulter counter

This device gets its name from its inventor.

The basic principles involved in the counter are as follows:
- A probe with two electrodes is placed into the culture sample being counted.
- One of the electrodes is enclosed in a glass tube.
- An electric current flows between the electrodes.
- The current passes through the sample.
- There is a narrow entrance, a small hole, in the glass tube surrounding the electrode.
- A vacuum pump pulls the cell suspension into the hole.
- A cell can pass through the hole.
- The cell lowers the electrical conductivity inside the probe.
- The size of the 'entrant' cell also affects the conductivity.
- Each change in conductivity can be recorded as an 'individual' count.
- Different cell types give different patterns of change and therefore can be recognised e.g. red and white blood cells, or different types of white blood cells.
- Modern counters incorporate a laser beam enabling recognition and counts of fluorescent labelled monoclonal antibodies.
- Labelled cancer cells or specific bacterial cells can be detected and counted.
- Computerised systems can process the data recorded.

Reasons for Coulter counter preference and the limitations of both systems

Technicians working in laboratories in the brewing industry or in pathology laboratories may prefer to use Coulter counters rather than direct cell counts using haemocytometers for a number of reasons. The counter is quicker. It gives a count based on a larger number of cells. It enables rapid repeats or larger sample numbers. It is automated and can provide data-processing through appropriate computer software.

Haemocytometer use is time-consuming but the equipment is relatively inexpensive. It may be difficult for a technician to distinguish between individual cells and those alive from those dead.

Coulter counters cannot distinguish between dead cells and live cells. Also, it cannot detect and ignore 'scores' produced by inanimate particles such as dust. The counter requires specialised personnel to set up and calibrate the machine.

Activity

Use the cell count for the 16 squares shown in Figure 2 to determine the number of cells per cm³ that would have been present in the sample used.

40 cells shown

Figure 3 Coulter counter

Source

The Beckman Coulter Company has a useful home page.

By the end of this spread, you should be able to:

* describe and explain how and why scientists in biomedical research and pathology laboratories study cells, cell counts and manifestations of cell changes

Cell biologists, microbiologists and biochemists working in laboratories employ their knowledge and skills in a wide variety of contexts. They may be employed in hospital pathology laboratories, forensic pathology laboratories, healthcare and food industries. Microbiologists work in hospital and public health laboratories. Fermentation based industries employ microbiologists and cell scientists in antibiotic manufacture and the production of materials such as insulin and interferon.

This is not intended to be a comprehensive survey. This represents a few examples only.

Two areas are explored below. These illustrate some of the ways in which the skills and knowledge of cell biologists and related scientists may be employed. The two areas are:
• biomedical research, including reference to diagnosis, disease and cancer in particular
• forensics.

Biomedical pathology and research laboratories
Diagnosis
Blood testing is a procedure commonly requested as part and parcel of most medical examinations. Blood samples are taken and analysed for cellular and molecular components.

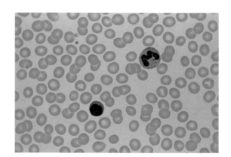

Figure 1 Blood smear

A peripheral blood film (blood smear) can be requested to see if the red blood cells, white blood cells and **platelets** are normal in appearance and number. An example of a blood smear is shown in Figure 1. (See also spread 4.5.1.)

A full blood count (FBC) may be requested for the same reasons but this time more information is made available and the technique is automated. (See also spread 4.5.1.)

DNA testing is carried out to investigate the possibility of certain genetic predispositions. It is used in oncology and in the study of infectious disorders such as HIV/AIDS and hepatitis.

Gene probes are use to investigate genetic disorders such as cystic fibrosis (CF), Huntington's disease (HD) and sickle cell anaemia.

Disease
Gene therapy is used in an attempt to cure genetic disorders such as CF, muscular dystrophy and certain types of cancer. The process involves replacing the defective gene by a normal one. Two techniques are available currently to introduce the normal gene. One uses viral vectors, using restriction enzymes and ligases. The other uses liposomes.
• Viral vectors are made from viruses by removing the disease causing component of the virus' genetics and replacing it by the therapeutic gene. CFTR gene therapy uses an adenovirus that targets the respiratory tract epithelial cells.
• Liposomes are artificial lipid-based vesicles that can fuse with the surface membrane of a cell, dissolve in it and empty their contents, the therapeutic DNA, into the interior of the cell. CFTR gene therapy involves delivering the liposomes in an aerosol spray similar to those used in the treatment of asthma.

Neither approach is particularly successful at present. In early experimental treatment the use of a viral vector produced about a 40% take up by respiratory cells but gene expression was short lived and there was some inflammatory response in the recipient. Liposomes produced a very low uptake, only about 5% of the epithelial cells took up the DNA.

AS **Unit 4**
Cells and molecules
4.4.3 Cells as evidence

Cancer

The observation and identification of cancer cells is one area of work cell biologists in pathology laboratories are likely to encounter.

Screening programmes will generate materials including blood samples (see above), cervical smears, **needle biopsies**, lymph node biopsies and bone and bone marrow tissue samples for microscopic examination.

Forensic pathology

Scientists working in this field may be involved in the analysis of evidence collected at a crime scene to provide evidence for the investigation of a criminal offence.

They may be employed in the analysis in terms of:
- forensic botany – wood, seeds, pollen
- forensic zoology – animal hairs, animal remains, insects
- evidence from blood, semen, sweat, skin, hair follicles, hair types, hair colour, presence of drug residue in hair, bones, dental structures
- DNA evidence from the above sources.

> **Key definition**
>
> A **needle biopsy** involves using a needle to pass through the skin to reach the tissue under examination. A core of cells is removed, sometimes with a vacuum applied, for microscopic analysis.

> **Case study**
>
> Radiologists sometimes carry out biopsies of more deeply-seated tissue. Use of the fine needle used to obtain the tissue sample is guided by ultrasound or CT scan.

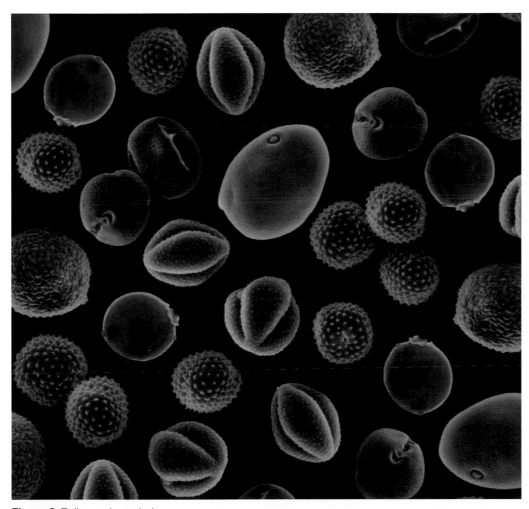

Figure 2 Pollen grain analysis

DNA finger printing may be used in litigation cases involving immigration, paternity issues, sibling relationships, biological family issues, insurance claims and inheritance.

External assessment

① Cells, genetics and disease

By the end of this spread, you should be able to:

* describe how cell counts can be used in the investigation of anaemia and leukaemia
* describe how cervical smear tests are analysed in a hospital pathology laboratory for positive and negative results
* describe the clinical symptoms of cystic fibrosis as an example of a genetic disease and its effect on the individual
* describe the clinical symptoms of Huntington's disease (Huntington's chorea) as an example of a genetic disease and its effect on the individual

Key definition

A **peripheral blood film** is a simple investigation. A sample of blood is spread into an even film on a glass slide. The film is dried and stained.

You can a blood smear in Figure 1 on spread 4.4.3.

Anaemia and leukaemia

Normal, healthy blood clots. An anticoagulant has to be added to a blood sample before it is examined or a blood count can take place. The sample is then tested using an automated analyser such as a Coulter counter. This, and other devices, can provide information about **haemoglobin** concentration, haematocrit (packed cell volume), red blood cell count, mean cell volume (MCV) and mean cell haemoglobin (MCH). The total number of white blood cells present can also be determined. In addition the numbers of white cells of different types can be analysed – a differential white-cell count. Finally it is possible to record the number of **platelets** in a sample. A **peripheral blood film** (blood smear) will also give a great deal of information about the donor.

Anaemia

The normal ranges for red blood cell factors mentioned in the introductory paragraph above are helpful in diagnosis. Values which are below the lower limit of these ranges may indicate the possibility of anaemia. Table 1 shows the ranges for one of these factors, i.e. red cell count.

Factor	Normal range	
	male	female
Red cell count	$4.4–5.8 \times 10^{12} \, dm^{-3}$	$4.0–5.2 \times 10^{12} \, dm^{-3}$

Table 1 Red cell count

Leukaemia

Table 2 shows some of the information that can be gained from a differential white-cell count.

White cell type	Normal levels $\times 10^9 \, dm^{-3}$
Leucocytes (all white cell types)	4.0–11.0
Lymphocytes	1.3–3.5

Table 2 Differential white-cell count

An increased number of any of the white cells listed in Table 2 may be indicative of leukaemia.

Cervical smear test

The Papanicolaou (Pap) smear, more commonly referred to simply as the cervical smear test, is carried out as part of a screening programme for precancerous or cancerous cells of the cervix. Cervical cancer is a disease caused by the uncontrolled division of cells in the cervix. Cervical cells are collected and smeared on a slide for microscopic examination. Atypical cells, those appearing different from normal cervical cells, may be precancerous but they can arise for reasons other than cancer. If they are precancerous then their abnormal appearance may become increasingly obvious over a period of time.

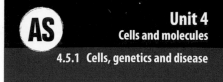

Left untreated these cells may develop into full-blown cancerous cells and metastasise to other parts of the body. Technicians working in the laboratories responsible for the testing look for any physical abnormality particularly with respect to the nuclei in the cervical cells present in the smear. See Figure 1.

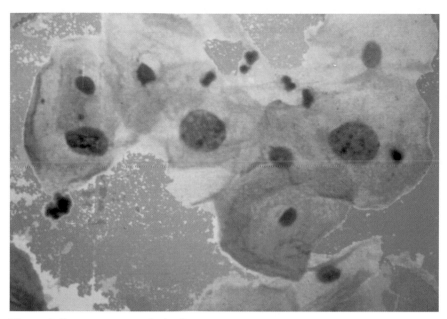

Figure 1 Precancerous cervical cells

Cystic fibrosis (CF)

CF is inherited as a recessive **allele**. This means that both alleles present in an individual's nuclei have to be recessive for disease symptoms to show up. Also, both parents must have been sufferers or carriers for CF. The disease is caused by changes in the gene that codes for a protein called the cystic fibrosis trans-membrane regulator (CFTR). CFTR is a membrane channel-protein that allows chloride ions to move across the outer surface membrane of some epithelial cells. The disease affects epithelial cells which produce mucus. They produce mucus that is abnormally thick and sticky. In particular the epithelia of the respiratory tract, pancreatic ducts and the intestine are affected. This makes CF a complex multisystem disease. Congestion of the lungs and blockages of the pancreatic duct and gut are common symptoms. Respiratory infections and impaired protein digestion are common symptoms. CF sufferers are often diabetic.

Huntington's disease (HD)

Huntington's disease (HD) is a disorder of the central nervous system characterized by uncontrollable irregular brief jerky movements. These symptoms were the reason for its original name of Huntington's chorea. HD is inherited in a dominant manner. HD normally shows up in people in their forties and fifties. It is a progressive disorder of motor, cognitive, and psychiatric disturbances. Symptoms include:

* personality changes
* psychiatric disorder (eg. depression)
* progressive chorea (jerky movements)
* dementia (deterioration of intellectual function such as memory).

The diagnosis of HD rests on positive family history, characteristic clinical findings, and the detection of an expansion in the HD gene, that is equal to or more than 36 CAG trinucleotide repeats. Diagnosis is usually confirmed by genetic testing using either restriction fragment analysis of polymerase chain reaction (PCR). The normal allele has fewer than or equal to 26 CAG repeats. The disease-causing mutant HD allele has 36 or more CAG repeats.

External assessment

By the end of this spread, you should be able to:

* explain the diagnostic test, to include the use of monoclonal antibodies, that can be used to identify genetic diseases
* discuss the moral and ethical implications of diagnostic testing for genetic disease

Testing for genetic disease

Genetic testing is available for a large number of disorders. Examples include:

* breast/ovarian cancer
* cystic fibrosis
* Duchenne muscular dystrophy
* haemophilia A
* Huntington's disease.

There are several ways in which genetic testing can be approached. The following list provides a summary:

* Cytogenetics. Microscopic examination of chromosomal preparations can be carried out to look for structural abnormalities at the **chromosome** level.
* Karyotyping. Here the number and shape of chromosomes is considered.
* Molecular genetics. This line of investigation uses DNA sequencing and polymerase chain reaction techniques. Recent evidence has shown that foetal DNA is found in maternal plasma. This provides a non-invasive prenatal diagnosis for a variety of complications or disorders. These include rhesus D, sex-linked and other inherited genetic disorders.
* Use of monoclonal antibodies and gene probes (see spread 3.3.3).
* Biochemical techniques can be employed. Markers indicating change in the function of a gene are explored through change in the gene-product e.g. enzyme and protein analysis.

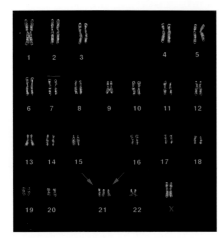

Figure 1 Karyogram of an individual with Down's syndrome

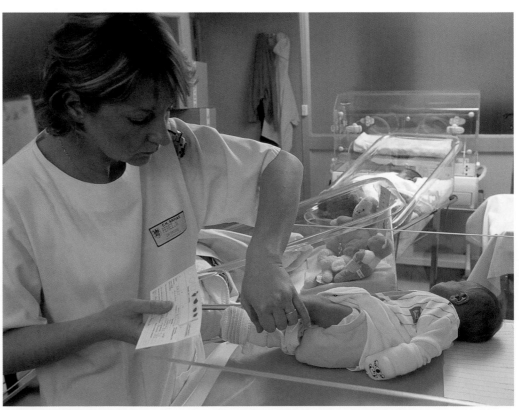

Figure 2 Newborn baby heel-stick test

Types of genetic tests

Two terms that may cause confusion are screening and diagnostic testing. In essence, screening assesses the level of risk involved for an individual. Diagnostic testing identifies whether or not the person tested is affected or not.

Screening is a process usually applied to large groups of individuals. Examples include screening different ethnic groups or prenatal screening. Some ethnic groups are more prone to blood disorders such as sickle cell anaemia. Ultrasound scans (see spread 3.5.2) are useful in prenatal screening to pick out potentially fatal genetic disorders. Screening by family history review can be useful in assessing level of risk. The screening process identifies high risk groups or individuals who would benefit from being tested.

If after a patient consultation a doctor feels there is sufficient clinical evidence, a *diagnostic genetic test* may be requested. This is carried out to confirm or reject the suspicion.

Sometimes it is necessary to test someone who is well but has a family history of a genetic disorder. Huntington's disease, breast cancer and ovarian cancer are examples of genetic disorder where this situation might arise. This type of pre-symptomatic test is described as a *predictive genetic test*.

Those genetic disorders that are caused by single recessive genes produce heterozygote individuals with the condition known as 'carriers'. Cystic fibrosis is a case in point (see spread 4.5.1). A 'carrier' will be well and never show cystic fibrotic symptoms. They will, however, produce 50% of their gametes with the recessive allele and may therefore transmit the disorder to their children in the future. A carrier is well and indistinguishable from a completely normal individual. Once more if family history screening suggests that there is a potential risk for an individual then genetic testing may be requested. This time a *carrier test* is undertaken to try to resolve this question as to whether an individual is a carrier or not.

Moral and ethical implications of genetic screening and testing

Screening and testing may raise many ethical issues since it is an extremely sensitive and emotive area. There are wide implications involving personal, social, emotional and economic issues. Some of the issues are listed below.

- There is always the possibility of error arising during diagnostic testing.
- There are many confidentiality issues resulting from genetic testing. Who has a right to know? Who needs to know? Family members may or may not want to know. Does an employer automatically have the right to know if their employee or other employees are put at risk as a result of a genetic disorder in one of their workforce? Are there circumstances where it would be in order for confidentiality to be broken with respect to retention of driving licence for example?
- Genetic information might be used to block applications for employment in 'employment screening' (as a disqualifier) resulting in occupational discrimination. A similar problem could arise in applying for health insurance or mortgage facility, this being particularly significant in genetic disorders that have a late onset e.g. Huntington's disease.
- Reproductive freedom and the question of sterilisation might be an issue.
- Prenatal testing for genetic disorder raises many contentious issues e.g. whether or not to pursue an abortion, how late on during pregnancy should termination be permitted? What constitutes a defect that is serious enough to justify having an elective abortion? Is society becoming less tolerant of disability?

External assessment

By the end of this spread, you should be able to:

* know what you will need to do for this portfolio
* be aware of the level of work required
* know how you will be assessed
* check your portfolio to see if you can improve it

The world in which we live is made up of elements, compounds and mixtures, each of which have different properties. Some dissolve in water, some conduct electricity, some react with grease, some are liquids and some are green. These are just a few possible properties. It is important that as scientists you understand how properties influence the use and importance of the many chemicals which we use.

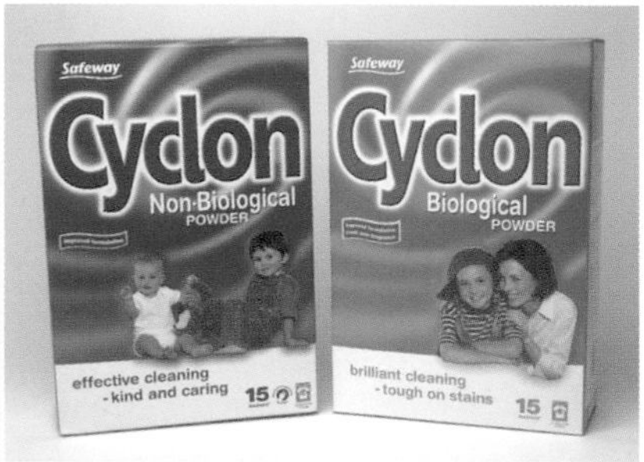

Assessment objective AO1

There are three strands in this section.

You have to:
* give four examples of chemical compounds (two inorganic and two organic) with formulas and properties (5 marks)
* link uses of each compound to their properties and to their structure (5 marks)
* write an in-depth account of the chemistry of a polymer or a detergent (11 marks).

Assessment objective AO2

There are two strands in this section.

You have to produce information which:
* outlines two industrial chemical processes (5 marks)
* gives a full account of catalysis and the social, economic and environmental impact of the process and the product (5 marks).

Useful chemicals such as fertilisers, acids, alkalis, and polymers can be made on a large scale. The chemicals must be produced as cheaply and as safely as possible. It is the conditions of the industrial process that affect the rate and the yield.

Assessment objective AO3

There are three strands in this section.

You should produce a written report that gives:
* a workable detailed method including risk assessments of the preparation, purification and analysis of a named product (6 marks)
* a coherent record of observations and measurements using different methods of presentation and showing some processing of data (7 marks)
* an evaluation of the method with workable suggestions for increasing the yield (6 marks).

Before a chemical is produced on a large scale, it is prepared in the laboratory. A calculation of the yield is needed to work out whether it is economically worthwhile to manufacture the chemical.

How did you do?

What grade did you think your work is worth?
Use the following checklists to get some idea of the likely standard at which you are working. Remember that these are only a guide and that you should always aim to work at as hard as you can to improve.

Figure 1 Chemicals in use

Figure 2 Chemicals manufactured on a large scale

Internal assessment

	Evidence	Form of evidence	Present	Missing
1a	Four examples of chemical compounds (two organic, two inorganic) with formulas Properties of these four compounds Uses of these four compounds	Formulae Pie charts Tables		
1b	Uses of these four compounds related to their structure	Report with clear diagrams		
1c	Detailed chemistry of a polymer or detergent	Report with: structural diagrams equations for reactions		
There must be plenty of background information about the chosen compounds and about the polymer or detergent.				
2a	Two industrial processes including: Conditions Raw materials Usefulness of products	Report with equations		
2b	Account of catalysis	Report with examples Report with analysis		
There must be plenty of resource information about the process that is chosen. The equation with state symbols for the reaction must be included. The role of a catalyst needs to be explained.				
3a	Detailed method for preparation, purification, and analysis including risk assessments	Report or copy of procedure with diagrams or photos		
3b	Observations and measurements, recorded to the accuracy of the instruments	Tables		
3c	Evaluation of method with ideas for improvements for a higher yield	Report		
Make sure that a risk assessment and labelled diagrams or photos of the apparatus are included. Observations about the changes in appearance of the reactants and measurements made such as mass of reactants used, temperature at which reaction takes place, melting point/boiling point of purified product should be displayed in a range of ways.				

Table 1 Assessment objectives checklist

If you have ticked all the 'Present' boxes your work is probably at Grade E or better.

Have you found any areas where you have left something important out?
Are there any ticks in the 'Missing' column? If there are you may have time to do something about it.

What do you need to do to improve your portfolio?
The evidence that is presented must be your own work and you must use your own words although guidance and helpful comments for improving the work can be obtained.

Check that you have selected material from the Internet and not just cut and pasted the information, and that all the sources have been listed.

The more detailed the information and the greater the range used to present the information the more likely is the achievement of a higher mark band.

Assessment tip

For AO1 for higher mark bands, be sure that:
- formulas are displayed to show the structure
- uses are related to the properties and the uses displayed in a wide variety of ways
- in-depth study has both physical and chemical properties of the compound and includes appropriate terminology.

Assessment tip

For AO2 for higher mark bands, be sure that:
- all the reactions involved in the processes are explained fully
- the social, economic and environmental impact of the processes are included.

Assessment tip

For AO3 for higher mark bands, be sure to include:
- results displayed in a range of ways e.g. tables, graphs
- suggestions for change in conditions with explanation
- an evaluation of each stage of the preparation.

Internal assessment

By the end of this spread, you should be able to:

✳ understand how the properties of a compound relate to its structure
✳ understand how the use of a compound is related to its properties (both physical and chemical)
✳ understand how to select two appropriate inorganic and two appropriate organic compounds and give their formulas, properties and uses
✳ identify a detergent, soap, polymer or detergent for an in-depth study

Chemical compounds: structure, properties and uses

A chemical compound:

• is formed when atoms of two or more elements combine in a definite ratio
• has a chemical formula that shows the number of each type of atom that combine to form that compound.

Potassium chloride has the formula KCl. It is an **inorganic** compound. Butane has the formula C_4H_{10}. It is an **organic** compound.

The atoms in a compound combine using bonds. Two types of bonds are ionic and covalent. The physical properties of a compound are linked to the type of bonding.

Potassium chloride with ionic bonding has the following physical properties:
• High melting point and boiling point;
• it is a solid at room temperature; and
• it is soluble in water.

Butane with covalent bonding has the following physical properties:
• Low melting point and boiling point;
• it is a gas at room temperature; and
• it is insoluble in water.

The uses of a compound will depend on its physical properties and its chemical reactions. The choice of the two inorganic compounds and two organic compounds for the portfolio work should be made so that the compounds:
• contain only a few different elements
• have properties about which there is detail and data (research Internet or chemistry text books)
• have uses which can be directly related to their structure and chemical reactions.

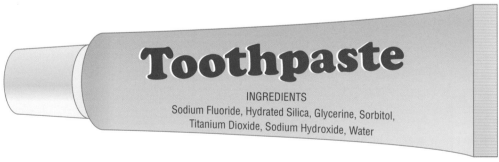

Figure 1 A tube of toothpaste

INGREDIENTS
Sodium Fluoride, Hydrated Silica, Glycerine, Sorbitol, Titanium Dioxide, Sodium Hydroxide, Water

In-depth study of a detergent, soap or polymer

The lifestyle of the developed world in the twenty first century is possible because of the properties of certain substances. A healthier life is due to cleaning agents, such as soaps and detergents, and the development of a vast range of synthetic polymers which gives a range of materials to support our needs.

Key definitions

Inorganic – compounds which are not carbon based (except carbon monoxide, carbon dioxide and carbonates).

Organic – compounds containing carbon.

Activity

Research ionic and covalent bonding

Activity

• Use labels on products such as yoghurt, fruit squashes, toiletries, DIY products, to identify some possible compounds.
• Give the formulas for the compounds in toothpaste.
• Identify which of the compounds in toothpaste are inorganic and which organic.
• Discuss the physical and chemical properties of these compounds.

For the in-depth study, detergents, soaps or polymers are suggested. Use the sources suggested to find suitable substances. Select one that has a structure that is understandable.

As detergents, soaps and polymers have organic functional groups, identify those groups and then research the reactions of the groups. An approach to the in-depth study is suggested below.

The polyester PET (polyethylene terephthalate)

PET is a polymer which could be used for the in-depth study. PET has a very high molecular mass as it is a polymer. It is therefore solid at room temperature. Polymers are large molecules in which a basic unit is repeated very many times. The basic unit in PET is $CO.C_6H_4.CO.O.CH_2.CH_2.O$ in which there are covalent bonds.

Figure 2 Displayed formula of the basic unit in PET.

PET is insoluble in water as the bonding is covalent and the molecule is large. PET is used for making bottles for soft drinks.

The basic unit of PET contains an ester grouping CO.O.C. The ester grouping is not very reactive.

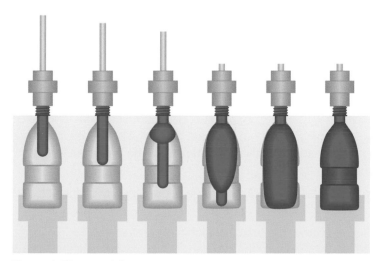

Figure 3 Soft drink bottle

The repeating unit in PET contains a benzene ring. When the molecules of the polymer are packed together the benzene rings give a rigid structure to the solid. The polymer is extruded to form the empty bottles. During extrusion the molecules are aligned. This gives extra rigidity to the bottles as there are more intermolecular forces present (Figure 4).

Figure 4 Blow moulding

Sources

Wikepedia contains a great deal of information. Selection is needed. Be sure that two sources provide the same information.

Book sources are 'The Chemical Industry', and 'The Plastics Industry', both produced by the Chemical Industry Education Centre, University of York.

Activity

- Write equations to represent the reactions of an ester group.
- Explain why PET, a polyester, is insoluble in water whereas an ester such as ethyl ethanoate is soluble in water.

Internal assessment

Activity

- Research the types of bonds formed between molecules (inter-molecular bonds) and their effect on the properties of the compound.
- Research the properties that enable a polymer to be adapted for another use i.e. recycled.
- Research the structure needed for a polymer to be biodegradable.

By the end of this spread, you should be able to:

✳ select suitable industrial chemical processes, in which useful products are manufactured
✳ outline the conditions of the processes and explain why these conditions were chosen
✳ understand catalysis

Many chemicals that are used daily are manufactured on a large scale; examples of such chemicals include sulfuric acid, nitric acid, sodium hydroxide and ammonium salts. Carboxylic acids which are made for use in foods (as preservatives and flavourings), in perfumes and in solvents are amongst many organic compounds that are made.

Choice of chemical process

The reactions involved in industrial processes often involve an **equilibrium reaction**. The hydrolysis of dinitrogen tetroxide, the last stage in the manufacture of nitric acid, is an example to show the approach that is needed to produce the assessed evidence for your portfolio.

The headings indicate topics that should be researched. Start with the equation for the process.

The equation for the hydrolysis of dinitrogen tetroxide is:

$$3N_2O_{4(g)} + 2H_2O_{(l)} \rightleftharpoons 4HNO_{3(aq)} + 2NO_{(g)} \; \Delta H = -103 \text{ kJ mol}^{-1}$$

Raw materials

Readily available raw materials cost less. In the hydrolysis of dinitrogen tetroxide:
- water is readily available and therefore inexpensive
- dinitrogen tetroxide does not occur naturally and has to be made and is therefore more expensive.

Hazards

The hazards to be considered are those associated with the:
- reactants and products
- use of high temperature and high pressure.

In the hydrolysis of dinitrogen tetroxide:
- there is no hazard associated with water as it is being used as the liquid
- the associated hazards for dinitrogen tetroxide are not immediately obvious (use Hazcards to find the information).

Conditions for the chemical process

Temperature

The temperature at which the industrial process is carried out is a commercial decision as the operating temperature will decide most of the energy requirements of the process and therefore affect the cost. A high temperature will increase the rate of reaction because it increases the:
- velocity of the particles so the number of collisions per unit time increases
- energy associated with each collision. A collision between reactant molecules must occur if there is to be a reaction. There is a greater chance that the total energy of a collision is greater than the **activation energy** and so an increased chance of a reaction if the energy is higher.

A high temperature can alter the yield of product. This depends on the actual equilibrium reaction.

In the hydrolysis of dinitrogen tetroxide a high temperature results in a lower amount of nitric acid being formed because the reaction in the forward direction is **exothermic**. When the temperature is changed, an equilibrium reaction moves in the direction

Key definitions

Activation energy is the minimum energy needed to break the bonds in the reactants.

Le Chatelier's principle states that when any of the conditions affecting the position of a dynamic equilibrium are changed then the position of that equilibrium will shift to minimise that change.

predicted by **Le Chatelier's principle** and in this case a high temperature favours formation of the reverse reaction (formation of N_2O_4 and H_2O).

Factors affecting the choice of operating temperature will be dependent on the:
* increase in the rate of reaction as the temperature increases
* change in yield of product as the temperature increases.

A compromise temperature between conflicting factors is usually chosen. In many processes heat produced in an exothermic reaction can be removed by a heat exchanger and used to heat reactants.

Pressure

Pressure needs to be considered in reactions involving gases. An increase in pressure:
* Increases the number of collisions per unit volume, increases the chance of a reaction and so increases the rate.
* Can change the direction of the reaction. The preferred direction of an equilibrium reaction depends on whether there is a change in volume as reactants form products. (Le Chatelier's principle.)
* Increases the cost of plant equipment and safety measures. Installation of pressure equipment must be cost effective if high pressure is used.

In the hydrolysis of dinitrogen tetroxide, high pressure results in more products as there is a reduction in volume from reactants to products (three volumes of reactant produce two volumes of product).

Concentration

Increase in concentration of reactants increases the number of collisions per unit time and so increases the chance of a reaction.

If one of the products is removed then by Le Chatelier's principle more products will be formed.

Nitrogen(II) oxide is a gas so it can be removed easily. Theoretically the reaction can go to completion

Catalysis

A catalyst is a substance which changes the rate at which a reaction occurs. It is the same chemically at the end of the reaction as at the start. A catalyst provides an alternative route of lower activation energy by which the reaction may occur.

Catalysts are used in industry to change the rate of reaction. The product will be produced more quickly if the catalyst speeds up the reaction and so less energy is used and therefore energy costs are reduced.

There are two types of catalyst

Heterogeneous, when the catalyst is in a different physical state from the reactants. In most examples the catalyst is a solid and gases or liquids flow over it. The catalyst is able to bring the reactants together by 'catching' the molecules on the surface and so bringing reactant molecules nearer together. These catalysts have to be pure. They are easily poisoned.

Homogeneous, when the catalyst is in the same physical state as the reactants. The catalyst reacts with a reactant molecule which then reacts further releasing a product and the catalyst molecule.

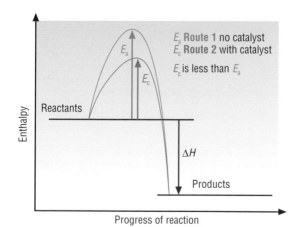

Figure 1 Diagram showing activation energy and the effect of the catalyst

Internal assessment

By the end of this spread, you should be able to:

* ✳ be aware of appropriate practical techniques to prepare, purify and assess purity of a product
* ✳ understand how to calculate theoretical yield and then the percentage yield
* ✳ understand how changes in the conditions could alter the yield and to suggest possible changes

Medicines to relieve pain are used all over the world. They improve your quality of life. These products not only need to be prepared but the purity needs to be checked. Cosmetics and skin products are big business but ensuring these products are both effective and safe, and not contaminated, is an important part of the industrial process.

Figure 1 Scientific research is carried out into ways of breaking down polymers into more useful materials

Sources

The Organic Preparations website gives a range of ideas for preparations.

Laboratory Hazcards often have a risk assessment for standard preparations on the back.

Details on techniques for preparation and assessing purity can be found in spread P.1.7 Techniques used in organic chemistry.

Assessment tip

Remember to put in your report:
* Full details of the method used with a risk assessment. The method need not be rewritten. A copy of the procedure is sufficient.
* Diagrams or photographs to show apparatus.
* An equation for the reaction.

Assessment tip

The observations and results should include:
* the actual masses/volumes of reactants (remember the units)
* appearance of reactants when mixed together at the start of the reaction
* appearance of the mixture as the reaction proceeds and at the end
* any vapour or any other substance that is given off or distilled off
* the actual masses/volumes of products at the end of this first stage of the preparation.

Preparation of a chemical product using different practical techniques

The chemical product chosen to be prepared and purified must:
* be safe to prepare in the laboratory;
* be prepared from readily available substances so does not cost too much (check with the laboratory technicians); and
* use techniques such as distillation or reflux in the preparation, recrystallisation, melting point determination, boiling point determination, chromatography in the purification and assessment of purity.

Organic compounds, such as aspirin and iodoform, are more easily purified than inorganic compounds.

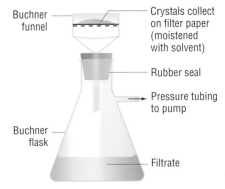

Labels: Buchner funnel — Crystals collect on filter paper (moistened with solvent); Rubber seal; Pressure tubing to pump; Buchner flask; Filtrate

Figure 2 Vacuum filtration

Purification of the product

The method chosen will depend upon whether the product is a liquid or a solid.
* If a liquid – this will involve a second distillation in a known temperature range.
* If a solid – this will involve recrystallisation using a solvent that may be flammable. (Vacuum filtration as a technique that could be used during recrystallisation.)

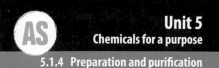
Assessing the purity

The physical properties of melting point for a solid and boiling point for a liquid can be used. If your product is aspirin, chromatography or a titration could be used to assess the purity.

Calculation of theoretical yield and percentage yield

The theoretical yield of products must be calculated using the chemical equation for the reaction.

All working must be shown and explained.

The percentage yield should be calculated using:

$$\% \text{ yield} = \frac{\text{actual number of moles of product}}{\text{theoretical number of moles of product}} \times 100$$

An example of the calculation of % yield.

Calculate the percentage yield of propanone if 1.45 g propanone is formed when 4.5 g propan-2-ol is oxidised using acidified potassium dichromate.

Step 1 Write the equation for the reaction. $CH_3CHOHCH_3 + [O] \rightarrow CH_3COCH_3 + H_2O$

Step 2 Calculate the number of moles of reactant

$$\text{Number of moles propan-2-ol} = \frac{\text{Mass of propan-2-ol}}{\text{Mass of 1 mole } C_3H_8O} = \frac{4.5}{60} = 0.075$$

Step 3 Using the ratio of moles in the equation calculate the number of moles of product formed.

In the equation the mole ratio is 1:1 as 1 mole $CH_3CHOHCH_3$ forms 1 mole CH_3COCH_3

Number of moles of product theoretically = 0.075

Step 4 Work out the actual number of moles of product obtained

$$\text{Number of moles propanone} = \frac{\text{Mass obtained of propanone}}{\text{Mass of 1 mole of propanone}} = \frac{1.45}{58} = 0.025$$

Step 5 Calculate % yield

$$\% \text{ yield} = \frac{\text{actual number of moles of product}}{\text{theoretical number of moles of product}} \times 100 = \frac{0.025}{0.075} \times 100 = 33\%$$

How changes in the conditions could alter the yield

Conditions can be altered and will affect the yield. Pressure in a laboratory cannot be easily altered

The following questions about the conditions used could be considered.

Temperature

- How was heat applied in the preparation? Did the mixture boil too vigorously?
- Did the mixture have to be maintained at a constant temperature for some time? How was this done? Could there have been a more satisfactory way?

Reactants and the reaction

- Would the reaction occur faster if the reactants were more concentrated?
- Was the size of apparatus correct?
- Were there any side reactions? Were there any other reactions that could have occurred?
- Was the product removed from the reaction? Did it react with any other chemical substances?

Internal assessment

Assessment tip

Take care to distinguish between conditions and techniques. Techniques will affect the yield but techniques can be improved with practice. It is conditions that are needed.

Examples of techniques include:
- careful pouring of liquids and handling of solids
- removal of all the chemical substances from one container into another.

Assessment tip

Possible changes in conditions.
- Each stage should be critically assessed.
- Explanations for less than 100% yield should be offered.
- Suggestions for alternative conditions should be given. Cost is not an issue.

By the end of this spread, you should be able to:

* ✱ know what you will need to do for this portfolio
* ✱ be aware of the level of work required
* ✱ know how you will be assessed
* ✱ be able to check your portfolio to see if you can improve it

Figure 1 Searching for evidence

Crime scene investigators use forensic methods to analyse evidence to try and identify a suspect. Forensic analysis uses principles which cover all branches of science i.e. biology, chemistry, geology, and physics.

The scientific skill of deduction from observations and measurements is used in analysing the evidence that has been collected.

Assessment objective AO1

There are three strands in this section.

You have to:
* show knowledge and understanding of the recording and preservation of the crime scene (5 marks)
* know how the evidence is collected safely and then visualised (12 marks)
* have an understanding of the ethical issues involved in retaining evidence (4 marks).

As forensic evidence changes with time, the crime scene must be recorded as quickly as possible using sketches and photographs. Evidence must be collected. All of this must be done carefully and systematically.

Assessment objective AO2

There are two strands in this section.

You have to produce
* a report on a forensic case study including the ways in which evidence is collected and analysed and then evaluated (6 marks)
* calculations on forensic data (4 marks).

Some crimes have never been solved because the evidence was insufficient. Some evidence has led to wrong convictions. The techniques for analysing evidence are constantly improving. In this assessment objective a forensic case study is used as the source of information on which to examine critically the evidence collected and analysed.

Assessment objective AO3

There are three strands in this section.

You should:
* carry out one forensic analysis safely in each of the four areas: visual and microscopic, biological and biochemical, chemical and physical (8 marks)
* record observations and/or measurements with appropriate precision for each analysis (5 marks)
* process and interpret each set of observations or measurements (6 marks).

Forensic scientists carry out the analyses on the evidence that has been collected and draw conclusions from the results in order to determine who committed the crime.

Internal assessment

How did you do?

What grade did you think your work is worth?

Use the following checklists to get some idea of the likely standard at which you are working. Remember that these are only a guide and that you should always aim to work as hard as you can to improve.

AO	Evidence	Form of evidence	Present			Missing
1a	Recording and preservation of the crime scene	Report outlining the techniques used				
1b	Techniques for visualising the evidence	Report with diagrams/ photos				
1c	Ethical issues. Sources should be given.	Report				
How the evidence is actually collected and then treated in order to give information should be described for AO1a and AO1b.						
2a	Forensic case study information analysed and criticised	Report				
2b	Calculations simple and complex using results from practical work	Work clearly set out showing all stages of the calculations				
A critical analysis of the treatment of evidence in a case should be given for AO2.						
3a	Forensic analyses in four areas including a risk assessment and using a range of techniques	Report with diagrams or photos of apparatus				
3b	Results of analyses	Report with appropriate tables				
3c	Processing and interpretation of results of analyses	Report including conclusions				
There are four forensic analyses required. Health and safety considerations may mean that one analysis has to be described. Processing of results can use data that has already been obtained.						

Table 1 Assessment objectives checklist

If you have ticked all the 'Present' boxes your work is probably at Grade E or better.

Have you found any areas where you have left something important out?
Are there any ticks in the 'Missing' column? If there are you may have time to do something about it.

What do you need to do to improve your portfolio?
It is likely that the evidence you have presented in your portfolio can be improved.

Use the information in the Assessment tip boxes to increase your chance of improving your work.

Assessment tip

For higher mark bands AO1:
- The techniques, chemical, biological, and physical, must be explained using scientific terms.
- An understanding of the need for an ethical code is discussed.

Assessment tip

For higher mark bands AO2 make sure that there is a discussion on the:
- limitations in the collection of evidence
- strengths and weaknesses of the analytical techniques
- probability of guilt.

For AO2b there should be evidence of complex calculations used in forensic measurements or observations.

The data from the practical work involving forensic analysis can be used for the calculations.

Assessment tip

For higher mark bands AO3 check that:
- there is an explanation of the wide range of techniques used
- all measurements have been repeated
- observations and measurements are recorded in a variety of ways and that measurements are given to the accuracy of the equipment
- a detailed interpretation of the results has been given.

Internal assessment

139

By the end of this spread, you should be able to:

∗ use techniques to record and preserve the crime scene
∗ use techniques to collect and understand the evidence
∗ use ethical issues in the collection and keeping of evidence

Recording the evidence at the crime scene

The priority for the police, firemen or ambulance crew who arrive first at the crime scene is to attend to anyone whose life is threatened. After that:

• contamination of the crime scene is minimised
• witnesses are interviewed
• the crime scene is recorded and the evidence collected by the police force and the forensic team.

Contamination of the crime scene by outside factors is minimised by the officials at the scene by

• putting tape around the scene to prevent access by unauthorised people
• the wearing of protective gear by the investigators.

Witnesses are identified, detained and interviewed by the police. Legal rights are explained in detail to witnesses before statements are taken or DNA samples collected.

Crime scene investigators (CSI) record the scene using:

• sketches which show the general layout of the scene
• photographs to show the position of the objects. Scale must be included. This can be done using a ruler or a tape measure
• digital photographs which can be produced instantaneously but have the disadvantage that they can be easily altered
• infrared photographs which can reveal hidden objects.

Preservation of evidence

Evidence is collected by the investigators. It is often photographed in place from several angles before removal. Any evidence removed from the scene of the crime must be put into a bag, sealed and labelled with date, location and signature of the collector.

Activity

Think about how each item of protective clothing worn by the investigator prevents contamination of the crime scene.

Figure 1 CSI in protective clothing

Collection and visualisation of evidence

Evidence is collected in several different ways depending on the type of evidence.

Visualisation of evidence refers to the way in which the evidence can be treated to reveal information.

The following table briefly outlines collection and visualisation of evidence. This is a starting point for further research to provide the detailed explanations needed. All collection techniques are not mentioned.

There are continuous improvements in collection techniques and in analysis of the evidence.

Type of evidence	Collection technique	Way in which evidence is treated	Extra information	Further treatment
Fingerprints	Physical	Dust with powder or use adhesive tape	Fingerprints are unique to any one person	Matching using data bank
Footprints Tyre marks Tool marks	Physical	Plaster of Paris casts	Distinctive patterns are revealed	Matching using provided data or using identified footprint or tool
Spent bullet	Physical	Examine under microscope	Rifling pattern noted	Test firing for comparison
Saliva and other biological fluids	Biological	Swabs	DNA is unique	DNA analysis
Blood	Chemical	Purple colour seen with test kit		
Ink	Chemical	Use of suitable solvent		Chromatography

Table 1 Evidence collection and visualisation

Ethical considerations

The ethics of evidence collection is concerned with whether it is right or wrong to:
- collect the evidence at all
- use the different techniques as ways to collect the evidence
- to keep the evidence once collected.

Some of the questions that could be thought about are:
- Have forensic scientists the right to collect any evidence that they want?
- Is agreement needed to collect evidence?
- For how long should the evidence be kept?
- Should all evidence be kept for the same length of time?

The collection and keeping of DNA samples is an example of a technique about which there is currently an ethical discussion.

Some of the points being discussed include:
- Should consent be given before a DNA sample is taken?
- Who should have access to DNA results?
- Should all DNA results be kept in a data bank?
- Should the DNA results of people found innocent be destroyed?

The laws concerning the collection of DNA samples are different in Scotland than in England and Wales.

Figure 2 Car crash scene

Internal assessment

By the end of this spread, you should be able to:

✳ select a forensic case study on which to base a report on evidence and proof
✳ question whether the evidence was collected objectively
✳ understand the strengths and limitations of the analytical techniques
✳ understand the strengths and limitations of using forensic evidence as proof

Figure1 A criminal trial

Source

News at bbc.co.uk is a good source of media coverage.

Crime scene ISBN 0-7513-4576-8 has case studies of forensic investigations.

Activity

DNA fingerprinting.
- Research who discovered DNA fingerprinting.
- Find out in what year DNA fingerprinting was first used.
- Find out the error in pinpointing an actual individual from a DNA fingerprint.
- Consider whether a match of DNA fingerprints is sufficient to convict a suspect.

Choice of forensic investigation

A report on evidence and proof is to be written using a forensic case study.

The forensic case study is chosen so that there is as much background information as possible. The background information may not be able to provide all the answers. You are not expected to read the actual proceedings of a trial!

The case study can be based on an actual forensic investigation or one in a television series.

Actual investigations will be the high profile ones such as O. J. Simpson, the dingo baby, as there will have been a great deal of media coverage.

Television forensic investigations in CSI in its many forms or 'Law and Order' can be used.

It must be remembered that although the collection and analysis of evidence should be the same in all countries, the legal system differs from country to country.

Collection of evidence

The ways in which the evidence was collected should be looked at critically. There should be several pieces of evidence collected. These should be listed in the report. Other evidence that might have been collected but was not in the background information should be listed in the report.

The information provided in spread 6.1.2 indicates how evidence in different forms is collected.

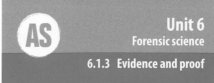

Strengths and limitations of analytical techniques

The report should contain the techniques used and an evaluation of the strengths and weaknesses of the actual techniques used. The information in spread 6.1.2 and the actual practical work done for AO3 will help.

The techniques used must produce reliable results. Discussion with other members of the class should indicate the reliability of the analyses done for AO3.

Analytical techniques have improved over the years. This has resulted in some different conclusions to the original one being made as in the case of Carl Bridgewater. Verdicts have been overturned when the original evidence has been re-examined using new techniques.

One analytical technique should be dealt with in detail.

In a case of breaking and entering a house a footprint has been left in the soil outside the window.

There are two ways of recording the footprint, by:
• making a cast of plaster of Paris
• taking a digital photo

Some of the strengths and limitations of each method is given in the table.

Figure 2 Photo of a footprint

Plaster of Paris cast		Digital photo	
Strengths	Limitations	Strengths	Limitations
Shows pattern of sole of shoe		Shows pattern of sole of shoe	
Shows wear of sole of shoe			Only indicates wear of sole
Indicates depth of footprint in soil			Cannot indicate depth of footprint in soil
	Relies on the skill of the person making the cast	Instantaneous	
	Depends on the state of the soil	Does not depend on the state of the soil.	
	Can only be made once	Can be repeated	

Table 1 Limitations in recording footprint data

Review of evidence for the forensic case study

A judgement has to be made as to whether the evidence that has been considered is sufficient to pinpoint and convict a suspect in the chosen forensic case study.

As there should be several points and as some points will be more important than others, it might be helpful to draw up a table with headings such as that below. The table only gives an indication of the approach. It is expected that there will be more points considered.

Technique	Accuracy	Limitations
Fingerprint collection	High, provided collector is competent	Could be smudged during collection
Fingerprint matching	High, as every fingerprint is unique	Prints on actual fingers can be removed by very drastic measures

Table 2 Fingerprinting

Activity

Use the information in Table 1 to decide whether more accurate information about a footprint in wet clay soil would be produced by a cast or a digital photo. Give reasons.

Case study

A paper boy, Carl Bridgewater, was shot in September 1978. In 1979 a verdict of guilty was given but this was overturned in 1997. The guilty verdict was based on the written confession which was shown later by electrostatic document analysis to have a forged signature.

Activities from this forensic case:
• Research the scientific principles behind electrostatic document analysis.
• Devise questions that should have been asked when the written confession was first shown at the trial.
• Find out what other evidence was presented at the trial.

By the end of this spread, you should be able to:

* understand the different types of forensic analyses (visual and microscopic, biological and biochemical, chemical, physical) that could be carried out in the laboratory
* record the observations and measurements for each analysis
* process and interpret the results for each analysis

Source

'The Forensic Science World', obtainable from Pfizer UK.

Case study

Matching fibres

A fibre found at a crime scene is examined using a microscope of a magnification which gives adequate detail into its structure. Other fibres taken from clothing of possible suspects are similarly examined.

All the fibres are handled using tweezers to prevent transfer of any other material.

All the fibres are illuminated using light coming in at the same angle.

A sketch is made of the image of the fibres seen in the microscope and labelled so that the different regions of the fibre are identified. For each sketch there is a description in words, the date of the observation, the name of the observer, and where the fibre was found.

If two fibres appear to be the same, further analysis would be needed to ensure that the dye was the same.

Internal assessment

Visual and/or microscopical analyses

These analyses are ones in which the evidence can be seen easily:
* by the naked eye e.g. fingerprints, footprints, tyre marks, tool marks
* when using an optical microscope e.g. fibres, hair, pollen grains.

In an actual crime scene the evidence is matched with other evidence:
* held in a data bank
* produced using an instrument thought to be involved in the crime such as the rifling on bullets.

Experimental work in which fibres and pollen are examined under the microscope, casts are made of footprints, can be easily carried out in the laboratory.

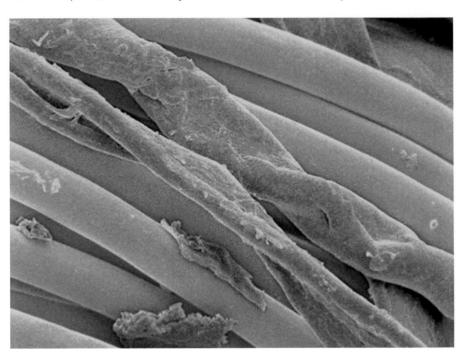

Figure 1 Fibres under the microscope

Biological and biochemical analysis

Such analyses are ones in which evidence comes from living organisms such as insects, humans (blood, semen, DNA). Health and safety considerations could restrict actual laboratory experimental work.

Experimental work in which a scenario similar to that in the case study could be analysed. Data on blowflies is obtainable on the Internet.

Using forensic entomology

The time of death of a victim can be deduced from the number of eggs, maggots, pupae and adult insects on the body and knowledge of the life cycle of that insect. An example is the blowfly. Blowflies lay their eggs on bodies within a few hours of death. Only a rough estimate of the time of death is possible as the life cycle of insects is affected by environmental factors.

Figure 2 Adult blowfly

Case study

A walker was reported as missing. After some time a corpse was seen by another party of walkers. Blowflies were found on the corpse. The time of death needed to be known. Samples of the eggs, maggots, pupae and adult blowflies were collected from different parts of the corpse using appropriate techniques and observing all necessary health and safety precautions.

Each sample was labelled with the location on the body, relevant temperatures, the time and date of collection, the name of the collector.

Think about:
• how the approximate time of death of the missing walker can be obtained from the life cycle of a blowfly
• whether an approximate time of death is a useful piece of evidence.

Chemical techniques

Use of chemical techniques involves:

• Chemical reactions. The identification of inorganic and organic substances using chemical tests is covered in spread 2.1.6. This method is used in the analysis of powders suspected to be a drug or a poison. Mass spectrometers are now used to analyse unknown substances as this is much quicker. The spectrometer is able to identify the chemical compounds present.
• Chromatography. This has been covered in spread 2.1.5. This method could be used to identify inks used in fraud cases. Gas chromatography linked to a mass spectrometer is used to identify drugs and alcohol.
• Infrared spectroscopy is used to identify burned plastics and synthetic materials.

Actual experimental work involving chemical techniques in the laboratory could be:
• qualitative analysis of an unknown powder (see spread 2.1.6)
• chromatography using dyes (see spread 2.1.5).

Physical techniques

Examples of physical techniques are:

• Determination of the refractive index of glass. Each type of glass has a specific refractive index.
• Blood spatter patterns. The pattern of blood splatter indicates the origin of the blood.
• Density gradients for soil. Soil can be analysed by shaking the soil with water and allowing the mixture to settle into layers which can then be examined and described.

Actual experimental work can be done using any of these examples.

Measurements and observations

Measurements and observations must be recorded clearly and in a range of ways such as:

• sketches for microscope work
• detailed observations in tables for biological and chemical analysis
• measurements in tables with clear headings for refractive index and blood splatter
• sketches with measurements of depth of each layer for soil analysis.

Processing and interpretation

The processing uses the measurements and observations from the actual evidence and will involve comparison with known standards.

Calculations will be needed in refractive index and blood splatter experiments. This contributes to AO2.

Source

Standard physics textbooks for refractive index.

'The Forensic Science World' published by Pfizer UK for blood splatter.

By the end of this spread, you should be able to:

* know what you will need to do for this portfolio
* be aware of the level of work required
* know how you will be assessed
* be able to check your portfolio to see if you can improve it

Assessment objectives AO1 and AO2

There are five strands in this section.

For each strand of AO1 you have to produce a leaflet about a particular aspect of sport. Three of your leaflets require additional content to meet the objectives of AO2:

* Measurement in sport. Five different units, devices and techniques for making measurements (AO1, 3 marks).
* Seeing in sport. Structure of the eye and formation of an image (AO1, 3 marks).
* Movement in sport. Energy transfer using muscles, bones and joints (AO1, 4 marks). Calculations based on information from *either* this leaflet or your techniques leaflet (AO2, 4 marks *either here or in techniques leaflet*).
* Choice of ball material. Information on properties of materials used in one type of ball (AO1, 3 marks). Use of principles linked to physical properties/energy change (AO2 3 marks).
* Equipment in sport. Information on properties of materials used in chosen sports equipment (AO1, 3 marks). Use of principles linked to physical properties/energy change (AO2, 3 marks).
* Techniques in sport. Knowledge of physics involved e.g. collisions (AO1, 5 marks). Calculations based on information from *either* this leaflet or your movement leaflet (AO2, 4 marks *either here or in techniques leaflet*).

When doing any piece of writing, it is important to think about who is intended to read it. In this case, your leaflets should be aimed at coaches at a sport or recreation centre to help them to answer technical questions.

Assessment objective AO3

There are three strands in this section to consider:

* Planning an experiment relating to one or more of your leaflets (6 marks)
* Safely carrying out your experiment using a range of equipment and techniques (6 marks)
* Interpreting and discussing your experiment (7 marks).

You may choose to summarise the conclusions of your experiment in your leaflet(s), but to score full marks for AO3 you are advised to report on your experiment separately from your leaflets.

How did you do?

What grade did you think your work is worth?

Use the following checklists to get some idea of the likely standard at which you are working. Remember that these are only guidelines and that you should always aim to work at as hard as you can to improve.

Internal assessment

Assessment tip

A leaflet is not the same thing as a full report. As a rough guide, aim for the equivalent of between two and four sides of A4 for each leaflet. You may wish to fold an A4 sheet in half or into three sections.

The challenge is to select your information carefully and present it concisely.

Figure 1 Swimmer

AO	Evidence	Form of evidence	Present	Missing
1a	Information on measurements of *five* quantities in sport. For each, include: units devices techniques.	Leaflet		
1b	Information on seeing in sport include: structure of the eye; how the eye forms an image; link to one chosen sport where vision is important.	Leaflet		
1c	Information on movement in sport include: conversion of chemical energy to mechanical work in the body; link to one chosen sport where efficient movement is important.	Leaflet		
1d	Information on choice of ball material include: material properties required how these are achieved for *one* type of ball.	Leaflet		
1e	Information on equipment in sport include: material properties required how these are achieved for *one or more* pieces of sports equipment.	Leaflet		
1f	Information on techniques in sport include *one* example related to a specified sport of *either* collisions, trajectories *or* lift	Leaflet		
	The challenge in producing leaflets is to present your information concisely and attractively. Remember that your audience needs technical information.			
2a	Selection and use of principles	Choice of ball material leaflet and equipment in sport leaflet		
	The additional AO2 marks for these two leaflets are for showing that you understand the links between scientific principles and the factual content of your leaflets.			
2a 2b	Basic calculations relating to your leaflet	*either* Movement in sport leaflet *or* Techniques in sport leaflet		
3a	Experimental plan and safe conduct of experiment	Report		
3b	Use of a range of equipment. Some results obtained	Report		
3c	Interpretation of results related to aim	Results		
	Record all your results clearly, with units and to an appropriate number of significant figures. Your reports should include the measurement instruments you have used.			

Table 1 Assessment objectives checklist

- If you have ticked all the 'Present' boxes your work is probably at Grade E or better.

Have you found any areas where you have left something important out?
Are there any ticks in the 'Missing' column? If there are you may have time to do something about it.

What do you need to do to improve your portfolio?
It is likely that the evidence you have presented in your portfolio can be improved.

Use the information in the Assessment tip margin boxes to increase the chance of your getting a better grade. There is an Assessment tip box for each of the assessment objectives. The advice given, if taken, could improve your grade up to Grade A.

Assessment tip

For higher mark bands AO1:
- no cut and paste
- show comprehensive and detailed knowledge
- show understanding.

Assessment tip

For higher mark bands AO2:
- accurately identify principles
- make your explanations clear, accurate and thorough
- use mathematical techniques confidently and accurately
- use your calculations to enhance the explanations in your leaflets.

Assessment tip

For higher mark bands AO3:
- draw up and follow a comprehensive and realistic risk assessment
- use a wide range of equipment and techniques
- obtain ample valid data
- repeat values and averages
- record data clearly and to appropriate precision
- interpret, calculate, evaluate.

Internal assessment

Internal assessment

By the end of this spread, you should be able to:

✻ know more about key SI units and their multiples and submultiples
✻ carry out calculations and conversions using SI and other units
✻ know about a range of devices and techniques for making measurements in sport and explain the need for calibration

If sport is to be fair, we aim for everybody to compete under the same conditions. We need to check that equipment is within the limits set down in the rules. We need to make sure that when we measure performance we do this in the same way for all competitors. We therefore need accurate and consistent measurement.

Units

Checklist

For each of your sports measurements you need to include:
- the units it is measured in
- what you measure it with
- how you measure it.

SI base units

There are six base units in the SI system. Base units are defined in terms of an actual physical object. For example the kilogram, the SI unit of mass, is defined as a mass equal to an actual lump of metal kept in Paris. You were introduced to the kilogram, the metre and the second earlier in this book. The SI base unit of temperature is the kelvin (K).

In everyday language we talk about the weight of something being measured in kilograms (kg).

In science we distinguish between *mass* which is measured in kg and *weight* which is measured in newtons (N).

Weight is the force due to gravity. If you ever go into space you will become weightless but you will still have a mass. Mass is defined by the force needed to accelerate an object.

SI derived units

SI derived units are defined in terms of the base units.

If you want to measure your velocity while running you could measure 100 m on a track and use a stop watch to find how many seconds it takes you to run the distance. Let's say it takes you 50 s.

$$v = \frac{s}{t}, \text{ where distance } s = 100 \text{ m, time } t = 50 \text{ s, } v = \frac{100}{50} = 2.0 \text{ m s}^{-1}$$

The unit of velocity is obtained by dividing the units of length by the units of time.

To work out a derived unit from the base units you start with the equation relating them.

$$\text{acceleration} = \frac{\text{velocity change}}{\text{time taken}}, \text{ so the unit of acceleration} = \frac{\text{unit of velocity}}{\text{unit of time}}, \text{m s}^{-1}/\text{s} = \text{m s}^{-2}$$

Force = mass × acceleration, so the unit of force is the unit of mass × the unit of acceleration, kg m s^{-2}

Because we use the units of force a lot we have a special name for this, the newton (N).

$$1 \text{ N} = 1 \text{ kg m s}^{-2}$$

Case study

You can calculate the weight of a mass *m* using the formula weight = *mg*

g = acceleration due to gravity
= 9.81 m s^{-2}

Source

If you want to see how much faster some British sprinters run see the BBC Sport website.

Assessment tip

When writing composite units like m s^{-1} notice there is a space between the units. If you wrote ms^{-1} the ms would mean per millisecond (1/1000 s)

Notice that the unit 'newton' is spelt with a small letter although the abbreviation N is a capital letter. If you write 'Newton' you are referring to Sir Isaac! This rule applies to other units as well.

Non SI units

Some other non SI units are often used in sport:
- Temperature is usually measured in °C. 0 °C = 273.15 K. The interval 1°C ≡ 1 K.
- Food energy is still sometimes measure in Calories.
- 1 nutritional Calorie (note capital C) = 4197 joules (1 joule (J) is the SI unit of energy).

There is also a unit called the calorie (small c). 1 Calorie = 1000 calorie.

Measurement instruments

In your measurement in sport leaflet, remember to include the device you use to measure with and justify your choice, even if it is a simple stopwatch as in Figure 1.

Think about the accuracy of your measurement. Most stopwatches measure to a hundredth of a second, but the reading is not usually that accurate because of the delay caused by our reaction time. If you are describing a sport where this kind of accuracy is needed the clocks are probably controlled by mechanical or light gates. Balances to measure mass can be obtained to measure to various degrees of precision.

Distance may be measured using:
- a simple tape measure
- vernier callipers which measure to the nearest 0.1 mm (see earlier in this book)
- micrometers which measure to the nearest 0.01 or 0.001 mm.

During training a coach may want to monitor an athlete's blood pressure, pulse rate and body temperature. See the Unit 3 spreads in this book for the instruments you need to measure these.

Radar

For many sports, speed is found by dividing distance travelled by time. Direct measurement of speed of, for example, cricket balls is done using radar. The principle is the same as the device used by police to check the speed of cars. You can buy one for the price of a good quality MP3 player!

Radar uses a pulsed beam of microwave radiation. If you point the beam at a ball or car coming towards you, the reflected pulses are closer together than if the target is still. This is called the Doppler effect.

Datalogging

Some sports such as formula one motor racing are highly dependent on computer monitoring and control.

Electronic datalogging is particularly useful for physiological measurement and for recording very fast events.

Source

The Heinemann weblinks include a useful site for converting units.

Figure 1 Stopwatch

Case study

It is important to check the calibration of measuring devices from time to time.

Imagine the effect if the marshal measuring the long jump had a tape measure that had stretched!

Internal assessment

Figure 2 Sophisticated electronic equipment is used to monitor the performance of racing cars

By the end of this spread, you should be able to:

∗ use formulae and equations to solve problems involving force, mass, acceleration, momentum, work, energy and power
∗ know and apply the principle of conservation of energy
∗ know that muscles are not very efficient at converting chemical energy to mechanical work done
∗ explain why exercise produces heat and its implications in endurance events such as marathon running
∗ apply the principle of moments to bone/muscle joints

Sports like snooker require excellent hand–eye coordination, but are less physically demanding than others. Marathon runners need to use their energy and keep their muscles moving efficiently for a sustained period of time. Competitors in the javelin train so that they can deliver a large amount of energy in a controlled manner for a very short period of time.

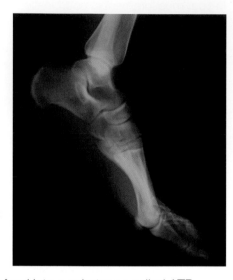

Figure 1 The foot is a kind of lever

Key definition

Energy is the capacity for doing work.

Source

The medbio weblink gives you more information about this.

Activity

Find the work done in striking a pool ball if the cue applies a constant force of 50 N for 0.62 m

50 × 0.62 = 31 J

Work and energy

Our bodies convert the chemical **energy** from our food into a substance called ATP (adenosine triphosphate). See spread 3.1.1.

Work is an activity where a force pushes or pulls something in the direction of the force.

Work done = force x distance moved in the direction of the force.

In our bodies the force is applied by our muscles. We use ATP to make our muscles contract. Muscles are attached to bones which are connected by joints. When the muscles contract, the bones move. Muscles on the opposite side to the contracting muscle are called antagonistic muscles. They contract when we want to move the bones back.

If your movement leaflet was about putting the shot, for example, you could use the equation above to find out how much work is done on the shot. From this you will know its kinetic energy.

The principle of conservation of energy states that energy can neither be created nor destroyed. The chemical energy in your muscles is converted into gravitational potential energy if you do weightlifting or the high jump. It is converted into kinetic energy when you throw a ball.

The process is not very efficient. A lot of the chemical energy in the ATP is converted into heat in your body and your surroundings. If you run along a flat track and then stop, you have no more kinetic or potential energy than when you started – but you probably feel a lot warmer!

Power – how fast do you work in your sport?

$$\text{Power} = \frac{\text{work done}}{\text{time taken}}$$

Compare a weightlifter and a mountain climber.

The weightlifter lifts a mass of 50 kg a height of 1.5 m.
 	
Force needed = weight
        = mass × g
        = mass × 9.81 ≈ 500 N
 	
The work done
= potential energy gained
= 500 × 1.5 = 750 J
	A mountain climber of mass 80 kg climbs 550 m up a cliff.
	
	Force needed = weight
	        = mass × g
	        = mass × 9.81 ≈ 800 N
	
	The work done
	= potential energy gained
	= 800 × 550 = 440 000 J

The mountain climber does much more work.

Now compare their *rate* of working – their power.

If the weightlifter takes 3 s,
power = 750/3
      = 250 W
	If the climber takes 3 hours,
	power = 440 000/(3 × 60 × 60)
	      = 41 W (to 2 sig. figs.)

The weightlifter delivers more power

Our bodies are full of levers

Your portfolio is likely to include some discussion of some of the muscles and bones used in your chosen sport. These form a kind of lever system.

A lever is any rigid object that can rotate about a point called a pivot. An effort will tend to push it round, so moving a load.

You should research the three classes of levers:

- Class one levers have the pivot between load and effort, like a crow-bar. In our bodies an example is the head pivoting on the neck.
- Class two levers have the load between the pivot and effort, like a wheel barrow. In our bodies this would be like our body weight, lifted by muscles at the heel and pivoted at out toes (see Figure 1).
- Class three levers have the effort between the pivot and load, like a pair of sugar tongs. In our bodies this is the same as our arm, pivoted at the elbow, lifted by the biceps attached close to the elbow and with the weight force further along the forearm (especially if you are lifting something in your hand).

Principle of moments

In some systems, including all class two levers, the effort can lift a bigger load. We say that the **mechanical advantage** is greater than 1. But nothing is for nothing! The penalty is that the effort has to move further than the load. We say that the **velocity ratio** is greater than 1.

In some other systems, including all class three levers, the effort is greater than the load. The compensation is that the effort has to move less distance than the load.

From the definition of the **moment of a force**, you can see that in Figures 2(a) and 2(b) the moment of the force F about the pivot A is $F \times y$.

In Figure 2(a), the moment is clockwise (imagine you put a nail through the book at the pivot and pulled in the direction of the force). In Figure 2(b), the moment is anticlockwise.

Principle of moments states that when a body is in *equilibrium* (i.e. balanced):

Sum of the anticlockwise moments about any point	=	The sum of the clockwise moments about that point

In Figure 2(c):

10 × 0.30 + 30 × 0.15	=	$F \times y$

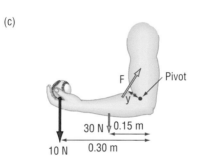

Figure 2 Diagrams showing: **a** force acting on a beam; **b** force acting on an arm; **c** a system in equilibrium

Internal assessment

Source

A good account of levers in the body is given in BCB (Department of Biodiversity and Conservation Biology at The University of the Western Cape).

Key definitions

Mechanical advantage = $\dfrac{\text{load}}{\text{effort}}$

Velocity ratio = $\dfrac{\text{distance moved by effort}}{\text{distance moved by load}}$

The **moment of a force** about a point = the force × the perpendicular distance of the force from the point.

By the end of this spread, you should be able to:

* apply conservation of momentum to simple sporting examples of collisions
* explain the effects of spin of a ball
* explain how sails and wings produce forces for motion and lift
* show that rotating objects have both kinetic energy and momentum
* explain how a change in shape may lead to a change in rate of rotation
* be aware of the need to use vectors to solve problems involving velocities or forces

Sachin Tendulkar is one of the best batsmen in the world. His batting depends on perfect balance, economy in the way he moves, and precision in the way he plays his strokes. Excellence in sport is not just a matter of strength and stamina. Good technique is firmly based in physical principles.

Collisions

Many sports involve collisions – either deliberately or accidentally! Energy may be lost to the surroundings during collisions. The energy is converted into heat, but *provided that no external forces act* one quantity, **momentum**, stays the same.

The principle of conservation of momentum states that:

* In isolated systems the total momentum of colliding bodies is the same before and after the collision.

Sometimes an isolated system is described as one where no external forces act. Friction with the ground is an example of an external force. The principle does not apply if there is friction.

The principle of conservation of momentum is useful when working out problems like colliding snooker balls. Their combined momentum is the same before and after a collision. Start you calculations with this equation:

momentum of cue ball before	+	momentum of object ball before	=	momentum of cue ball after	+	momentum of object ball after

Spin

Sportsmen and women deliberately spin balls to change their path.

You learnt in the previous spread that work done by your muscles can give a ball kinetic energy and potential energy:

* Potential energy is due to position. The ball may be higher or squashed.
* Kinetic energy is due to movement.

You can calculate kinetic energy for translational movement using $E = \frac{1}{2} mv^2$. (Movement from point A to point B along a straight line or a curve is called translational movement.)

Key definition

Momentum = mass x velocity.

Units: $kg\,m\,s^{-1}$

Figure 1 Conservation of momentum is at the heart of playing pool

---

Activity

A white pool ball has a mass of 0.16 kg. Find its momentum if it is travelling at 11 m s⁻¹.

The white ball hits the centre of a stationary coloured ball with the same mass and stops completely. Find the velocity of the coloured ball after the collision.

$0.16 \times 11 = 1.76 = 1.8$ kg m s⁻¹ (to 2 significant figures).

total momentum before	=	total momentum after

$1.8 + 0 = 0 + 0.16\,v$

$v = 11$ m s⁻¹ (to 2 significant figures).

If the ball is spinning about its axis it has rotational kinetic energy as well as the translational kinetic energy.

A spinning ball also has rotational momentum. Really clever snooker players can transfer rotational momentum from the cue ball to the object ball when they collide!

Have you ever seen a spinning ball behave in strange ways when it bounces? The spin causes the surface they bounce off to apply a force on the ball along the surface. This increases or decreases the component of their velocity in that direction.

Specially shaped objects like the discus and javelin have their own peculiarities. If you are keen on cricket you may want to find out more about the effect of the stitching on ball movement.

If you are writing about ball techniques in your portfolio find out if they have a special shape. For example:
- Dimples in golf balls make them go faster. Asymmetric dimple patterns on some balls are said to reduce accidental side-spin!
- Ten pin bowling balls are not symmetrical. Like those used on bowling greens, this is a deliberate way of making the path of the balls curve.
- The distinctive shape of rugby balls has more to do with the shape of a pig's bladder, from which the early ones were made!

Lift and bending it 'like Beckham'
Aeroplanes fly because the upper surfaces of their wings are more curved than the under surfaces. This special shape is called an aerofoil. Air has to go faster over the longer surfaces. The Bernoulli effect tells us that the air travelling faster will be at a lower pressure (surprising but true). If the pressure under the wing is higher than the pressure above it this will hold the aircraft up.

The same principle is used in sports like:
- parasurfing (see Figure 2)
- paragliding
- sailing – the aerofoil is on its side so that the force is horizontal to push the boat along
- motor racing – the upside-down wings on racing cars provide downforce (see gpracing weblink)

Spinning balls curve in flight. This is used in many sports, but most famously by David Beckham who can make the ball lift as well as move sideways. The BBC science topic web link includes a clear animation showing what happens.

If you want to find out more about this look up the Magnus effect. The Geocities web link explains how the 'whirlpool' of air around the ball increases the velocity and reduces the pressure on the side where the motion is in the same direction as the airstream.

Direction makes a difference

If you run once round a race track there is a big difference between the distance you have run (maybe 250 m) and your displacement (your distance from your starting point which is zero).

Displacement, velocity and force are examples of vector quantities. They have magnitude (size) and direction.

Distance travelled and speed are called scalar quantities. They have magnitude only.

There are special rules for adding vectors together and these rules become important if your sport involves forces and velocities at different angles. Here are two examples:
- Combining the change of velocity of a ball caused by a cricket bat or tennis racket with its original velocity as it comes towards you.
- Sailing boats move forward due to the combined forces of the wind pushing on the sail and the water pushing on the centre-board or keel. These forces are at different angles.

Assessment tip

One of the things that make sport fun is that we do not live in a simple world. Your leaflet may include some of these complications. Air resistance particularly affects objects that are wide, slow, and/or light.

Sources

See the Heinemann diracdelta web link for a more detailed explanation of this.

Figure 2 Parasurfing

Internal assessment

⑥ Your experiment and your seeing in sport leaflet

By the end of this spread, you should be able to:

* design and carry out a safe experiment to determine the coefficient of restitution for a ball of your choice
* know the basic anatomy of the eye and describe the optical function of each of its parts
* describe the formation of a real image with a lens and relate this to the eye
* describe how the use of coloured contact lenses may help sports players

Internal assessment

Your experiment

Bouncing ball

Measuring the bouncing properties of a ball is just one example of an experiment that meets the requirement for a related experimental investigation. You may choose other experiments instead.

Balls used for different sports vary in many ways. They vary most particularly in size, weight and how much they bounce. This experiment is about measuring the bouncing properties of a ball – properly called its coefficient of restitution.

As a ball falls from a height it converts gravitational potential energy into kinetic energy. During contact with the ground the ball is compressed. The energy is stored as elastic potential energy. The ball actually stops. The process is then reversed.

Very little energy is likely to be lost due to air drag (unless you were to do the experiment with a shuttle cock!). Depending on the material of the ball (and to a lesser extent the type of surface) energy is likely to be converted into heat during the bounce. The ball does not return to its original height.

The coefficient of restitution is a measure of the bounciness of the ball and ground surface. It is always a number less than one.

$$\text{Coefficent of restitution} = \frac{\text{velocity after bounce}}{\text{velocity before bounce}}$$

It is easier to measure the height the ball is released from and the height of bounce.

The equation you use to process your results is:

$$\text{Coefficent of restitution} = \sqrt{\frac{\text{height after bounce}}{\text{height before bounce}}}$$

Things to think about when designing your experiment:
- If you are measuring the bounce height by eye you must be level with the ball.
- If your rule is resting on the surface measure to the bottom of the ball – why?
- If you have a very bouncy ball you might let it bounce several times – but then take care with the sums!
- Remember to repeat your readings and take an average. Estimate your errors from the spread of your results.
- Think about how you can extend your investigation. For example you could investigate how the coefficient of restitution of squash balls varies with temperature. Think how you will change and measure the temperature of the ball.
- Does the starting height have any effect?
- Keep things you are not intending to change, like the surface, constant.
- Is there any way you could use a light gate or video camera to get more accurate readings?

Case study

Squash balls are made in different grades for different types of players. Good players hit the ball so hard and fast that the ball heats up more. This makes it more bouncy. Beginners can use balls that are bouncy even at lower temperatures. See 'squashplayer' weblink.

Assessment tip

This is an experiment than can be performed very simply. Read the AO3 mark band 3 criteria carefully ('… wide range of techniques and equipment… ample data… precision') to make sure that you do the job thoroughly enough!

Case study

To relate coefficient of restitution to height:

Kinetic energy = ½ mv^2

Kinetic energy gained = potential energy lost

Gravitational potential energy = mgh

$mgh = ½ mv^2$
$gh = ½ v^2$
$v^2 = 2gh$
$v = \sqrt{2gh}$

$$\frac{\text{velocity after bounce}}{\text{velocity before bounce}}$$

$$\sqrt{\frac{2\,g \times \text{height after bounce}}{2\,g \times \text{height before bounce}}}$$

Structure of the eye

Good eyesight is important for many sports.

The organisation British Blind Sport does remarkable work to enable people who are blind or partially sighted to take part in a wide range of sports including cricket, archery and shooting. This brings home to those with good eyesight just how important a part this plays in their sporting performance.

You should know the basic structure of the eye (see Figure 1).

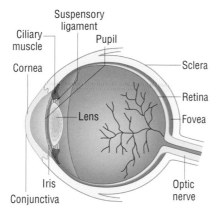

Figure 1 The eye is critical for most sports

Source

The BBC bitesize website includes further details about the basic parts and structure of the eye. See weblink.

Image formation

The lens in your eye is convex (it bulges in the middle). When light goes from air into the cornea and lens material it turns a slight corner. The amount of bending varies. Rays that started from the same point on an object come back together when they get to the retina. This forms the image (see Figure 2).

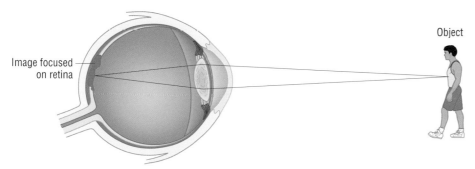

Figure 2 Rays forming an image in the eye

The image will only be in focus for objects at a limited range of distances.

To focus your eye, you use your ciliary muscles to squash or stretch the lens to bring the image into focus. Sports people sometimes have to do this very quickly if, for example, a ball is coming towards them fast. Unlike a camera, the distance from the lens to the retina is fixed.

Coloured lenses for sports

A recent development in contact lenses is light-filtering tints. The idea is enhance certain colours compared to others:

- Tennis players can wear yellow lenses which are the same colour as tennis balls. The ball is easier to see against the background.
- Golfers can use lenses that help them to distinguish between the different greens on a golf course.
- Baseball players wear amber lenses to filter out blue light. This makes it easier to see the baseball.

Source

The sportslens weblink – tinted lenses and other eyewear for sport.

The scotman weblink – tinted lenses for sports.

The eveshamoptometry weblink – other opticians help sports people.

Internal assessment

By the end of this spread, you should be able to:

✱ **know what you will need to do for this portfolio**
✱ **be aware of the level of work required**
✱ **know how you will be assessed**
✱ **be able to check your portfolio to see if you can improve it**

Research scientists need to plan and document all the work they complete and it is important to record work that did not go to plan, you never know you may discover something new!

Assessment objective AO1

There are two strands in this section.
You have to:

- complete a workable and clearly presented plan with aims and objectives, including scientific principles (5 marks)
- carry out research for your project and related health and safety requirements, set and keep to deadlines and be aware of the constraints of your work (5 marks).

The plan you produce needs to be a holistic representation of what you intend to do during your investigation. It should be a work plan showing dates and times, a schedule of the work you intend to do, a record of what you actually did and comments on any changes you need to make.

Research using biotechnological techniques such as recombining DNA has led to the production of substances including human insulin and growth hormone. Many scientists work on the Human Genome Project to isolate genes and determine their function, which leads to discoveries linked to genes associated to specific diseases. Other work includes commercial applications in the food industry, agriculture and DNA fingerprinting. Investigative work in science is the key to improved knowledge to support a changing world.

Assessment objective AO2

There are three strands in this section.

You have to produce information which shows:
- a record of the data collected with suitable detail and explanations (5 marks)
- processing, interpretation and analysis of your data (5 marks)
- a range of calculations linked to the work you have carried out (4 marks).

Recording and presentation of data is key to the success of research projects. Data collected needs to be easily understood by those who are reading it. You may know what you have carried out, but does any one else! Clear labelling, inclusion of units, organised tables all result in good recording of results. It is important that this is completed for your investigative work.

Assessment objective AO3

There are five strands in this section.

You should produce in your written report:
- evidence that you have safely completed a range of practical activities each with related risk assessments which link to the aim of your investigation (6 marks)
- information showing how you monitored your plan throughout your project (5 marks)
- the outcomes and findings of your investigative work (7 marks)
- information showing interpretation of your data (4 marks)
- an evaluation of the investigation you have carried out (4 marks).

Case study

Scottish research assistant Alexander Fleming discovered the antibiotic penicillin after noticing a mould attacking bacteria in a set of culture dishes.

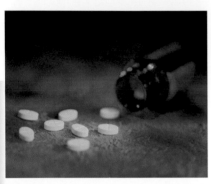

Figure 1 Antibiotics are commonly used

Figure 2 Biotechnology used on a commercial scale

Assessment tip

Practical work needs to be logically and accurately performed. Working scientists need to set realistic targets and organise their workload to fit the constraints of the project they are investigating. A well organised scientist makes sure the correct equipment is used and suitable time is allocated to both complete the experimental work and its review in the case of obtaining anomalous results.

How did you do?

What grade did you think your work is worth?

Use the following checklists to get some idea of the likely standard at which you are working. Remember that these are only a guide and that you should always aim to work at as hard as you can to improve.

AO	Evidence	Form of evidence	Present	Missing
1a and 1b	A plan and research to include: aim of your project objectives (tasks you intend to do) time allocation resources needed health and safety requirements scientific principles involved any ethical implications deadlines constraints.	A record of a plan either in tabular form or written in a lab notebook A record of your research		
3b	A record that you followed your plan and any changes made.			
You should include evidence of a selection of secondary sources and include information of the validity of your research. You must write this plan before you carry out your project. It is important that you use it as you are completing the work.				
2a	Work which includes: results set out in suitable formats/grouped where required suitable explanation of what results indicate.	Work included within report of investigation		
2b and 2c	Suitable processing of data – to include suitable: calculations graphs display and explanation of any qualitative data.			
Data needs to show evidence of collection from individual work but can also include group data. Take care to check calculations are accurate and all answers recorded to the correct number of significant figures. Indicate use of primary and secondary data where appropriate.				
3a, 3c, 3d and 3e	Report to include: evidence of any trials and main practical work has been completed, with suitable use of risk assessments any instructions you followed (you do not need to rewrite these) to be included. the outcomes of your investigation. information showing interpretation of your data and how your work achieved its aims some evaluation of your work.	Work recorded as an organised detailed report		
Your report needs to be written as a scientific document. Do not use 'I did this etc.' Organise your report logical – it is useful to use side headings.				

Table 1 Assessment objectives checklist

If you have ticked all the 'Present' boxes your work is probably at Grade E or better.

Have you found any areas where you have left something important out?

Are there any ticks in the 'Missing' column? If there are you may have time to do something about it.

What do you need to do to improve your portfolio?

It is likely that the evidence you have presented in your portfolio can be improved.

To improve your work from mark band 1 check you have completed the extra detail. Use the information in the Assessment tip boxes to help you improve.

Assessment tip

For higher marks in AO1 your research and plan needs to:
- give evidence of comprehensive and selective research showing the vocational link and detailed scientific principles
- show sufficient detail of health and safety guidelines.

Assessment tip

For higher marks in AO2 your records need to show:
- more than one set of results organised in formats decided on by yourself
- information explaining the results and why they were collected
- processing of data showing a range of complex calculations. Answers quoted to the correct number of significant figures.

Assessment tip

For higher marks in AO3 your report should include evidence:
- of completion of a number of different experimental techniques
- that risk assessments are completed and used
- of your plan being implemented and monitored with suitable explanations and strategies to improve the overall aim
- a high level of knowledge and independent understanding of the scientific principles and skills that you have used
- of a critical and well structured evaluation giving suitable amendments where appropriate.

Internal assessment

By the end of this spread, you should be able to:

✳ know what is needed to complete a detailed and workable plan for your investigation
✳ understand what is required for research and knowledge on scientific principles

Activity

It is a good idea to discuss what you need to think about when planning an investigation. Use this following information to help you decide on what you are going to do:

- topic
- research needed
- practical work that can be done
- measurements/data to be collected
- what is needed to plan.

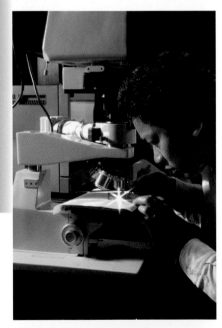

Figure 1 A scientist at work

Key definitions

The **aim** of your investigation is what you intend to find out and understand usually with a scientific reason behind it.

The **objectives** are the tasks you are going to carry out in order to achieve your aim.

Planning your investigation

Your choice of investigation needs to build on knowledge and practical skills that you have covered in other units of Applied Science. The investigative work needs to show a vocational link which needs to be supported by research and practical skills. You may be given a topic but here are a number of suggestions you may wish to use.

Biological investigations

Biological scientists study living organisms and their link to the environment. They use their biological knowledge in medical research, drugs, treatments and medical testing. Environmental issues may include biofuels, crop yields, pollution etc. Recent advances in biotechnology are changing the type of work biological scientists carry out. The opportunities are huge and the research exciting.

Your investigation could be based on the work you covered in:

- Unit 3 – extending work on cardiac recovery/fitness and health/healthy eating and diet.
- Unit 4 – focusing on biochemistry – include food tests/link with organic chemistry preparations/amino acids/microorganisms/antibiotics/microscopy work.
- Unit 14 – an extension of the investigation you studied in this unit.
- Unit 15 – an extension work on catalysis, biological and/or chemical/rates of reactions.

Chemical investigations

Chemical research has led to the discovery and development of new and improved materials. Chemists' work involves research and development of different materials including synthetic fibres, adhesives, lubricants, medicines, paints etc.

Your investigation could follow on from Units 2, 6, 5 or 10 and can extend both theoretical chemical knowledge and build on independent and competent use of qualitative and quantitative analysis or organic preparative work. For Unit 12, extension of electrolytic work or redox could be completed.

Physics investigations

Physicists investigate and identify basic principles and laws. They look at structure and behaviour of matter and energy. They apply their knowledge of physics to the development of advanced materials, electronic and optical devices and medical equipment.

This investigative work could be extended:

- Unit 2 – investigation involving energy production/efficiency/fuels.
- Units 7 and 11 – the investigations based on this work are wide ranging – physics linked to strength/material investigative work.

Having chosen your topic you need to decide on the **aims** and **objectives** of your investigation.

Student could have decided to investigate painkillers

The aim of the investigation could be:

- To investigate the active ingredients in painkillers on offer to the public, to understand how they work and how they could be prepared both in the laboratory or in an industrial setting.

The objectives would be:

- The different tasks you need to carry out in order to cover the aim.
- Research on types of painkillers; what are 'active ingredients'; how they work.

- Practical work: preparation of a painkiller and analysis of a suitable 'active ingredient'.
- Investigate reaction route.
- % yield.
- Compare manufactured product and costs.

Student could decide to investigate materials in everyday use

The aim of this investigation could be:
- To investigate the properties of a range of materials, to understand how they are used to improve performance in sport and every day life.

The objectives would be:
- Decide on the materials you want to investigate and what you want them to improve.
- Research on how the materials are used to improve the selected performance – include visit to where materials are being used.
- Research on properties needed or how a new material may improve performance.
- Practical work to look at a range of properties and carry out a number of tasks involving suitable measurements and observations to investigate the properties of the materials being investigated.

Producing a plan

Organisation is key to success, so before you begin your investigation you need to produce a plan for all of your work. The following steps should help:
- Find out how long you have, you should be working towards 60 hours, this may not all be in the laboratory, you will need time to carry out practical: time researching and time writing up your project.
- You can write your plan either electronically or paper based: suggested headings are shown in Figure 2.
- You will also need to monitor the progress of your plan; see spread 8.1.4.

Date/Time	Task	Requirements/Things to do	Outcome
Session 1 4th Sept 2 hour session	Research work on materials List materials Find out properties Discuss practical availability with tutor	Internet access Book practical equipment for session 5	Found information on investigation topic – materials Decided on materials to study Found out about practical Ordered equipment
Session 2 5th September 1 hour session	Write up aims of investigation	Computer access	Started AO1 – research and aims – written up

The tasks you need to think about including in your plan:
- Start with the research you need to do: include background to the topic and scientific principles.
- You then will need time to research and carry out the practical work.
- You may need time to do some trials/tests or preliminary work, research on health and safety and don't forget to include the ordering of your equipment.
- Include time to do some of your writing up as you go along as well as at the end.
- Include time for discussions with your tutor and time to check and monitor your plan.

How much research?

You need to include in your introduction to your investigation:
- Research on the topic which makes the investigation 'vocational'.
- Information on the scientific principles needed in order to understand the work you intend to carry out.

For an investigation on pain killers you need to:
Discuss types of painkillers/look at packets from products available from pharmacists.
Carry out an Internet search: to focus on one or two types of active ingredient e.g. paracetamol/Aspirin.
Scientific principles include – structure of compound/preparation of compound to include types of reactions/ information on type of practical techniques/work on calculating the yield.

You will need to ask your teacher to direct you to the instructions on how to prepare your chosen compound – you may need to find out about the type of reactions involved.

Assessment tip

In your plan remember to include time for:
- research work
- practical details and if you need to repeat or extend your work
- writing up the outcomes of your work as you go along and your final report.

③ **Investigative work**

By the end of this spread, you should be able to:

✱ to carry out your investigation
✱ know what is needed in order to record and process data collected

Carrying out the investigation

The practical you will carry out will obviously be linked with your chosen topic, however listed below are some practical techniques that you could use for your investigation. Following your initial research, you will need to find out about the practical instructions that you will need to follow for your investigation.

Biological practical activities

These may include:

* Monitoring of a sample of people carrying out a number of tests/exercises.
* Building on the experimental work completed in a psychology unit.
  (If this is the case you need to make sure that they have completed a risk assessment before they begin. An example is given below.)

You will be told the reason for completing the test.
Explanations of any measurements which may be made will be explained to you.
The time the testing will take and if any repeat testing will be needed.
Results will be available to the participants.
All data will be kept anonymous.
Any discussion re the outcomes will remain anonymous.
Signature _____ Date _____

Table 1 Guidelines to be followed when completing tests for experimental purposes

Figure 1 These students will measure fitness after completing a cycling task

* Within your investigation microscopy work may be included, see P.1.8. For basic work on preparing a temporary slide see Unit 4 information for additional detail.
* If your investigation includes microorganisms you may need to use aseptic techniques, see spread P.1.8.
* Enzyme technology, bio-reactors can be found in Unit 14.
* Food test information can be found in Unit 4.

Chemical practical activities

There are a vast number of chemical practical activities that can be used in your investigations. You will need to incorporate a range of different exercises within your work to ensure you reach mark band 3.

Assessment tip

Remember to complete a risk assessment before you complete any practical activity. You can use a given format – but make sure the information you record relates to what you are doing and is not just a generic statement.

Activity

Household bleach is a dangerous material that causes burns and is toxic. The active ingredient in most chlorine bleaches is $NaOCl$, sodium hypochlorite. The oxidising action of the OCl^- ion kills germs and also decolourises stains. Research work on this and discuss the types of practical work that could be used to analyse household bleach.

Organic work could include:

- Preparation of an organic compound to include refluxing for initial preparation, distilling for separating, recrystallisation for purification and filtration under pressure. See spread P1.7 and Unit 10.
- In addition to the basic preparation you could look at varying reagents and measuring yields.
- You could also analyse the products using different types of chromatography or by using spectra, or testing for functional groups.

Inorganic work could include:

- Volumetric analysis: titrations, preparation of standard solutions, see spread P.1.6. Titration techniques can be used in preparing samples when exact quantities are required. Colorimetry used for finding concentration, see spread 2.1.5.
- Qualitative analysis of anions and cations, see spread P.1.5.
- Preparations: these usually involve following a set procedure – practical techniques used are usually quite straightforward: reacting usually involves heat; filtration; evaporation; crystallisation.

Physics practical activities

Physics practical work often involves using mathematical expressions to test theories or prove relationships. Physicists find ways to apply laws and theories to problems in a wide range of different areas: optics, materials, energy, communications, medical work etc. Investigative work in this field may lead you to work in using a range of laws:

- Looking at energy and its involvement in heat transfer/setting up circuits to look at temperature control systems.
- Looking at safety requirements in vehicles: include material testing/crumple zones/ experiments involving friction/momentum/forces.
- Working on properties of materials related to strength/heat treatment/annealing, see Unit 11.
- Working on physics of sport, see Unit 7.

Recording and processing data

It is essential in all practical work to keep an accurate record. Just jotting odd numbers or colours of solutions is not enough. Before you begin your experimental work draw out a suitable table and record all observations or measurements as you go along:

- Give table headings;
- include units; and
- check significant figures – record to the accuracy of the equipment you are using.

Processing your data could involve plotting graphs, see spread P.1.11:

- Remember to label axes and give units where appropriate;
- check scale – to ensure you use all the graph paper
- check you do not join points dot-to-dot – use line of best fit where appropriate.

Carrying out calculation, see spread P.1.12:

- Watch that the number of significant figures in the answer is the same as those used in the recording;
- check you have some two and three step calculations included in your work; and
- show all your working and check answers – think about estimated values.

Calculating the errors, see spread P.1.11:

- Include % errors;
- compound errors – remember these occur whenever measurements are combined in calculations; and
- errors can be estimated by finding the percentage error for each measurement made. Remember percentage error depends on the mathematical operation of the quantities, sums and differences.

Activity

Your task is to monitor the rate of reaction of the action of acid rain on a limestone surface:

- Suggest an experimental set-up.
- What you would measure?
- How you would record your results?
- What processing would you carry out?

Assessment tip

Remember that the order you present your results in your report may not be in the order you carried out the practical. You need to arrange them in a logical sequence.

By the end of this spread, you should be able to:

✷ monitor and evidence completion of your work

✷ complete an evaluative report

Monitoring your plan

One of the key tasks of a scientist is to record what is carried out but also to monitor what has not worked and what changes could be made to improve. You need to update your original plan throughout your investigation. The detail will depend on the mark band at which you are working. Examples below show plan monitoring.

Date	Scheduled work	Actual work	Comments
	Test fruit and vegetables Use method to quantitatively assess vitamin C	Completed – took longer than expected Additional time is now needed to carry out practical work Trial method completed – modifications needed to be made	A blender was needed to prepare the sample rather than a pestle and mortar

Date/ time	Task	Requirements/ things to do	Outcome/ monitoring	Affect
	Visit health club to review availability of use of equipment	Check – appointment made with health club Permission letter Questions to be prepared	Visit successful Arranged 3 further dates to monitor exercise	Kept to original plan But check next time to leave 1 hour for visit 30 min insufficient

The following points can act as a guide for monitoring your plan.

- Is the time allocation suitable?
- Did your experimental work fulfil the requirements?
- Did your work go as planned or do you need to change the order of your original ideas?
- Did you remember to order all your equipment or does anything new need to be ordered?
- Have you access to the correct facilities: laboratories/ computer access/library facilities?
- Is there a member of staff available to help you?
- Are you going out of college at all – have you completed all the relevant paperwork and have obtained permission?
- Can you extend the work to raise your marks – have you left enough time for this?

Evidence of completion of practical work

It is important to include in your work evidence that you have actually completed the practical work. Risk assessments should now be completed by you as a matter of course. See P.1.5 if you need a reminder of what to include.

A certificate could be included. This needs to indicate the level at which you have been working.

This is to certify that

....

completed trials and experimental procedures

Correctly carried these out and repeated experimental where necessary and used risk assessments	which included different experimental techniques that have been safely & skilfully completed and used detailed risk assessments Appropriate degree of accuracy was used in practical work	which included the independent completion of a number of different techniques that have been safely & skilfully completed and produced and used detailed risk assessment which you have produced have been used. Appropriate degree of accuracy was used in practical work

What needs to be included in your report

Your report needs to be suitably structured and written appropriately. Do not use 'I completed the experimental techniques'.

- Aims and objectives need to be clearly explained with scientific principles included to support your work.
- The data that you have collected should link to the objectives (the tasks you have carried out).
- Check that your results link to the scientific principles you have quoted.
- You need to interpret the data you have collected – make sure that you have at least two sets of primary data.
- You need to assess the reliability of the data you have collected and for this you need to consider the accuracy of the equipment used and any anomalous results – did you repeat your work?

You may want to support your report with a scientific poster or presentation

A scientific poster is a visual display of the results of an investigation, usually mounted on card. Posters are used at scientific meetings, to communicate research findings. The poster needs to attract attention but needs to be as informative and interesting as possible. Keep text to a minimum and aim to use 500 words in your poster.

Although most students feel very nervous about giving a presentation, it is a fundamental method of scientific communication and is therefore an important skill to learn. Another way of supporting the outcome of your investigation is by giving an oral presentation. Adopt the following suggestions.

Plan your presentation in terms of the duration and structure. Aim to include:

- Introduction: which explains the structure of your talk: the aims and objectives of the investigation: your approach to your scientific work.
- The main information: includes your experimental results presented in a suitable format: discuss each point as it is raised. Keep details of methods to a minimum. This is not the place for a detailed description of equipment and experimental procedures. Final results and analyses need to be discussed.
- Concluding remarks: these need to provide the audience with key points from your investigation. You can indicate the end of your talk by 'finally or concluding …'

Many accomplished speakers use abbreviated notes for guidance rather than reading from a detailed script. Aim to talk to your audience and not read to them. Project your voice. And watch your time.

You need to evaluate your work

An evaluation is a process that critically looks at the experimental work that has been carried out. It involves reviewing and analysing the data collected in order to make a judgement on how well the practical achieved its aims. Include in this review

- the suitability of the apparatus used: include accuracy, precision and sensitivity
- the reliability of the data collected: look at possible sources of error, repeated results, anomalous values
- suggest ways with explanations that if the practical work was repeated how it could be improved.

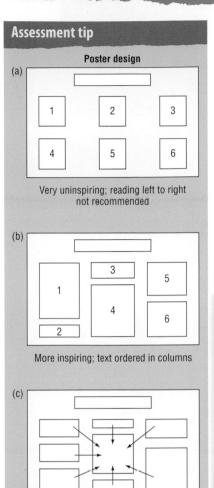

By the end of this spread, you should know about:

✳ the general content of this unit
✳ how it is assessed

Techniques and processes

This unit has no detailed specification content. Instead, the emphasis is on the techniques and processes used when analysing and identifying materials. You may need to use existing techniques and processes and modify them as necessary so that they are more suitable for your purposes.

You will need to think about how particular samples are selected and how these samples are tested for their purity and for their suitability for a variety of uses. Sometimes samples are taken to assess the amount of pollution present. An example is the analysis of air samples around factories.

Once you have obtained your samples you will need to know where to find methods describing how to analyse them. These details are generally found electronically, in books, or by asking those skilled in particular techniques.

Project work

Practical work is an important part of this unit. Your experimental work might include new work especially designed for this unit or an extension of experimental work from other units.

The chemical analysis of materials is in two parts:
• qualitative analysis – to find out what is present
• quantitative analysis – to find out how much of a particular substance is present.

For example, you could collect samples of soil at various distances from a factory where lead is produced from its ore and find out if excessive quantities of lead are present in the soil and also how the amount of lead present varies with the distance away from the factory.

Figure 1 Student carrying out volumetric analysis using titration

Another approach for project work might be to make a mixture of materials for a particular purpose. One example might be making a mixture that is suitable for washing clothes.

Mixtures for washing clothes

There are a number of factors that you need to consider. These include:

* Are the starting materials safe and readily available?
* How much of each substance is required?
* At which temperature will the mixture be expected to operate?
* What extra considerations are needed if your product was to be produced on a much larger scale?

When you have made your product you should assess its effectiveness. For example, you might consider whether your washing product is more effective as a powder, when it may dissolve more quickly or whether granules are better because they do not become a paste when water is added.

Evaluation

An important aspect of practical work is evaluation. You should firstly ask some general questions:

* Is it safe, not only for me but for others who may follow my instructions?
* Does my method work effectively or does it need modification?

Assessment

This unit is assessed through a written examination in which questions are based on two case studies. These case studies are circulated a few weeks before the examination. The final question in the examination is not based on case study material. The topic for this question may be unfamiliar, but the questions can be answered through your background knowledge of the ideas behind sampling, testing and processing.

What do you need to look for in the case studies?

The case studies will focus on the sampling methods used and the various techniques used in testing. Unfamiliar methods may be mentioned and you should have researched these to understand the basic principles involved. You should be able to comment on the accuracy and reliability of a particular method when compared with other methods.

You should find out the meanings of any unfamiliar key scientific words.

You will need to be able to:

* alter the subject of a simple mathematical equation
* calculate percentages
* draw and interpret graphs and bar charts
* use square roots
* change units.

Processing materials

Part of the examination will test the processing of materials. This might involve describing how to make small quantities of a particular product. For this you should be familiar with the names and uses of basic chemical apparatus. You should also be able to describe simple techniques such as crystallisation, distillation and chromatography.

Assessment tip

Each case study will have a main focus.

This might be a topic of environmental concern such as the contamination of water from copper mining.

You should be aware of how to take samples, including health and safety considerations.

Another topic might concern a commodity, like cocoa or coffee, and the problems caused by inadequate plant nutrition or pest attack.

By the end of this spread, you will be able to recognise why samples are:

✳ collected in a particular way
✳ stored under carefully controlled conditions

Sample collection

When samples are collected, your health and safety must be the first consideration.

Apart from the physical hazards of collecting environmental samples from, for example, rocks and quarries, there are the added problems of the toxicity of the sample materials themselves.

There are obviously special considerations if your samples are of biological origin. For environmental samples you should consider the hazards of dust inhalation and the ingestion of material from your hands.

It is always important to carry out a risk assessment before you start work. You must always consider the appropriate use of personal protective equipment, whether you are working in a laboratory or outside.

In areas where copper or lead mining has occurred, a common project is to collect samples from the mine spoil heaps where low-grade ore, of little economic value, has been dumped. When collecting samples from a spoil heap you must consider whether your samples are representative of the spoil heap as a whole. A single sample will almost certainly give a false impression of the overall mineral content of the spoil heap. You should collect samples from various parts of the spoil heap and not just from the surface, because specimens at the surface may have been affected by weathering. This type of sampling is called representative sampling and should always be used where the composition varies.

The size of the sample

Another factor that you need to consider when you are sampling is the size of the sample that you should collect. Too large a sample may cause transport problems, but if the sample is too small there may be an increased chance of inaccuracies during analysis, particularly if the percentage of the mineral present is very small. For example if a sample of lead ore contains around 6% of lead, then a 250 g sample will contain a total of around 15 g of lead and several analyses can be carried out from this sample. If a small sample of mass 2.5 g is collected the total amount of lead present will be about 0.15 g and the whole of the sample would probably be needed if the percentage of lead present was to be found using gravimetric analysis. The margin of error would be much greater for this smaller sample.

> ### Key definitions
>
> A **representative sample** is obtained by taking samples from a number of different areas in the location.
>
> A **homogeneous sample** is one where the composition is the same throughout the sample.

Figure 1 Spoil heap

External assessment

However, quantitative analysis for metals is now usually carried out by instrumental methods such as atomic absorption spectroscopy, which gives accurate results from very small samples.

Safety when collecting samples

When samples are collected from rivers you will need to remember that the results obtained will be affected by weather conditions, which will affect the flow rate of the water. You will also need to think about where in the river to collect your samples – from the bank, or in mid-stream and at what depth. Water samples can also be obtained by filtering the sediment from the bottom of the river.

There are added risks when collecting water samples. You cannot be certain that the water does not contain biological toxins that can cause disease. For this reason appropriate personal protective equipment should always be used. There are potential problems in the actual collecting of these samples and you should seek advice about the safest method of collection.

When samples of air are to be collected there are additional factors that need to be considered.

Contaminated air would generally only contain a few percent of the impurity and it is therefore necessary to collect a large volume of air but this is not very practical. Another method would be to use a pump and pass the air through a substance that will react with the contaminant in the air. If this method is used then a flow meter is needed to measure the actual volume of air passing through the equipment. Another method would be to draw air through a tube packed with activated charcoal to absorb volatile organic hydrocarbons. The absorbed material can then be extracted in the laboratory and separated and analysed by gas chromatography.

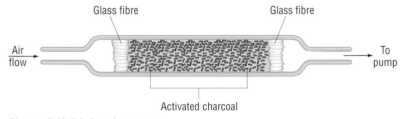

Figure 2 Solid absorbent tube

Sample storage

When you have collected your samples you will need to think how best to store them. Ask yourself whether the samples will be affected by changes in temperature, humidity or light. Perhaps they slowly deteriorate on keeping. If they do it is important to test them quickly and on the same day. They may be affected slowly when exposed to air. For your results to be comparable the samples should all be stored under the same conditions. They should be kept in a sealed container to prevent contamination and labelled with the name of the sample and the date of collection. If the sample is hazardous the container should have the correct warning label and stored in an appropriate place.

Many of the samples will be analysed. It is very important to avoid contamination through unclean equipment and this includes storage bottles. You should be aware of safe methods to dispose of unwanted samples. This is particularly true of biological samples and chemical solutions that contain irritant or toxic materials but is equally important for disposing of solid materials containing heavy metals. This may involve you in finding out about acceptable local methods of removal and disposal.

External assessment

By the end of this spread, you should be able to:

✦ use the given criteria so that you can choose a suitable method for testing
✳ interpret and evaluate the results of your tests

Choosing a suitable test

Once you have decided which property of your sample you are going to test, you will need to find out about suitable testing methods. For this purpose scientific books and other paper-based resources are still in use, although the use of the Internet for this purpose is increasing. You should be able to compare the advantages of one method with another method. It is often difficult to be able to do this and you should seek advice from your teachers or those with experience in this topic. It may be that the method you choose needs adapting to make it more suitable for your intended use.

Once you have chosen a suitable method you will need to do a risk assessment for your procedure. Then you will need to prepare the sample for the test. It is essential that your apparatus and equipment are absolutely clean to avoid contamination. At the end of the test you will need to clean the apparatus and equipment ready for their next use.

If you are going to find the percentage of a metal in an ore, the first stage might be crushing the sample in a suitable way. Depending on the hardness of the sample this might be done by using a pestle and mortar, or mechanically using a ball mill or roller mill. A solution is then made from a known mass of the crushed sample.

There are a number of methods that can be used for testing the sample. For example if you are going to find the percentage of calcium in a sample of limestone, one method would be to use volumetric analysis in a complexometric titration using ethylenediaminetetraacetic acid (EDTA). Other methods include the weighing of an insoluble calcium salt, or using flame emission spectroscopy.

When you choose a suitable testing method you should consider a number of factors. They might include:
- Health and safety considerations – if there is a choice, a method should be chosen that uses safe materials, lower temperatures and which does not produce irritant or toxic products.
- The size of the sample needed – sometimes only small quantities of the sample are available and this might limit the method.
- How easy is it to carry out – technician training may not have to be so detailed when compared with other more complicated methods.
- The type of equipment needed and its availability – although more sophisticated equipment will often give quicker and more accurate results, this may not be readily available to use.
- The time taken – if a test takes less time, then you can carry out more determinations in the time available.
- The accuracy of the result – you should choose the most accurate appropriate method.

External assessment

Working with your results and evaluating your method

Once you have taken measurements or made observations from your tests, they need to be recorded in such a way that both you and others can understand them and easily work with them.

There are accepted ways to present both volumetric results and the results of weighings. The box shows one acceptable way of presenting the results of a titration.

> Burette volume at the end = 26.30 cm³
> Burette volume at the start = 00.00 cm³
> ∴ Volume used = 26.30 cm³

If your results have units these should always be given. The results can be shown in a table or as a graph. It is usual, when giving tables of results, for the numbers to become larger down the table. Presenting the results in a jumbled order is incorrect. If a result does not fit in with the pattern, you should consider whether to repeat the measurement or to disregard it.

The question of how many significant figures to choose causes problems for a number of students.

As a general rule your answer should be given to the same number of significant figures as the least accurate of your readings. The box shows the results of an experiment to find the percentage of copper in a sample of copper sulfate.

> Mass of copper sulfate taken = 12.47 g
>
> Mass of copper obtained = 3.18 g
>
> Percentage of copper in copper sulfate $= \dfrac{3.18 \times 100}{12.47}$
>
> $= 25.5\%$
>
> If a student gave the answer 25.5012025% the answer is not valid as the copper has only been weighed to three significant figures.
>
> An answer of 26% would not be satisfactory as that could imply any number between 25.6 and 26.4.

You will need to report on the significance and implications of your results. If, for example, you are finding the concentration of aluminium in samples of drinking water, you will need to know the maximum allowable concentration of aluminium. In your report you will need to indicate if any of your samples are above the acceptable level.

Assessment tip

Do not simply write 'cost' as a response when you are asked why a particular method is chosen. You must always give more details to obtain credit.

Assessment tip

When drawing the line of best fit on a graph, you must always consider whether it should go through the origin.

Figure 1 A volumetric flask

External assessment

By the end of this spread, you should be able to:

* be aware of some of the techniques used to prepare materials in the laboratory
* identify or devise a suitable method to prepare your material
* evaluate your method
* explain the meaning of some scientific terms used in this unit

Choosing a suitable method

If you are asked to prepare small quantities of a material in the laboratory, you will need to know why this is being done. It may be that the material is required as a reference standard in analysis. Another use for small scale processing is to prepare the material and then to consider whether this process is suitable to use on a larger manufacturing scale.

Once you have found the reasons for producing this material it is necessary to find a suitable method.

The ways of finding out methods of preparation are similar to those described for testing in spread 9.1.3.

Sometimes you will find that the method you have chosen is not entirely suitable for your task and will need adapting before you can use it. It may be that you cannot find any method that is suitable for your needs and you would then need to devise a method.

When choosing a suitable method of preparation you should consider a number of factors that include:
* Identifying any hazards and assessing the risks – are the starting materials irritant, corrosive or toxic?
* What temperatures are required? The higher the temperature used the greater is the risk.
* How easy is it to carry out? – A method that is run at room temperature or requires simple refluxing is preferable to more complicated procedures like fractional distillation or solvent extraction.
* Availability of equipment – is the normal glassware suitable or does more complicated apparatus have to be made or bought?
* The time taken – if you are making the material by a batch process, then a shorter process will enable more material to be made in the available time.
* The relative yield of your product – if the material is eventually to be made on a commercial scale, then you should consider the overall percentage yield.
* The purity of the product – you will need to consider the uses for the material.

Carrying out your method

Once you have chosen a suitable method you should ensure that your apparatus is clean both before and after your work and appropriate in size for the quantities that you are using.

If a mixture is to be heated, then you should consider the most appropriate and safest method. Although heating using a Bunsen burner is effective, it is only suitable for relatively small quantities and should not be used at all if you are using flammable liquids unless the vapour of these can be contained.

Electrical heating mantles can be obtained in a number of sizes and are safer and easier to use.

You will need to be familiar with common laboratory techniques including crystallisation, distillation and solvent extraction using a separating funnel.

Key definition

Two solvents that do not mix are described as **immiscible**.

In solvent extraction an immiscible solvent is added to a solution of the solid using a separating funnel.

Figure 1 Using a separating funnel

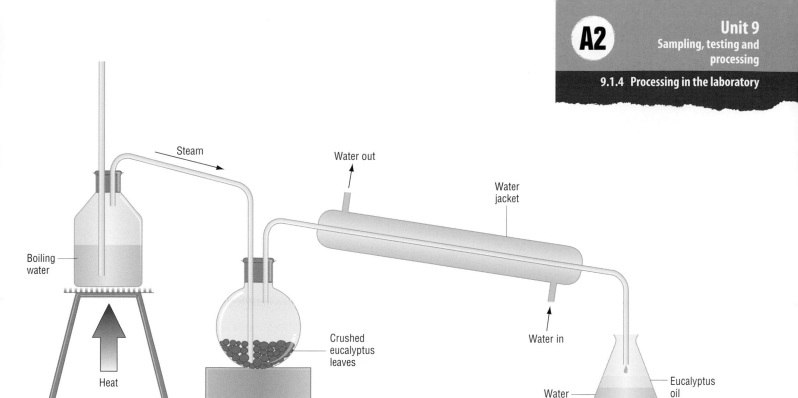

Figure 2 Steam distillation

Steam distillation is used where the required product may be destroyed by heating the mixture to the higher temperatures needed for ordinary distillation. Steam is passed through the mixture and evaporates the product, which is then carried over with the steam and condenses. Steam distillation is used in the perfumery industry for extracting oils from plant material.

Evaluating your product

Once your product has been made you will need to assess its purity against the requirements given.

There are many methods for finding the purity of materials. You should be aware of some possible methods but detailed knowledge is not required. One method is to take the melting point of your product and to compare the value with the book value. Use can also be made of **thin layer chromatography** to see if impurities are present.

If your product is a liquid, then it should boil at the expected temperature. You can also assess the purity of your product using gas-liquid chromatography.

If your product turns out to contain an unacceptable level of impurities you should consider finding a method to purify your product, such as recrystallisation or fractional distillation. Alternatively you could use a different method of producing your material where the amount of impurities present is less, or adapt your present method by changing the conditions to reduce the quantity of by-products.

An important part of successful small scale processing is to make recommendations for production of the material on a larger scale. There are a number of factors to be considered. These may include:

- using a heating method where heat losses are kept to a minimum
- the use of heat produced in an exothermic process
- the recycling of solvents
- keeping any fire risks to a minimum
- if toxic gases are used or produced, you will need to consider how these can be contained.

Key definition

Thin layer chromatography uses an absorbent solid mounted on plastic or glass.

The separated compounds appear as coloured spots.

Figure 3 Thin layer chromatography

The preservation of books

Paper in older books was made from cotton or linen rags but around 1860 paper began to be made from wood pulp.

Unfortunately wood pulp is slightly acidic and the acid present slowly attacks the cellulose polymer of the paper, breaking it in shorter lengths until, eventually, the strength of the paper is lost and the paper's structure is lost.

As a result, many books produced over the last 150 years are slowly disintegrating and the only answer to prevent further breakdown of the cellulose is to try and neutralise this acidity.

Methods of deacidification

For over eighty years different methods of 'deacidification' have been tried, with varying degrees of success. One problem that methods have also tried to overcome is that the treatment should protect against secondary build up of acidic substances. This may come from further degradation of the paper or from outside.

The lifespan of paper is determined by the amount of alkaline substances present in the paper to overcome acidity. One problem with adding strongly alkaline substances is that they attack the cellulose structure of the paper itself and therefore methods used in the past have generally relied on calcium or magnesium carbonates being impregnated into the paper.

One of the first efforts in this direction was in 1936 when a patent was published for the conservation of wallpaper using an aqueous solution of calcium hydrogencarbonate, which, when dry, gave a deposit of calcium carbonate within the paper.

A number of problems occur if the technique is extended to books. For maximum effect the book has to be taken apart and each page treated separately. Another problem with the use of water-based materials is that they may attack the adhesive in the binding and also the inks used. Extensive drying is necessary, which would cause difficulties when done on a large scale. When each page has been treated the dried pages then have to be reassembled and bound together. It is obvious that the costs involved in this are huge, particularly when we realise that the British Library contains many hundreds of thousands of books and journals, many of them already in a fragile state. An article in 1989 described the cost of treating each book in this way as upwards of £150 for each book.

It was obvious that a new method was needed. In the 1960s a **non-aqueous** deacidification technique using a magnesium compound dissolved in a small quantity of methanol was developed. The main solvent for this process was a chlorofluorocarbon (CFC). However, the use of CFCs is now severely restricted, owing to their destruction of ozone in the upper atmosphere. They are being replaced by **volatile** liquid hydrofluorocarbons.

In the late 1980s a new method was developed in the United States using the toxic flammable material diethylzinc, DEZ. This compound is very hazardous to use since it bursts into flames when in contact with air. However, it will react with acids in the paper and neutralise them, giving zinc salts and ethane gas. In addition, residual moisture in the paper reacts with DEZ to give zinc oxide. This zinc oxide is itself beneficial in that it neutralises external acidic materials, such as the polluting atmospheric gas sulfur dioxide.

In the DEZ method, the books are gently heated under vacuum to remove as much moisture as possible and they are then placed in a closed chamber. The chamber is flushed with dry nitrogen to remove air and DEZ is introduced into the nitrogen stream for several hours. Any DEZ that has not reacted is recycled and the ethane removed. After treatment, the chamber is again flushed with nitrogen.

Key definitions

Non-aqueous – a process that uses a solvent that does not contain water. A suitable solvent might be methanol or a chlorofluorocarbon.

Volatile – a description of a liquid that evaporates easily at lower temperatures.

External assessment

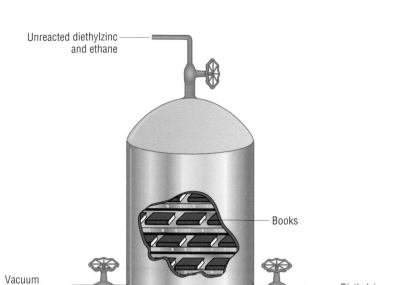

Unreacted diethylzinc and ethane

Books

Vacuum pump

Diethylzinc

Figure 1 Treating books with diethylzinc

The DEZ method takes three days and costs around £2 per book. The cost of producing a microfilm copy of the book is very much greater. This process adds about 2% of zinc oxide to the mass of the book; much of this zinc oxide is deposited near the edges of each page.

Unfortunately, in the mid-1990s trials with the DEZ method were stopped when a number of continuing problems were identified. These included:

- Degradation of books by the 80 °C temperature needed to remove trace water from the books.
- Reaction of DEZ with the adhesives and bindings of the book.

Other problems affecting book preservation

Books are not only subject to deterioration by acidity. The paper may be subject to microbial attack and some work has been done to find methods to reduce this effect. Any method must not cause damage to the fabric of the books themselves. Books have been fumigated with the gas ethylene oxide and any residual ethylene oxide present in the books measured by gas chromatography. The amounts of residual gas reported to be present have varied between laboratories, probably due to the non-standardisation of the methods of **gas chromatography** used.

Beta radiation has also been found to be effective in destroying fungi present on paper. Unfortunately, the high doses of radiation necessary have attacked the cellulose molecules present in the paper. The use of beta radiation cannot therefore be recommended. Microwave radiation has also been tried and has a fungicidal effect, although without significant effects on the chemical structure of the paper.

Another problem with long-term storage of paper is attack by insects. The use of artificial insecticides has been shown to be effective but these are generally harmful to humans and chemically attack the paper. A natural insecticide has been isolated from the seeds of the neem tree (*Azadirachta indica*).

Whether it will be effective against pest attack on books remains to be seen.

The move to digital technology may be the answer to the problem of information storage, but obviously it cannot help in the preservation of the actual books themselves.

Key definition

Gas chromatography – a method of separating liquids and gases by the use of a carrier gas that passes the mixture through a column. The materials present in the column separate the mixture into individual components.

Assessment tip

In this case study it is not necessary to research extra details of the processes outlined. It is important however to be able to relate the case study to the needs of the specification of this unit.

You could research the processes outlined on the Internet and find out how the researchers have attempted to solve the problems outlined.

External assessment

Questions and answers based on case study 1

(a) In 1936 wallpaper was treated with a solution of calcium hydrogencarbonate in an attempt to preserve wallpaper against acid degradation. If you were to repeat this method of preservation using three identical samples of wallpaper, state two other factors that should be kept constant.

1 *Concentration of the calcium hydrogencarbonate solution.*
2 *The time the wallpaper is immersed in this solution.*

(b) State one reason why the calcium hydrogencarbonate solution method is unsuitable for the preservation of books, apart from the cost.

Attacks the adhesive/ink.

(c) You are given newspaper samples from different years.
Describe a test to investigate the strength of the newspaper samples so that you can determine the effect of ageing on the strength of the newspaper.

Cut the newspaper samples into strips of the same stated size. Support the strip and hang masses on the free end until the paper breaks. Record the mass needed. Repeat the exercise with strips of the same age and then with strips of different ages.

(d) Suggest and explain two factors, other than the age of the newspaper, which could affect the results of your tests.

The chemical composition of newspaper may vary even though the age is the same/ the type of paper used may be different/the strength is also affected by moisture content/the thickness of the paper may vary.

(e) If you were to carry out the DEZ method of book preservation, state two hazards of the method and how you would minimise these risks.

1 *DEZ is highly flammable in the presence of oxygen – ensure that the equipment is thoroughly flushed through with nitrogen.*
2 *DEZ is toxic – it must be used in a controlled environment.*

(f) The DEZ method deposits more of the zinc oxide towards the edges of each page. Suggest why this has occurred and how this could be remedied.

The DEZ has not sufficiently penetrated towards the centre of each page. Leave the books for a longer period in contact with DEZ/increase the concentration of DEZ.

(g) (i) Small scale processing shows that 30 g of DEZ is required to treat a book of mass 1 kg.
The cost of treating each book is £2.
Use these values to calculate the cost of 1 kg of DEZ.

30 g costs £2. ∴ *1 g costs £2/30* ∴ *1 kg costs £2000/30 = £66*

(ii) State one assumption that you made when working out your answer to (i).

The cost of processing each book is simply the cost of the DEZ used.

(h) Ethylene oxide has been used to prevent microbial attack on books.
Suggest one environmental problem with this method.

*Some ethylene oxide is retained in the books; the toxicity of this compound needs
to be evaluated.*

Assessment tip

(a) and (b) There may be other acceptable answers to these open ended questions.

(c) This question requires a free response and carries several marks. There would be a mark too for the quality of written communication.

(d) There are a number of other factors here that are acceptable. Marking would be to a maximum of two.

(e) The answers are given in the case study. Any other relevant correct answers would gain credit.

External assessment

Defeating the rhinoceros beetle

Advertisers suggest that coconuts represent a taste of tropical paradise but for the rhinoceros beetle (*Oryctes rhinoceros*) they represent a home, food and a maternity ward for its larvae.

The rhinoceros beetle is a large beetle, up to 10 cm in length, that can reproduce four or five times a month and can destroy coconut plantations in a matter of weeks. The adult beetle feeds on young buds and bores into unopened palm fronds. This devastation can lead to a reduction of as much as 75% of the coconut crop of an individual tree. An estimate suggests that up to 35% of the coconut crop in the Philippines is lost each year to the rhinoceros beetle. Since the Philippines produce around three million tonnes of coconuts each year, this is a substantial loss.

Coconuts have many varied uses and this is why producing countries cannot afford to lose a substantial proportion of their crop to the rhinoceros beetle. Uses for coconuts include the:

- white flesh for confectionery and foods such as cakes
- fibre for matting and brushes
- coconut 'milk' in pharmacy – as this is naturally sterile
- oil for cooking and as a base for cosmetics such as sunscreens
- wood as a construction material
- leaves as 'wrappers' and 'plates'.

Figure 1 Rhinoceros beetle

Figure 2 Coconut palms

Problems start to arise during the rainy season, when trees felled by typhoons start to decay and provide an ideal breeding site for the beetles. Removal of the decaying coconut tree stumps is a labour intensive and expensive process but does have a localised effect. The use of naturally occurring and synthetic insecticides is another option but this is hazardous and may destroy environmentally friendly organisms and predators of the rhinoceros beetle.

Since the beetles are large, they can be removed using long hooked poles but this too is a difficult task.

The beetles do have some natural predators and these help in the effort to reduce the damage done to the coconut palms but on a relatively limited scale.

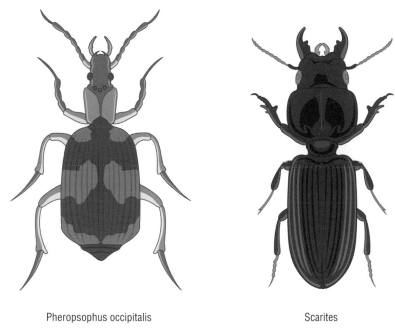

Pheropsophus occipitalis   Scarites

Figure 3 Natural predators of the rhinoceros beetle

Newer methods of beetle eradication

Two methods have been developed to try and reduce the effects of this pest. One method is to infect beetle grubs with a baculovirus (OBV); this kills them in 15 to 20 days. It also affects the adult beetles, it reduces the length of time that they live and also their fertility. The mid-gut of an OBV infected grub of the rhinoceros beetle is removed and ground up, together with water, in a mortar. This fine suspension can then be fed to about six healthy grubs. The procedure is then repeated to obtain a stock of the baculovirus. To infect healthy beetles the fine suspension containing OBV is placed on the base of a trough and 10 to 15 healthy beetles are allowed to crawl in the trough for half an hour. The beetles, hopefully now infected with the baculovirus, are then released into the coconut plantation. This application of the baculovirus is time consuming and the results can only have only a limited effect on this massive problem, considering the method of application.

Recently, researchers in the Philippines have studied the effect of the green muscardine fungus (GMF) (*Metarhizium anisopliae*) on the beetles. This new method of beetle eradication has proved to be very effective, particularly as it only affects the rhinoceros beetle. Farmers can buy GMF directly from the Philippine Coconut Authority. This fungal pathogen is mass produced in the laboratory and then mixed with powdered coconut or cow dung and sprinkled over the beetles' breeding sites. Alternatively, a **suspension** of the spores can be injected into infected logs using a home-made bamboo syringe – an example of a 'low technology' application. A further variation is to introduce infected larvae into the breeding site. After 30 days the fungus will have spread throughout the particular beetle population. Researchers have found that 1 kilogram of the fungal spores will cover 10 **hectares** of a coconut plantation.

Reports suggest that 65% of the treated beetle larvae and 87% of adult beetles are destroyed using the GMF method. This fungal method costs 120 pesos per hectare. Each hectare has around 160 coconut palms. The method is 300 pesos per hectare cheaper than the next most economical method.

External assessment

Key definitions

A **suspension** contains insoluble particles throughout a liquid.

A **hectare** is an area of land measuring 100 metres by 100 metres.

Assessment tip

When numbers are given in the article it is likely that calculation questions will be asked about this information.

Questions and answers based on case study 2

(a) Students from the Philippines were studying methods of reducing the crop losses of coconuts. They found that the Philippines produce 3 million tonnes of coconuts each year but the rhinoceros beetles destroy 35% of this crop.
Calculate the mass of coconuts destroyed each year by the beetles.

$\dfrac{3 \times 35}{100}$ = 1.1 million tonnes

(b) Synthetic insecticides help to control infestation by rhinoceros beetles.
State two problems that may occur with the use of synthetic insecticides.

1 *Kills other useful insects.*
2 *Toxic to humans.*

(c) These large beetles can sometimes be removed from coconut palms by the use of a long hooked pole.
Suggest why the students thought that this method of pest control was relatively inefficient.

It can only catch/reach a limited number.

(d) The use of a baculovirus can destroy up to two-thirds of the larvae and a larger percentage of the adult beetles.
Suggest one disadvantage of this type of pest control.

Only effective on a local scale/danger of viral transfer to other species/leaves a substantial minority of the larvae still alive.

(e) The newest method uses a fungal pathogen.
State the meaning of the term pathogen.

An agent that causes disease/illness/death.

(f) The fungal method is described in the article as 'low technology'.
State an advantage of this type of method.

Its method of application uses easily available/inexpensive materials.

(g) The students found that a coconut plantation covered 25 hectares.

(i) Calculate the cost, in pesos, of the material needed to treat this area using the fungal method.

120 pesos per hectare ∴ 25 × 120 = 3000 pesos

(ii) Each hectare of this plantation contains 160 coconut palms.
Calculate the average cost of treating each palm by the fungal method.

Total number of palms = 25 × 160 = 4000

Cost per palm = $\dfrac{3000}{4000}$ = 0.75 peso

(h) Another method of beetle eradication is to use the seeds of the neem tree (*Azadirachta indica*). The seeds are pressed to provide neem oil and then mixed with soapy water to give an aqueous solution. Alternatively, the ground-up seeds can be mixed with sand to give a powdered insecticide.
You are to produce these neem tree extracts for sale.

   (i) Suggest three important factors that would need to be considered by coconut farmers before they bought your products, apart from safety of use and cost.

   Harmless to plants   Effectiveness   Easy application   Good shelf life
   Long lasting in use   Biodegradable   Selective in use   Availabilty

   (ii) If you were a coconut farmer, state which one of the two neem tree products you would choose, giving a reason for you answer.

   Aqueous solution – more effective penetration/easier to use.
   Powder – less likely to be washed off by rain.

(i) The group of students from the Philippines wished to test the effectiveness of the various methods of rhinoceros beetle control in a coconut growing area. It is important to use particular methods of sampling so that the evaluation of each method of beetle control is scientifically meaningful.
State five factors that should be considered when the students take samples to test the effectiveness of the methods used.

   The sampling should be representative.
   Choose areas of similar climate/altitude.
   Sample at the same time of the year.
   Samples should be of sufficient size.
   Same time span since treatment.

(j) Devise a method for catching live rhinoceros beetles for scientific study.
The method should be both effective for attracting and retaining these insects.
In this question one mark is available for the quality of written communication.

   The method needs to describe a suitable receptacle in which the insects become trapped. It should suggest the bait used and the method should indicate how it is secure against escape.

Assessment tip

In numerical questions give answers to the same number of significant figures as the least accurate value given in the question.

Assessment tip

Part (j) has a mark for the quality of written communication. The answer should have relevant information organised clearly and coherently, using specialist scientific vocabulary when appropriate.

External assessment

Groundwater pollution by arsenic

Communities throughout Bangladesh are drinking poisoned water from wells, which they have been assured are safe.

Regular drinking water supply is a problem for hot countries like Bangladesh and in the 1970s and 1980s international agencies such as UNICEF sank millions of tube wells across the country in an effort to solve the problem of drought.

After a period of time it emerged that the water from a large number of these wells was contaminated with arsenic. The arsenic originated in the Himalayas by the breakdown of mica in rocks, from where it **leached** into water and then combined with particles of iron hydroxide. This solid material was carried down by rivers and eventually settled, giving thick layers of sediments containing high concentrations of arsenic. Iron-seeking bacteria then attacked these particles, releasing soluble arsenic compounds into the water. The arsenic is now concentrated in groundwater up to 50 metres above the sediment. Water is tapped from this depth by wells that provide water for everyday use.

> **Key definition**
>
> **Leaching** – this is a process that occurs when water reacts with solid particles (particularly rocks) and dissolves out those compounds that are soluble.

Figure 1 A tube well in Bangladesh

The water from these wells is now being tested for arsenic and results show that up to half of the country's 10 million tube wells may be providing water that contains unsafe levels of arsenic. Those wells that have been declared safe are painted green and those wells that have unsafe levels of arsenic are painted red.

However, there is a major problem in that checks have shown that the testing kits are regularly giving the wrong results and that some wells passed as safe contain more arsenic than was previously detected and vice versa. More accurate analysis has shown that two-thirds of previously 'safe' wells are dangerously contaminated and one-third of 'contaminated' wells are actually safe.

The testing kits used are only really reliable at relatively high concentrations of arsenic and the minimum concentration that they can detect is 100 parts per billion (1 part of arsenic in 10 million parts of water). At lower levels, these tests are unreliable. The problem is exacerbated because the arsenic level in the water is displayed as a colour change in a liquid that can be interpreted differently by technicians, particularly if they are inexperienced. The safe limit set by the Bangladeshi government is 50 parts per billion, whereas the World Health Organisation sets the safe limit at 10 parts per billion of arsenic.

More reliable and accurate testing kits that are capable of measuring much lower concentrations of arsenic are available but are not in regular use. A more satisfactory method would be to collect water samples from the wells and send them to a laboratory for detailed analysis.

One way of solving the problem of drinking water which has high levels of arsenic would be to drill deeper wells, as tests show that wells sunk to a depth of 80 metres or deeper contain very little arsenic in the groundwater.

An additional problem that has recently been highlighted is that water from these wells is also used to irrigate fields in which rice is grown. Tests for the levels of arsenic in this rice show that the concentration of arsenic present depends on the amount of arsenic in local groundwater. The concentration of arsenic in rice varies from 50 to 1800 parts per billion. It is not clear how much arsenic the body can absorb from contaminated rice or, if when cooking rice, it can absorb even more arsenic from the water. Fortunately, some species of rice, spinach and beans do not accumulate arsenic even when they are grown in contaminated groundwater.

Arsenic poisoning is a serious problem in Bangladesh and it is estimated that 10% of all deaths occurring in the south of Bangladesh will, within the next few years, be caused by arsenic poisoning.

What is needed, until deeper wells can be bored, is a simple and effective solution to this problem of contamination. Some success has been achieved by pumping up well water and then adding soluble iron compounds to it and then leaving it in full sunlight for a day. The ultraviolet light from the sun oxidises the arsenic compounds present, which then react with the iron present to give an insoluble sludge that is then removed. Scientists in India, where there is a similar problem in some areas with arsenic in drinking water, have distributed chlorination tablets to villagers whose water supply is contaminated. The chlorine produced has a similar effect to ultraviolet light and helps to produce a sludge that contains the arsenic present.

It is unfortunate that international agencies, in trying to solve water supply problems in Bangladesh, have inadvertently introduced an additional serious problem that is proving difficult to resolve.

Assessment tip

The article describes testing for arsenic using a method based on the development of a colour. You should find out about this technique, which is called colorimetry.

External assessment

Questions and answers based on case study 3

(a) Use the article to suggest what the engineers should have done before installing the tube wells.

They should have tested the well water for the presence of arsenic.

(b) You are helping Abid to collect water samples from a tube well in Bangladesh. He says that it is only necessary to collect one water sample as the source is homogeneous.

(i) Explain the meaning of the term 'homogeneous'.

All samples have the same composition.

(ii) Suggest one environmental factor which might lead to you believe that Abid's assumption is wrong.

Seasonal demand for water/variable rain water percolation into sediments.

(c) Suggest two reasons why the article states that it is more satisfactory to send the water samples back to a laboratory for analysis.

More accurate readings can be taken/measurements can be taken of low concentrations of arsenic/technicians are more experienced.

(d) A group of students measured the quantity of arsenic in samples of two different varieties of rice before, and after, cooking in arsenic contaminated water. The results are shown in the table.

Sample	Mass of arsenic present before cooking/μg	Mass of arsenic present after cooking/μg
A	19.2	19.2
B	28.8	57.6

(i) State two factors that should be kept constant so that the two samples can be compared.

The mass of the rice samples should be the same/the rice should be grown under the same conditions.

(ii) State two conclusions that can be made about the results.

Sample B has absorbed more arsenic in growing than sample A/sample A does not absorb arsenic when cooked in contaminated water or sample B absorbs arsenic from the water when it is cooked.

(iii) The mass of rice sample A before cooking was 50.0 g. Calculate the concentration of arsenic in μg kg^{-1} (parts per billion)

50.0 g contain 19.2 μg of arsenic.
∴ 1000 g of rice contain   1000/50.0 × 19.2 = 384 μg

Assessment tip

Question (b) (i) asks for the meaning of the term 'homogeneous'. You should find out the meanings of unfamiliar words in the case study and relevant words in previous papers.

Assessment tip

Questions are set that try to be realistic to actual situations.

For this reason you should be familiar with both large and small units of mass and volume and the relationships between them and grams and cm³.

These will include μg, mg and tonne.

A cubic metre (m³) is 1×10^6 cm³.

(e) Technicians testing for arsenic in well water use a colorimetric method. A test card is dipped into a sample of the well water. A blue colour develops and its intensity is compared against a colour chart to find the quantity of arsenic present. In the laboratory this can be measured more accurately using a colorimeter. A technician finds that the absorption due to the blue colour depends on the amount of arsenic present by the equation:

Absorption = 0.00200 × concentration of arsenic in µg dm^{-3}

Calculate the concentration of arsenic present if a water sample gives an absorption reading of 1.10.

Concentration of arsenic $= \dfrac{1.10}{0.00200} = 550$ *µg dm^{-3}*

The use of iron(II) sulfate in the water industry

Iron(II) sulfate is used to make substances for the treatment of drinking water.

The raw material arrives at the factory as a lumpy, impure, green/blue solid. On standing, this raw material slowly reacts with moisture and oxygen giving unwanted products.

The raw material is tested for its iron(II) sulfate content before further use.

(a) A technician takes small samples from each batch of raw material just before the batch is about to be processed. The technician takes samples from various parts of the batch.
Why do various parts of the batch need to be sampled?

To obtain a representative sample, as the material may not be homogeneous.

(b) A number of methods could be used to analyse the material.
State two reasons for choosing any particular method.

Is it feasible/gives accurate results/gives reproducible or reliable results/is it quick/ easy/efficient/is it economical/does it use readily available equipment/safe.

Assessment tip

Students find it difficult to give simple steps in a sensible order. To answer (c), think of what you would do in the laboratory if you had lumps of salt mixed with sand and you needed to make salt solution.

(c) The lumps of raw material contain some insoluble material as well as the water-soluble iron(II) sulfate. The technician takes the samples into the quality control laboratory and makes up a solution of the iron(II) sulfate to determine its purity. Outline four stages necessary to produce an aqueous solution of iron(II) sulfate that is free from insoluble material.

Crush lumps/produce powder → add to water → stir → filter

(d) In a typical analysis, 7.5 g of impure iron(II) sulfate was treated and made up to 250 cm³ of solution.
25.0 cm³ of this solution reacted with 12.0 cm³ of potassium manganate(VII) solution. Use the graph in Figure 1 to help you calculate the percentage purity of the impure iron(II) sulfate.

You may find the equation below useful.

$$\text{percentage purity} = \frac{\text{mass of pure iron(II) sulfate} \times 100}{\text{mass of impure iron sulfate}}$$

From the graph 12.0 cm³ of potassium manganate(VII) solution is equivalent to a solution of pure iron(II) sulfate of concentration 24.0 g cm⁻³

250 cm³ of solution was used, this must have contained $\frac{24 \times 250}{1000} = 6.0$ g of pure iron(II) sulfate

$$\text{percentage purity} = \frac{6.0 \times 100}{7.5} = 80$$

Assessment tip

Analysis of materials often involves percentages.

Make sure that that you clearly understand how to do these. The answer is never more than 100%.

(e) Explain why it is important that sampling and analysis of the raw material is done just before its use in the manufacturing process.

The answer will be wrong owing to reaction with oxygen and moisture.
The purity of the iron(II) sulfate will be too high.

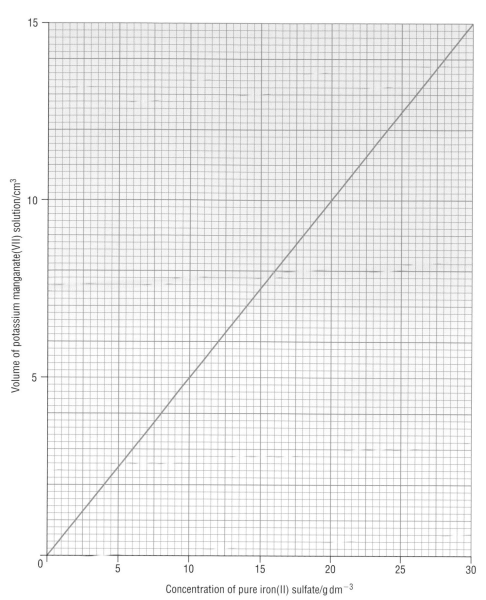

Figure 1 A graph of volume of potassium manganate(VII) solution against concentration of pure iron(II) sulfate

(f) (i) In a new pilot scale method for turning iron(II) sulfate into other substances, the chemist finds that the conversion is very efficient. However, the reaction becomes very warm and gives off toxic gases. These can be passed through an alkaline solution for safe removal by absorption.

Use a labelled drawing to show how these two problems could be overcome in this pilot scale experiment.

The drawing needs to show:
- *an enclosed system*
- *some kind of heat sink (for example cooling pipes)*
- *a pump for removing the gas or similar idea*
- *piped off to alkaline solution*
- *method of gas absorption prevents 'suck back'.*

(ii) Suggest two ways in which the cost effectiveness of this process could be improved when large scale production is planned.

The heat produced can be used for other processes in the plant.
A use can be found for the toxic co-product so that absorption into alkali is not necessary.

Assessment tip

Many students find designing apparatus and scaling up existing apparatus very hard. Look at the mark schemes for previous papers to see what the examiners expect. The focus is often on efficient, economical and safe methods of heating and cooling.

The way in which reactants and products are delivered and collected is also important.

External assessment

By the end of this spread, you should be able to:

* know what you will need to do for this portfolio
* be aware of the level of work required
* know how you will be assessed
* be able to check your portfolio to see if you can improve it

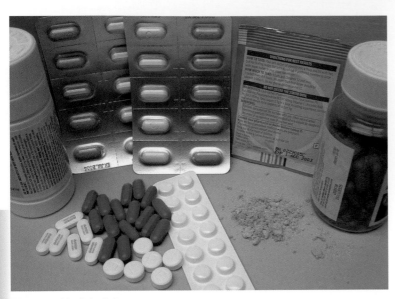

Figure 1 Medicinal drugs

Assessment objective AO1

There are three strands in this section.

You have to show:

* knowledge and understanding of the classifications of organic compounds and the importance of different types of isomerism (3 marks)
* understanding of reaction types (3 marks)
* knowledge and understanding of drug types and their action (4 marks).

Organic compounds work together to keep the human body alive. There are millions of possible organic compounds. It is important to understand the properties of organic compounds so that drugs for treating complaints such as headaches and illnesses such as cancer can be manufactured.

Organic compounds can be grouped depending on the functional group present in their structure. The reaction of a compound is determined by the functional group or groups.

Assessment objective AO2

There are three strands in this section.

You have to produce:

* information on a process used to manufacture an organic compound and the range of factors that have to be considered (5 marks)
* information on the costs and benefits to individuals, companies and society of manufacturing the compound (5 marks)
* calculations related to the research and preparations of the organic compounds (4 marks).

Pharmaceutical companies manufacture medicinal drugs on a global scale. One pharmaceutical company had an income of $10.4 billion in one year.

Assessment objective AO3

There are five strands in this section.

You should produce written reports with appropriate diagrams of two preparations of organic compounds one of which must be an anti-inflammatory drug. The reports should show that:

* risk assessments have been produced (4 marks)
* preparations have been planned and carried out safely using a range of techniques (8 marks)
* observations and measurements have been recorded logically and accurately (4 marks)
* results have been processed (6 marks)
* conclusions have been made, explanations for the results have been produced and suggestions for improvements made (7 marks).

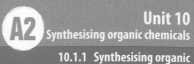

How did you do?

What grade did you think your work is worth?

Use the following checklists to get some idea of the likely standard at which you are working. Remember that these are only a guide and that you should always aim to work at as hard as you can to improve.

AO	Evidence	Form of evidence	Present	Missing
1a	Knowledge and understanding of the classifications of organic compounds: homologous series named functional groups stated. Actual examples named and displayed formulas drawn The importance of different types of isomerism with examples	Summary table Displayed formulas should be clearly drawn		
1b	Understanding of reaction types and how related to specific functional group	Summary as report or table Equations included		
1c	Knowledge and understanding of drug types and their action Scientific terminology used correctly	Summary table Structures can be drawn schematically		
	There is a great amount of background information that can be found for AO1. A brief summary will be all that can be expected given time restraints.			
2a	Process used to manufacture an organic compound indicating a clear understanding of the reaction involved Discussion on as many factors as possible that are involved in the process	Report with flow diagram Sources of information listed and compared		
2b	Calculations based on results from practical preparation of two organic compounds Work should include both simple and complex calculations	Clearly set out Working showing all stages of calculations		
	Information from a wide range of sources should be presented clearly, concisely and logically.			
3a and 3b	The safe completion of two practical tasks indicating equipment and techniques used Use of risk assessments based on COSHH data	Record of safe completion of both tasks with details of method		
3c	A record of relevant observations and measurements from each of the practical tasks	Suitable results tables that you have devised		
3d	Processing of results from the practical work	Calculations set out clearly and logically		
3e	Conclusions drawn Suggestions for improvement Consideration of alternative techniques	Report probably with bulleted points		
	As much detail as possible about the observations and measurements should be included whatever the yield. If necessary, 3d (Processing of results) can use results from another source but this must be stated.			

Table 1 Assessment objectives checklist

If you have ticked all the 'Present' boxes your work is probably at Grade E or better.

Have you found any areas where you have left something important out?

Are there any ticks in the 'Missing' column? If there are you may have time to do something about it.

What do you need to do to improve your portfolio?

It is likely that the evidence you have presented in your portfolio can be improved.

Use the information on the Assessment tip boxes to increase your chance of improving your work.

Assessment tip

For higher mark bands in AO1, note that:
- A great deal of information is needed for this objective so summarising the information is essential.
- Specific examples of isomers are needed.
- Displayed formula should be drawn out.
- All reaction types should be covered.
- Action of the drug with examples are required.
- Evaluation of the use of the drug is needed.

Assessment tip

For higher mark bands in AO2

For AO2a and b:
- explain why the reference sources were used and how accurate each source was
- evaluate the benefits or otherwise to society of the organic product that was manufactured.

For AO2c successful completion of more complex calculations. The percentage yield is calculated and working shown. Errors in measurements included.

Assessment tip

For higher mark bands in AO3, the reports should show:
- independent planning of experiments
- risk assessments based on COSHH data
- explanation of techniques used
- all relevant results recorded to the appropriate precision and displayed clearly
- results accurately processed with conclusions drawn and work suitably evaluated
- alternative techniques considered.

Internal assessment

By the end of this spread, you should be able to:

* research the different functional groups in organic chemicals
* research the different types of isomerism
* research the different reaction types
* research the action of different drug types and the effective functional groups in a drug's chemical structure

Functional groups in organic chemicals

Organic compounds can be grouped into **homologous series** in which all the compounds contain the same functional group and have the same general formula. The functional group present in an organic compound is indicated by the ending of its name (its suffix). Thus hex*ane* C_6H_{14} is an alkane containing the bonds C–C and C–H.

Organic compounds contain carbon:

* Carbon can have four covalent bonds.
* Carbon atoms can combine with other carbon atoms in a long chain or in a branched chain or in a ring.
* Carbon atoms can be linked by single bonds C–C as in alkanes and by double bonds >C=C< as in alkenes.
* Carbon can combine with oxygen by a single bond C–OH, as in alcohols, by a double bond >C=O, as in aldehydes and ketones, by a combination of a single and a double bond $\overset{O}{\underset{\parallel}{-C}}-O-H$ as in carboxylic acids or $\overset{O}{\underset{\parallel}{-C}}-O-C$ as in esters and by a single bond from a benzene ring C_6H_5OH as in phenol.
* Carbon can combine with nitrogen by a single bond $C–NH_2$ as in amines or by a single bond from a benzene ring $C_6H_5NH_2$ as in phenylamine. Amides contain the grouping $–C=O.NH_2$.

The homologous series that must be researched are alkanes, alkenes, alcohols, aldehydes, ketones, carboxylic acids, esters, amines, amides, phenols, phenylamines.

The first part of the name of an organic compound (its prefix) indicates the number of carbon atoms present. In *hex*ane there are six carbons. Meth –1C; Eth –2C; Prop –3C; But –4C; and Pent –5C.

Isomerism

Isomerism occurs because atoms can be arranged differently within molecules of the same molecular formula. There are two types of isomerism:

* Structural isomerism – which depends on the arrangement of atoms within the molecule.
* Stereo isomerism – which depends on the orientation of atoms within the molecule (there are two types of stereo isomerism, geometric and optical).

Isomerism is important in the human body as some reactions will occur only when the atoms are linked in a specific orientation. This is very important in medicinal drugs.

Pentene has the molecular formula is C_5H_{10}. However there is more than one possible way in which the atoms can be arranged as shown in Figure 1.

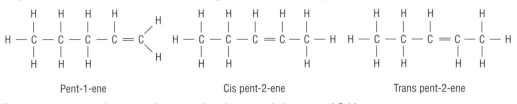

Pent-1-ene   Cis pent-2-ene   Trans pent-2-ene

Figure 1 Displayed formulas of structural and geometric isomers of C_5H_{10}

Reaction types

Each functional group has its own characteristic type of reactions.

The reaction types that need to be researched are: addition, diazotisation, esterification, hydrolysis, polymerisation, redox and substitution.

However the reaction of one group may be modified by the presence of another as in for example the carboxylic group –COOH which appears to be made up of >C=O and –OH.

The functional group >C=O in aldehydes and ketones can be oxidised by acidified potassium dichromate solution to –COOH in a redox reaction.

Although containing >C=O, –COOH is not oxidised by acidified potassium dichromate solution.

–COOH reacts with an alcohol to form an ester and water. It is the –OH that appears to react. However, the –OH group in alcohols does not react with other alcohols to form an ester. The equation for a reaction between –COOH in a carboxylic acid and a –OH grouping of an alcohol is:

$$CH_3COOH + C_2H_5OH \rightleftharpoons CH_3COOC_2H_5 + H_2O.$$

Action of different drug types and the effective functional groups in the drug's chemical structure

The seven different drug types that need to be researched are: antibiotics, antiviral, analgesic, antihistamine, antihypertension, anti-inflammatory and anaesthetic.

The information extracted from sources must be at a level that is understandable by another student doing the same course. Some of the information found in different sources will be very detailed.

Only a summary of each drug type is needed so the easiest format will be a table. Part of such a table is shown as an example.

Drug type	Example	Mode of action
Analgesic	Aspirin	Prevents production of an enzyme of a type of hormone known as a prostaglandin which transmits pain information to the brain. It is the acetyl group $\begin{smallmatrix}O\\||\\-C-O\end{smallmatrix}$ which reacts
Anti-inflammatory	Aspirin	Reduces blood clotting

Table 1 Drug type summary example

Activity

- Draw out the displayed formula of aspirin. The molecular formula of aspirin is $C_9H_8O_4$. Its systematic name is 2-ethanoyloxybenzenecarboxylic acid.
- Ring and name the functional groups in aspirin.
- Draw out the displayed formula of 2-hydroxylbenzoic acid which has a similar effect to aspirin in relieving pain but causes irritating side effects. Ring the group that is NOT the same in the two displayed formulas.
- Aspirin is used as both an analgesic and an anti-inflammatory. Find out if the dose required is the same.
- What percentage of an aspirin tablet is actually aspirin? Show your working.

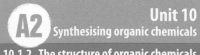
Activity

Benzene, cyclohexene and hex-1-ene react with chlorine. For benzene, cyclohexene and hex-1-ene

- Draw the displayed and skeletal formulas.
- State the conditions and write the equations in words and symbols for the reactions with chlorine (benzene reacts under two different conditions with chlorine).

Assessment tip

Summarise in a table for each reaction type:
- Name of the reaction type;
- name of homologous group;
- functional group; and
- one example of the reaction type with equation.

Here is an example:
- substitution
- alkanes
- C–C
- propane + bromine → bromopropane + hydrogen bromide
  $C_3H_8 + Br_2 \rightarrow C_3H_7Br + HBr$.

Source

The appropriate section in www.chemguide.co.uk has information on homologous series.

Source of information of medicinal drugs

Wikipedia will provide a starting point for each type of drug. But do a double check with another source.

10.1 ③ Manufacturing organic compounds

By the end of this spread, you should be able to:

✳ research for information on the manufacturing process of an organic compound
✳ understand the factors that have to be considered in the manufacturing process
✳ research for information on the costs and benefits of the manufacture of the chosen compound

Research for information on a manufacturing process of an organic compound

The organic compound must be selected. It should have a structure that can be easily understood. Examples of manufactured organic compounds are given in the Assessment tip.

Factors that have to be considered in the manufacturing process

The actual chemical reaction or reactions

On an industrial scale an organic chemical must be produced:
• as quickly as possible (this is rate of reaction and is covered in spread 5.1.3)
• in as high a yield as possible.

The yield is influenced by:
• Whether the reaction is an equilibrium reaction. Le Chatelier's principle must be applied for temperature, pressure and concentration if it is an equilibrium reaction. This is covered in spread 5.1.3.
• How many reactions are involved in the process. As there is hardly ever 100% conversion of reactants to products, the more reactions in the process, the lower will be the yield.
• The transfer of substances from one reaction vessel to another will also result in a loss.

The actual chemical reaction or reactions must be considered first. The equation for the reaction including the states of reactants and products must be given (see Case study 1). Raw materials cost and hazards should be discussed.

Plant design

The aim is for minimum capital cost.

If large quantities of the product are needed then a continuous process is used.

If small quantities of the product are needed then a batch process is used.

Continuous process

Such a process will run without stopping. It will be automated and controlled by sensors, so fewer workers are required, so the wage bill is reduced.

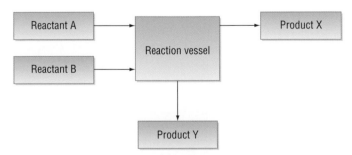

Figure 1 A simple flow diagram for the manufacture of an organic compound using a continuous process

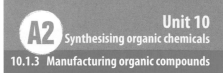
Batch process

In a batch process all the reactants are put into one single reaction vessel at the same time. The mixture is left there for some time, possibly with a mechanical stirrer mixing the reactants. At the end the mixture is removed and separated into its components. The reaction vessel has to be cleaned between batches and so there is more manual input making the wage bill higher.

The following points need to be considered before the manufacturing plant is designed:

- Whether the reaction in the main reaction vessel is exothermic or endothermic. Does heat need to be added or removed? If heat is removed can it be used elsewhere in the process? Can heat exchangers be used?
- The physical state of the reactants and products is important. Reactants and products can be most easily moved in and out of vessels if they are gases or liquids, i.e. they flow. In a continuous process the reactants and products must flow.
- Effective mixing of reactants. Counter-flow of fluids for a continuous process will achieve this.
- Purification of reactants is important. Impurities in the reactants can cause side reactions.
- Separation of products.
- Whether any unreacted reactant is left. This could be recycled.

Health and safety and environmental considerations

- The hazards associated with the reactants and products and any solvents should be researched. (The Hazcards in the laboratory will provide information.)
- The disposal of the waste must be considered. More and more legislation is coming into force. Carbon dioxide emission is regulated because of the effect on the climate.

Figure 2 Diagram of a batch reactor

Research for information on the costs and benefits of the manufacture process to individuals, companies and society

The benefits of some manufactured organic compounds are immediately obvious e.g. the use of PET for bottles. (Refer to Case study 2.) A search on the Internet should produce the home pages of a manufacturer but the search must be world wide. Substances are manufactured on a global scale wherever the process can be done cheaply. This usually means low wage costs.

Case study 2

PET is used in bottles as it is:
- less hazardous than glass on breaking
- lighter than glass so transported more cheaply.

Case study 1

Synthesis gas. Although synthesis gas is not an organic compound, it is used to manufacture the organic compound methanol. The production of synthesis gas indicates the approach needed for this assessment objective.

When steam and methane are passed over a catalyst synthesis gas (mixture of carbon monoxide and hydrogen) is formed. The catalyst is a coating of nickel oxide on pellets of calcium aluminate.

$$CH_{4(g)} + H_2O_{(g)} \rightarrow 3H_{2(g)} + CO_{(g)}$$
$$\Delta H = +210 \text{ kJ mol}^{-1}$$

- The process is a continuous process as large quantities of synthesis gas are needed. Methane and water must flow so temperature must be greater than 100 °C for water to be the vapour, steam. Methane is a gas.
- Water is plentiful therefore cheap.
- Catalyst of nickel oxide is heterogeneous. It speeds up the reaction that occurs at the surface so nickel oxide is spread on calcium aluminate to increase surface area and reduce cost. Methane must be pure otherwise the catalyst is poisoned
- Endothermic reaction, so high temperature produces more products and higher reaction rate. Operating temperature is 1000 K so high energy costs.
- Increase in volume from reactants to products so low pressure ideally. However high pressure used (10–20 atm) as that increases the concentration of both gases.
- High steam to methane ratio as steam is cheaper than methane and forces the reaction to right by Le Chatelier's principle.

Sources

- Chem Guide
- Doctor Brown

Internal assessment

By the end of this spread, you should be able to:

* know what you will need to do for this portfolio
* be aware of the level of work required
* know how you will be assessed
* be able to check your portfolio to see if you can improve it

Figure 1 Planes need modern lightweight materials

Modern materials allow us to make things that do their job better than ever. Contrast the clothes worn by early mountaineers with the specialised clothing available today. Compare the early biplanes with today's jets.

Assessment objective AO1

There are two strands in this section.

You have to produce a poster and accompanying leaflet which includes a description with diagrams of more than two examples each of:

* polymers and metals relating their structures to their physical properties (5 marks)
* ceramics/glasses and composite materials relating their structures to their physical properties (5 marks).

For each of your chosen materials you need to research their

* structure, describing it and giving a diagram
* properties relating them to their structure.

For example if you chose rubber, one of the important properties is that it can be stretched. This is because one feature of its structure is that the molecules are coiled up.

It is a good idea to choose your examples from different categories. For example choose one thermosetting polymer and one thermoplastic. Choose one pure metal and one alloy.

Assessment objective AO2

There are three strands in this section.

* You have to produce reports on *two* case studies. Start by stating the articles for which you are going to choose materials. Then, in each case, select a material from stated alternatives and explain why you have chosen it, using data about its properties (5 marks each).
* You have to show calculations of stress, strain, the Young modulus and toughness from a graph of force against extension. You will also be given information about the length and cross-sectional area of the sample (8 marks).

Applied scientists need to know about materials so that they can make good choices of materials for particular purposes – new and old. Tents and sails are now made from modern fibres. These are stronger and lighter than old fashioned canvas.

Assessment objective AO3

There are four strands in this section.

You have to produce reports on:

* an experiment to measure how the extension of *two* different samples varies with tension (8 marks)
* your design and tests of an impact testing machine (8 marks)
* tests on samples you have work-hardened, annealed and tempered together with control samples (5 marks).

You will produce results for each of your experiments to measure thermal conductivity, electrical conductivity and specific heat capacity (5 marks).

We base our choice of materials on data about their properties. First-hand experience of measuring these properties is the best way to understand their significance.

Figure 2 Bottles for recycling. When choosing materials we need to think about whether they can be recycled after use

How did you do?

What grade did you think your work is worth?

Use the following checklist to get some idea of the likely standard at which you are working. Remember that these are only guidelines and that you should always aim to work hard as you can to improve.

AO	Evidence	Form of evidence	Present	Missing
1a	Information on at least one example of: polymer; metal.	Poster and leaflet		
1b	Information on a poster of at least one example of: ceramics or glasses composites.	Poster and leaflet		
	Include details of your sources.			
2a and 2b	Clearly stated purpose Shortlist at least two materials that could be used Give information about the properties of these materials (get this from published data) State which of your shortlisted materials you have selected as best and why	Case study 1 Case study 2		
2c	Calculation of: stress; strain; the Young's modulus; toughness.	Calculations with workings shown		
	In your case studies be sure to give your reasons for each step of the process. Take care in your calculations to be accurate and to record all answers to the correct number of significant figures.			
3a	Results of your experiment to measure extension of a sample against tension This may either be from a wire-stretching experiment, or you may have been fortunate enough to use a tensometer	Report		
3b	Design and testing of an impact testing machine include: plan; safety precautions; description and diagram; sample results from testing.	Report		
3c	Reports on tests carried out on samples: work-hardened; annealed; tempered; controls used.	Report		
3d	Results on experiments carried out to measure: thermal conductivity; electrical conductivity; specific heat capacity; calculations of related values.	Results recorded in suitable format e.g. tables		
	Record all your results clearly, with units and to an appropriate number of significant figures. Your reports should include the measurement instruments you have used.			

Table 1 Assessment objectives checklist

If you have ticked all the 'Present' boxes your work is probably at Grade E or better.

Have you found any areas where you have left something important out?

Are there any ticks in the 'Missing' column? If there are you may have time to do something about it.

What do you need to do to improve your portfolio?

It is likely that the evidence you have presented in your portfolio can be improved.

Use the information in the Assessment tip margin boxes to increase the chance of your getting a better grade. There is an Assessment tip box for each of the assessment objectives. The advice given, if taken, could improve your grade up to Grade A.

Assessment tip

For higher mark bands AO1:
- show detailed and *relevant* information
- more than two examples of each class
- include diagrams, physical properties and structures. Relate properties to structure.

Assessment tip

For higher mark bands AO2:
- state clearly what your material has to do (e.g. support a heavy load), and things that may limit your choice (e.g. it has to be cheap or lightweight)
- shortlist at least three possible materials that could be used for your stated purpose
- fully justified choice
- range of complex calculations. Answers given to appropriate accuracy. Done unaided.

Assessment tip

For higher mark bands AO3:
- your plan and risk assessment should be done without help
- lay out your report in clearly headed sections and use scientific words
- repeat values and averages – estimates of uncertainty
- at least two samples and comments on why they differ for AO3a
- improvements from prototype and comparison with industrial standards in AO3b
- evaluation for AO3c and d.

Assessment tip

Graphs should be drawn so that they use up as much of your graph paper as possible. Draw big triangles to find the gradient. You have taken a lot of trouble to get precise results. Small graphs throw this away!

Internal assessment

197

By the end of this spread, you will:

* ✱ know about stress and related illness
* ✱ know about functions of the nervous system

A healthy person is considered healthy if they exist in a state of equilibrium of mind, body and soul. Health psychology attempts to prevent illness by understanding how mental states can influence health behaviour. Psychologists interested in the area of health and illness refer to **psychophysiological** symptoms that can be caused or worsened by emotional factors e.g. ulcers, headaches, asthma.

Stress is one of the areas in which the interaction between psychology and health is most obvious.

The mind, stress and illness

The psychological definition of **stress** relates to the ability of an organism to cope, to adapt and respond to the demands of any situation. If the demands are perceived as being too great or the individual feels unable to respond then they may 'feel stressed'. Stress is a psychophysiological disorder and will have an effect upon emotional well being and can also result in physical symptoms e.g. migraines, asthma, ulcers, raised blood pressure.

Any definition or description needs to consider the following:

* Stress can result from **external** and/or **internal** factors. Examples include the physical environment (external), negative self talk (internal).
* Different theories exist as to the causes and sources of stress.
* Individuals may respond differently to the same situation (stressors). You could put 10 people in the same situation and they may all respond differently. Why do you think that this might be?
* There are potentially **psychological**, **behavioural** and **physiological** responses to stress. Examples include depression and confusion (psychological), increased alcohol intake (behavioural) and palpitations and sweating (physiological).
* The **measurement** of stress i.e. measuring physical symptoms. These include increases in blood pressure and heart rate. The measurement of 'life events and hassles'.
* The **management and control** of stress. Often the initial difficulty lies with individuals recognising that they may be stressed. Once they do techniques can be employed to reduce stress. They may involve changing behaviour e.g. exercise, meditation, yoga, changing thinking by counselling and therapy, or changing the activity of the nervous system by drug treatment.

Figure 1 Feeling stressed?

Activity

Investigate the readings of Rene Descartes (1595–1650) for relating the mind to the body.

Key definition

The physical science definition of **stress** is that of pressure or load.

Activity

Some theories to research: Seyle (1936)/Lazarus (1966)/ Friedman and Rosenhan (1959).

Activity

Complete the Holmes and Rahe (1967) Social Readjustment Scale.

Activity

Discussion: Is it always possible to tell how stressed someone is?

Activity

Everyday stress – ask your friends and family to identify three things that have recently made them feel stressed. How did they feel and how did they deal with the situation?

Assessment tip

The highest level work will:
* use everyday language
* identify the link between stress and mental health
* recognise that stress is not necessarily all bad
* be evaluative
* provide statistics related to stress e.g. cost to the workforce and employers.

Sources

Family Doctor

Natural Health School

Mind-body-health

BBC Health

Health and safety executive – statistics

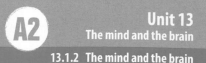

The brain and nervous system

Many behavioural problems can be brought on by brain abnormalities as a result of damage or disease. For many years researchers have attempted to observe directly or make inferences about the functioning of the brain and other parts of the nervous system in their efforts to understand both normal and abnormal psychological functioning. If a person is stressed the body has to deal with the demand caused by the stress. It does this via the nervous system and via hormones.

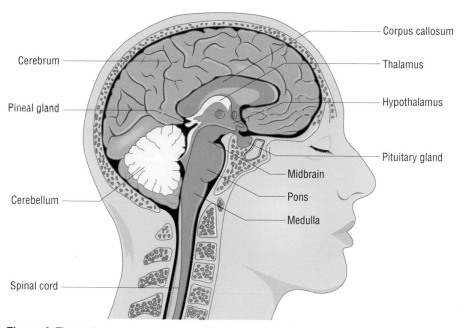

Figure 2 The main structures of the **central nervous system**

The brain

The brain is located within the protective coating of the skull. Viewed from the top the brain is divided by a midline fissure into two mirror image **cerebral hemispheres**. The major connection between the two hemispheres is a band of nerve fibres called the **corpus callosum**. Deep fissures divide the cerebral hemispheres into several distinct areas called **lobes**. Different functions tend to be localised in particular areas of the lobes e.g. vision in the occipital lobe.

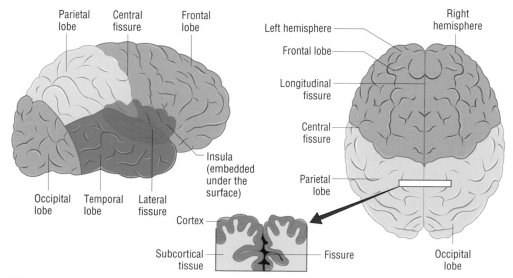

Figure 3 Lateral view of cerebral lobes

Brain damage can be caused by a number of factors including accident or injury, the effects of illness, the effects of drug or alcohol abuse.

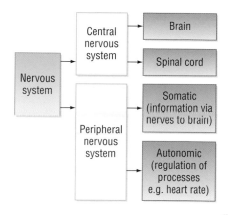

Internal assessment

Activity

Draw and label diagrams of the brain, outlining the function of each area or structure.

Activity

Investigate and present a case study relating to an illness, e.g. Alzheimer's disease, or schizophrenia or drug abuse, e.g. cocaine or Prozac.

Activity

Discuss the affect on the brain, how the brain may attempt to deal with damage itself and pharmacological treatment.

Sources

British Neuroscience Association

Headway

British Psychological Society

By the end of this spread, you should be able to:

* know about he methods and techniques used in studying the brain
* know about ethical issues in brain research
* understand the aims of psychological research

For many years researchers and clinicians have tried to either observe the brain directly or to make inferences about the functioning of the brain via other measures.

Techniques for studying the brain

Direct methods of studying brain function

There are techniques for studying the brain directly and include:

* CAT (computerised axial tomography) scan
* PET (positron emission tomography) scan
* NMR (nuclear magnetic response imaging) scan
* FMRI (functional magnetic response imaging) scan
* direct recording of neural activity via microelectrodes placed within the brain
* EEG (electroencephalograms).

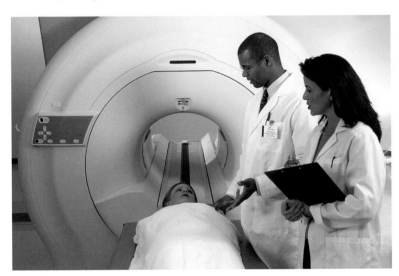

Figure 1 A brain scan

Indirect methods of studying brain function

Many brain abnormalities and injuries, however, involve such subtle changes in structure that they are not picked up via direct examination techniques. In such instances neuropsychological tests have some validity in the assessment of brain damage.

Damaged brains

A brain may become damaged accidentally, through illness or deliberately. Researchers can compare the alteration in psychological functioning with the location of the damage.

Naturally occurring and experimental exposure effects may influence brain physiology and functioning by using environmental excess (alcohol, drugs) or deprivation (water). If you consider alcohol as an example – how might excessive alcohol intake affect the functioning of the brain? Compare an individual who chooses to drink too much alcohol with an experimental situation in which individuals may be subjected to too much alcohol. What are the ethical implications in each situation?

Assessment tip

Describe and evaluate techniques in terms of:
* invasive nature
* implications of for the individual
* ethical implications
* expense.

Activity

Investigate the practice of removing areas of the brain to reduce aggression within psychiatric patients in the 1950s.

Have you read or seen the film 'One flew over the cuckoo's nest'? Discuss the treatments used with patients.

Assessment tip

Distinguish between the role of a neurologist and a neuropsychologist in your introduction to alternative and non-direct methods.

Activity

Discuss the concept of validity with specific relation to neuropsychological tests. Examples include: Halstead-Reitan battery, Luria-Nebraska battery.

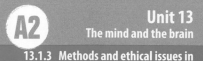
Take care to note the issues that exist when making assumptions about relationships between results on tests and the working of the brain! There is no clear 1:1 relationship between a CAT scan finding or a score on a neuropsychological test (e.g. Speech Sounds Perception Test) and psychological dysfunction. Assessment instruments are rarely perfect and we do not have a complete and total understanding of how the brain actually functions. The concept of **holism** is relevant here; as is the fact that we are all individuals and that we find ways of compensating for poor brain functions in many varying ways.

Ethical restraints on research

Ethical restraints exist in order to protect individuals from unnecessary harm, risk, humiliation and invasion of privacy. Several international codes of ethics have been produced with regards to humans and animals. This is because scientists in the past have carried out brutal experiments in the name of science.

You need to be able to link and evaluate the ethical aspects of brain research methods to the codes of practice.

Ethics of future technologies
Consider elements such as:
- Whether brain scanning should be used as a predictor of a tendency towards behaviours such as aggression and the ethical implications that this could have.
- Gene research and therapy and other various medical advances should be used to enhance cognitive function.

Psychological research

The aim of research in psychology is to gather data to describe and to test out ideas about behaviour and experience. Psychologists use a variety of methods to carry out research. These include:
- experiments – laboratory, field and natural
- observations
- case studies
- correlations
- surveys and questionnaires
- content analysis.

The methods vary in terms of the types of data that can be collected and the assumptions that can be made from the data that are relevant to the whole population.

It is essential that all psychological research must be ethical and overseen by someone that is fully aware of all ethical guidelines.

Research generally follows a pattern:
- Deciding upon a research question;
- establishing aims and writing hypotheses to test;
- choosing the most appropriate method in order to carry out the investigation;
- operationalising the variables and the design of the study**;
- collecting and analysing the data – either via descriptive (averages and variances) or inferential statistics (statistical tests); and
- evaluating the investigation.

(** Identifying the variables to be controlled and those to be measured in the way of results and deciding whether to use the same subjects under different conditions or to use different subjects in each condition.)

Internal assessment

219

By the end of this spread, you will:

✱ **know about everyday cognition**
✱ **know about experimental work to evaluate cognitive functions**

Everyday cognition

Cognition refers to the processes we use to think about our experiences. It refers to aspects of thinking such as: attention, perception, memory, language, problem solving and the development of attitudes. Often we take such abilities for granted and don't question how we are able to do such things. Everyday cognition informs us of how people carry out everyday activities, how they organise and use their knowledge in order to behave appropriately in the world in which they live.

Activity

Define the word: memory. Include a distinction between the working (or short term) and long term memory. Include the concepts of encoding, storage and retrieval.

Focus on memory

Psychologists make different distinctions about memory and their biological bases:

- The first concerns three stages of memory: encoding, storage and retrieval.
- The second deals with different memories for storing information for short and long periods.
- The third refers to different memories being used for different events (personal memories, skill, facts).

There is evidence that all distinctions noted above are mediated in different structures in the brain. Evidence from brain damaged patients can reveal restricted ability with one type of memory, whilst remaining unimpaired in the other type of memory. Brain scanning studies of long term memory indicate that most brain regions activated during encoding are left hemisphere and most for retrieval are right hemisphere.

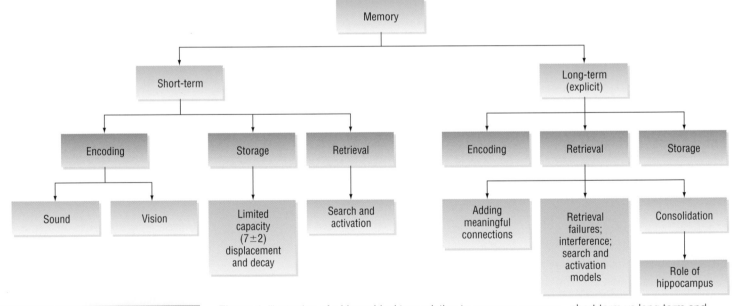

Figure 1 Illustration of a hierarchical tree relating to memory: memory – short term vs long term and branches for encoding, storage and retrieval

Source

Squire, L. R. (1987), *Memory and Brain*, New York, Oxford University Press

Atkinson, R. L. Atkinson, R. C. Smith, E. E. Bem, D. J. and Hoeksema, S. N. (1996), *Hilgard's Introduction to Psychology*, Harcourt Brace and Co.

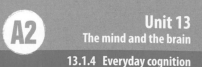

Eye witness testimony

Testimony given to police or in court is often assumed to be accurate. However, many factors influence the preciseness of such testimony. Examples include:

Social factors e.g. attitudes, prejudice, status of interviewer

Situational factors e.g. duration of event, type of crime, lighting

Individual factors e.g. personality, ethnicity, sex, background

Interrogational factors e.g. wording of questions, photofits, ID parades.

Consider some key studies (Loftus 1974, Loftus and Palmer 1974, Malpass and Devine 1981, Pickel 1988) to identify elements that affect the reliability of witness testimony.

PHANTOMBILD LKA NRW 251 / 07

Figure 2 Photofit picture and ID parade

Memory loss

- Can result from: brain damage, illness, old age, repression etc.
- Look at all factors that can affect forgetting referring to retrieval failures, storage failures or interference.
- Investigate the role of the hippocampus in the consolidation of new memories.
- Amnesia: how is it cognitively assessed and treated?

Case study: Memory loss

Investigate and detail a case study of memory loss.

Identify the type and onset of the memory loss. Identify the assessment of memory loss and techniques employed to reduce the memory loss.

Assessment tip for case study

Use the appropriate psychological terminology in relation to the memory loss. You may find an example in your reading or someone known to you, in which case, do not detail their name. Remember ethics – privacy.

Internal assessment

By the end of this spread, you should be able to:

* plan and investigate a research problem
* display, interpret and evaluate data
* write up a psychology practical

Figure 1 Can you do numbers?

Internal assessment

Activity: Reminder of the aims of research

Look back at spread 13.1.3 to remind yourself of the broad aims of psychological research.

Assessment tip

Select the correct statistical test. Look at the design of your study: Related sample (matched subjects or repeated measures) or Unrelated (independent) sample. What level of data do you have? The answers will lead you to identify the test.

Practical research

- Research any aspect of cognitive functioning.
- It can be based on a replication of a known practical (e.g. Stroop effect on attention, Craik and Lochart – levels of processing). You may have found some element in your studying of memory that you found particularly interesting and want to investigate further.
- You design, plan and carry out the project. Don't forget your hypotheses!
- You will justify your plan and ensure that you use the most appropriate method to carry out the research.
- You will demonstrate consideration of ethical guidelines throughout.
- You will collect data and use both appropriate descriptive and inferential statistics to interpret your results.
- You will link your research to theory and evaluate your research.
- You will present your research in the standard format of a psychological report.

The format of a psychology report

Follow the format below, starting each section on a new page.

Title: To indicate the precise nature (experiment or survey etc.) of the topic being investigated.

Abstract: A summary of no longer than 100 words. What you did, the method used, what you found.

Introduction: Answer the following questions:
- What is the general nature of the area?
- What have others said and done in relation to the area?
- Why is this project being carried out and what is going to be done?
- Statement of your hypothesis (experimental or alternate). Is it one or two tailed? What is the null hypothesis?

Method: Always written in the past tense with four sub headings:
1 Participants: The number of participants. Information on age, sex, background. How were they selected?
2 Apparatus: Description with purpose and diagrams if necessary.
3 Procedure: Describe exactly what happened so that a reader could exactly replicate the research.
4 Design: A formal statement of the design (you may need help with this from your teacher), and the planned statistical analysis. You should also refer to all relevant variables.

Results: Often the shortest section. Descriptive statistics (means, standard deviations, bar charts, etc) and inferential statistics (results of statistical tests) (see P.1.13). Raw data can slot into the Appendix.

Conclusion: An answer to the project question or hypothesis. Is the null hypothesis rejected in favour of your experimental/alternate hypothesis?

Discussion: You can start with repeating the main verbal findings in the results.

Do the results indicate the need for further or additional research? Suggest outlines if so.

How have the results moved knowledge along?

Link with theories and previous research identified in the Introduction.

How could the research be improved? Were there any problems?

Have you drawn any additional conclusions that were not initially identified?

Appendix: All raw data, lengthy instructions etc. Labelled and referred to through the main text.

References: Full and alphabetical.

Scatter graphs

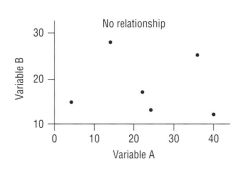

Barchart

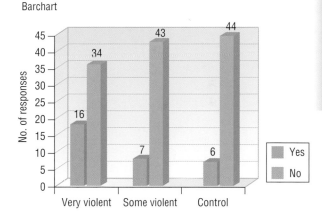

Frequency polygons

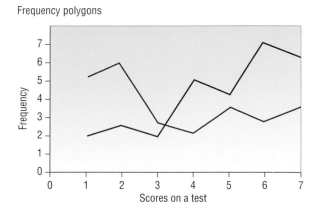

Histogram

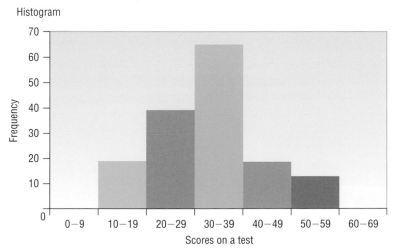

Figure 2 Descriptive statistics

① Ecology and managing the environment

By the end of this spread, you should be able to:

* know what you will need to do for this portfolio
* be aware of the level of work required
* know how you will be assessed
* check your portfolio to see if you can improve it

Our environment is coming under considerable pressure. Man's activities are accelerating the natural processes of change. Some of these changes are undesirable and avoidable. This unit considers some of the issues involved.

Assessment objective AO1

There are two strands in this section:

* Extracting relevant information, from as many relevant sources as you can, about the relationship between organisms and their environment and each other and produce a report (5 marks).
* Make sure that you research and consider the three areas specified, namely agricultural practice, human habitation and greenhouse gas production and produce a report (5 marks).

Assessment objective AO2

There are three strands in this section:

* Identify and report on scientific, moral and ethical reasons for preserving ecosystems and species diversity (4 marks).
* Produce a report to describe methods used to manage ecosystems and preserve species diversity and an evaluation of one, specific management project (5 marks).
* Carry out calculations on ecological data probably but not exclusively linked to your investigation of an ecosystem under AO3 below (5 marks).

Assessment objective AO3

You should produce an illustrated, written report that includes and covers the four strands in this section for a planned investigation of an ecosystem:

* Make observations and carry out measurements of environmental factors using a range of techniques and equipment in a way that meets the requirements of a risk assessment you have produced (8 marks).
* Record these observations and measurements (6 marks).
* Display this ecological data (4 marks).
* Use the information gained during your work in sections AO1 and AO2 to interpret the results of your investigation and draw conclusions (8 marks).

Figure 1 RSPB reserve sign

How did you do?

What grade did you think your work is worth?

Use the following checklists to get some idea of the likely standard at which you are working. Remember that these are only a guide and that you should always aim to work at as hard as you can to improve.

AO	Evidence	Form of evidence	Present	Missing
1a and 1b	Some research which shows knowledge and understanding of the effects of change on ecosystems	Report		
	Some research which shows knowledge and understanding of the effects of change on biodiversity	Report		
	Some research which shows knowledge and understanding of the relationship between organisms and their physical environment and each other	Report		
	Evidence of basic work on ecological succession	Report		
	Your own work that has been suitably selected and referenced and shows appropriate use of scientific terms and conventions	Report		
	Research showing selected work of your own (not cut and paste) on: (1) agricultural practice; (2) human habitation; and (3) greenhouse gas production	Report		
	Information giving reasons for choice of resources	Report		
2a and 2b	Some discussion of the scientific, moral and ethical reasons for preserving ecosystems and species diversity	Report		
	Research of a method used to manage an ecosystem and preserve species diversity with a description of the success of the project. Some interpretation of any data collected	Report		
2c	Calculations based on results of practical field study carried out or second hand ecological data. Completion of some straightforward calculations	Report		
3a, 3b and 3c	Individual experimental work required. Evidence needs to show some structure and independent research	Work recorded as an organised detailed report		
	Plan has been followed. Your teacher has signed to say that you have worked safely			
	Evidence that a number of different techniques have been employed complete with risk assessments			
	Measurements taken. Some evidence of repeats where appropriate			
	Accurate use of scientific terminology			
	Group results can be collated and used for display and for calculations			
	Data collected has been displayed in different ways			
	Data collected has been interpreted			

Table 1 Assessment objectives checklist

If you have ticked all the 'Present' boxes your work is probably at Grade E or better.

Have you found any areas where you have left something important out?
Are there any ticks in the 'Missing' column? If there are you may have time to do something about it.

What do you need to do to improve your portfolio?
It is likely that the evidence you have presented in your portfolio can be improved.

Use the information in the Assessment tip margin boxes to increase the chance of your getting a better grade. There is an Assessment tip box for each of the assessment objectives. The advice given, if taken, could improve your grade up to Grade A.

Internal assessment

By the end of this spread, you should be able to:

⚓ Investigate the effects of those changes on ecosystems (succession) caused by human activity

The effects of change on ecosystems

Ecosystem

It is important that you are familiar with the basic ecological terms and principles used in reporting this area of study.

The external surroundings in which we and all other animals and plants live form our environment. Our external environment will include not only all those other living things but also all those other things that affect us such as temperature, whether it's light or dark, or whether it's wet or dry. These and many other factors in our physical world will differ depending where we are, what time of year it is, what time of day it is, and so on. Our 'personal world' has, therefore, a living (biotic) component and a non-living (abiotic) component peculiar to where we live. The animals and plants that live around us and the physical world we occupy together is called an ecosystem. Different groups of animals and plants living in different physical conditions live in different ecosystems. Ecosystems can be small or very big.

Succession

The plants and animals that make up a community within an ecosystem may change over time. This process of change is called succession. The first organisms to colonise an area of bare rock or a new pond or lake are called pioneer species. Those organisms growing on bare ground usually mosses or lichens start the process of soil formation. New plants are then able to colonise the area. These too will, by growing there, bring about further change. The natural end point for this series of changes in most parts of the United Kingdom would be oak woodland. This is described as the climax community and would include all the dependent animal populations found there too. Climax communities are rare.

Assessment tip

- This area of work in your portfolio is worth 20% of the marks.

Sources

The Offwell Woodland Wildlife Trust is an excellent source of information. Make sure that you visit the links page too.

Activity

Discuss the following terms:
- population
- community
- autotroph
- heterotroph
- herbivore
- carnivore
- omnivore
- trophic level
- food chain
- food web.

Figure 1 Pioneer species

Figure 2 Climax woodland

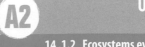
Agricultural practice

About 70% of the UK land area is farmland. The way in which farmland is used is a major factor driving change in the ecosystem.

Figure 3 Man-made ecosystem: 'prairie' farmland

The adoption of more environmentally aware agricultural practices will have a positive effect on habitats and the communities living there.

Biodiversity

An ecosystem is likely to involve a variety of habitats. Each habitat will have a community living within it. A community has plant and animal populations that interact with each other through food webs for example. The term biodiversity is used to describe the variety or diversity shown in terms of the different habitats and different species of organisms. Many factors affect biodiversity. One of the main factors is human activity.

Human habitation

A growing human population generates increasing demand for land. This is required for housing, schools, hospitals, supermarkets, factories, roads, airports and so on. The knock-on effect on the ecosystem and biodiversity is not difficult to imagine.

Greenhouse gas production

One consequence of population growth is an increase in demand and consumption of energy. This generally leads to increased greenhouse gas production. There is strong evidence to suggest that this has an effect on our ecosystem in terms of climate change. This in turn may drive ecosystem change and bring about change in biodiversity.

Activity

Areas that you might research include:
- monoculture
- hedgerow removal
- use of fertilisers and pesticides
- bioaccumulation
- eutrophication.

Case study

Man's activities are not the only sources of greenhouse gases. Natural production of greenhouse gases includes:
- waste gases produced during digestion in ruminants
- methane released from peat bogs, marshes, paddy fields and other similar habitats.

Internal assessment

Figure 4 Land-clearance for building

14.1 ③ Why and how do we need to manage change?

By the end of this spread, you should be able to:

* investigate the reasons for preserving ecosystems and biodiversity
* investigate and evaluate methods of management of ecosystems

The management of ecosystems

Scientific, moral and ethical issues

Scientific reasons for preserving biodiversity include:

- collectively organisms possess an enormous reservoir of genetic material – potential for DNA technology
- variety of food
- raw materials for a variety of products.

What are morals and ethics – are they different? As a working definition you can think of morals as views or standards agreed by society as to what's right and what's wrong. Ethics can be interpreted as a code of conduct or behaviour based on those accepted moral judgements. In your research you may see reference to business ethics, journalistic ethics, legal ethics or medical ethics. These are the views or standards agreed by society as a whole and a particular group, for example the medical profession, to determine acceptable practice. They determine the accepted code of conduct of all the members of that group.

Is it right to:

- clear tropical forest to provide land to grow crops to support the people who live there?
- cut down native woodland and grow palm oil as a biofuel for export?
- fell and clear a woodland area to provide housing?

Members of industrial corporations have to take decisions as to whether to develop an area for trade. Planning authorities have to take decisions about whether to allow consent for an area to be developed. These are examples of situations where moral and ethical issues arise as a result of human activity impacting on ecosystems.

Sustainable practice in agriculture and natural resources

How do you recognise sustainable practice in agriculture? One set of criteria (defined in an Environment Agency document 'Agriculture and Natural Resources May 2002') refers to four farm systems. These are, in order of increasing sustainability:

- Conventional: narrow rotations and intensive use of inorganic fertilisers and pesticides.
- Reduced-tillage: minimal turning of the soil, with narrow rotations and intensive use of inorganic fertilisers and pesticides.
- Integrated: diverse crop rotations and less use of inorganic fertilisers and pesticides.
- Organic: diverse crop rotations and mechanical tillage replacing all agrochemical inputs.

Management of designated areas

Public awareness of the need for conservation and preservation of biodiversity has seen a dramatic increase in the recent past. People are being asked to play a more proactive role in conservation and to engage in a more 'sustainable' lifestyle.

This might be represented by:

- Local activity groups linked to county wildlife trusts
- Conservation areas, national parks, WWT, fisheries, wildlife parks, RSPB reserves
- Reclamation projects – e.g. bioremediation to remove toxic material
- Travel agents promoting ecotourism.

Internal assessment

Assessment tip

The following would be useful areas to research to provide you with information for your report:
- Animal welfare
- Deforestation
- Desertification
- Maintenance of rural economy and rural life
- Public access
- Recreation of habitats
- Set-aside
- Soil management
- Water management.

Activity

Discuss the four farm systems. Starting with reduced-tillage, try to identify how any one system differs from the system before it in the list.

Activity

There are other techniques used to indicate how sustainable a particular agricultural practice is. One method, for example, uses criteria focusing on how 'environmentally friendly' the farming is. Discuss what these criteria might be.

Figure 1 Wetland reclamation site

Carbon dioxide audit

Evaluate methods used to decrease emissions:

- cleaner industrial processes including manufacturing and power generation
- carbon sinks e.g. reforestation.

Management of an ecosystem

How do you start to manage an ecosystem with a view to conserving the ecosystem and maintaining biodiversity?

Management usually involves:

- Establishing the structure of the ecosystem as it is, gathering data about biotic and abiotic components.
- Establishing what the structure should be.
- Producing a management plan that attempts to 'maintain', or 'restore', or 'recreate' the ecosystem in question or probably all three.
- Producing action plans and actioning them.
- Evaluate the effectiveness of methods/management techniques used.

Activity

How could you investigate to what degree ecosystem management is happening in your area?

Assessment tip

What you need to do for your portfolio is, for one specified ecosystem, obtain data with respect to the management of that ecosystem by a scientist or team of scientists. Your report should describe their approach including data and evidence of effectiveness.

NB It will be easy to overrun your time allocation here. Take care!

By the end of this spread, you should be able to:

✱ plan an investigation of an ecosystem including an appropriate risk assessment
✱ make and record observations and measurements of environmental factors
✱ carry out calculations (AO2 strand 3)
✱ display and interpret the data, draw conclusions and evaluate the investigation

Planning

The first thing you need to do is to plan what you want to do. Remember that you have a fixed amount of time. Perhaps you might set up a diary so that you can organise your time. You are then more likely to achieve what you want to get done. The main things you are going to need to consider are listed below:

- Decide which ecosystem you would like to investigate.
- Define its location, grid reference, aspect, topography.
- Decide on the title, prediction, justification.
- Discuss the feasibility of your choice with your teacher.
- Identify any possible problems in terms of travel, cost, and equipment.
- Preliminary work that would need to be done – with reasons.
- Identify the number and range of measurements you would have to take.
- Identify any variables that may affect the validity of your investigation.
- Main investigation, detailed instructions as to what you intend to do, what equipment will be required, design an appropriate risk assessment.

Observing and measuring

Principles of sampling

Most ecosystems are too big and involve too many individual organisms to count every individual present. Most quantitative work carried out in the field involves the use of a sampling technique of some description. Two things you will have to decide are:

- sample size
- how to avoid bias.

Fieldwork techniques available

The fieldwork techniques that you employ for your investigation will obviously depend on the demands of your investigation. Techniques appropriate for investigating the composition, number and distribution of plant populations might not be appropriate for motile animal populations. They might, however, be usable with sedentary animals such as barnacles.

The list below includes equipment and methodology that you should research to decide what you need to do for your particular investigation. It is not a comprehensive list. You may be given others by your teacher. Your research may extend the list further:

- quadrat, point quadrats
- pitfall trap, water trap, light trap, Longworth small mammal trap, sweep net, pooter
- transect – line, belt
- frequency, density, percentage cover
- mark and recapture.

Figure 1 A quadrat in use

Activity

- Discuss the possible areas where you might carry out field work in your locality.
- Make a list of possible sites.
- Identify and write down the type of work you might be able to do at each site.
- Make your choice.

Assessment tip

A preliminary visit to the site where you intend to carry out your work might save you a lot of time. Go and see what's there, what the difficulties or problems might be. Be prepared.

Assessment tip

Make sure your method avoids bias. Your sampling for example should be done randomly. Within a selected area don't go for those places that are an easy option e.g. the goal mouth area of a playing field. Equally don't select places because there are lots of specimens. Using random number tables to provide coordinates for sampling areas would be more scientific.

Physical factors

In addition to recording the composition and distribution of the organisms in your chosen ecosystem you may wish to investigate its abiotic component. Some of the physical factors that may affect the number and distribution of organisms in an ecosystem include: temperature; light; humidity; wind strength; slope; exposure; oxygen availability; soil pH; soil nutrient levels.

Once more, there may be other factors that you might need to add to this list. You may record field data manually or using datalogging equipment.

Calculations

You will need to be able to use some or all of the following statistical calculations in the processing of your data: mean; standard deviation; Simpson's diversity index; chi-squared or t-test; correlation coefficient (see P.1.13).

Display

You will need to be able to use some or all of the following styles in the display of your data: line and bar graphs; histograms; pie charts; pictographs; kite diagrams.

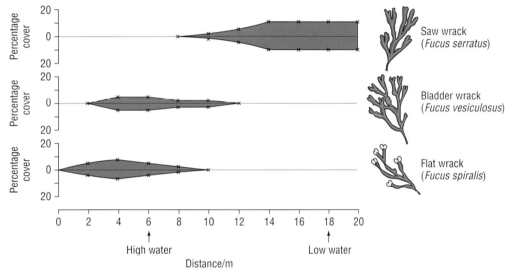

Figure 2 Example of data display using kite diagrams.

Analysis and interpretation

Use statistics to summarise, manipulate, and validate your data.

Evaluation

When writing an evaluation you should make positive statements about your evidence. If you have carried out statistical tests and your results were significant at the 5% level remember that there is still a 1 in 20 chance that your results did arise by chance. There should be evidence of repeats. Comment on any errors that have arisen. Make and explain suggestions for improvement.

Internal assessment

By the end of this spread, you should be able to:

✽ **know what you will need to do for this portfolio**

✽ **be aware of the level of work required**

✽ **know how you will be assessed**

✽ **be able to check your portfolio to see if you can improve it**

Assessment tip

Each of your public information booklets should:

• be researched and produced in about five hours of your time – they are meant to be 'booklets' *NOT* 'big books'!

• summarise the scientific information involved

• be written using 'man in the street language' with minimal 'jargon'

• use diagrams/photos wherever appropriate.

Humans have been using living things and their products for thousands of years. Biotechnology is the application of science and technology to this activity. It employs microorganisms or biological processes in the production of food, drink, medicine or for other benefits to the human race, or other animal species.

Assessment objective AO1

There are two strands in this section.

You have to produce a public information booklet about:

• the science of genetic engineering (5 marks)

• the use of recombinant DNA technology in medicine *or* agriculture (5 marks).

Assessment objective AO2

There are three strands in this section.

You have to produce a report which:

• identifies information on how successful recombinant DNA technology has been in solving food production problems (5 marks)

• include calculations you have carried out on financial and statistical data relating to the use of recombinant DNA technology (3 marks)

• identifies and reports on moral, ethical and environmental issues relating to the use of recombinant DNA technology in the production of GM plants and the constraints put on scientists working in this field (6 marks).

Assessment objective AO3

You should produce an illustrated, written report that includes and covers the four strands in this section for a planned practical investigation into enzyme technology, involving the construction of a simple bioreactor and its use in investigating the effect of temperature on enzyme activity. Your report should include:

• a plan of your investigation including risk assessments, description of the construction of a simple bioreactor and the production and use of an immobilised enzyme (5 marks)

• observations and measurements made on an immobilised enzyme system in action in the bioreactor (5 marks)

• a record of the observations and measurements with data displayed in the most appropriate way, including calculations and the use of statistics where appropriate (9 marks)

• use of the information gained during your work on enzyme technology in interpreting the results of your investigation and drawing conclusions (7 marks).

How did you do?

What grade did you think your work is worth?

Use the following checklists to get some idea of the likely standard at which you are working. Remember that these are only a guide and that you should always aim to work at as hard as you can to improve.

AO	Evidence	Form of evidence	Present	Missing
1a and 1b	Some research which shows knowledge and understanding of genetic engineering.	Public information booklet		
	Some research which shows knowledge and understanding of the use of recombinant DNA technology in medicine **OR** agriculture.	Public information booklet		
	Your own work that has been suitably selected and referenced.	In booklets		
2a	Some discussion of how successful recombinant DNA is in solving problems associated with food production and some conclusions about possible benefits of the technology. Specific examples.	Report		
2b	Calculations based on financial and or statistical data. Some straightforward calculations completed and some attempts at complex calculations.	Data and calculations clearly presented		
2c	Your own analysis of the moral and ethical issues of using recombinant DNA technology in the production of GM plants. Includes an explanation of **one** of the controls placed on scientists working in this field.	Report In report		
3a, 3b and 3c	Plan has been followed. Your teacher has signed to say that you have worked safely.	Work recorded in an organised, detailed report		
	Simple bioreactor produced.			
	Immobilised enzyme produced.			
	Effect of temperature on chosen enzyme completed.			
	A number of different techniques have been used accompanied by appropriate risk assessments.			
	Some repeats carried out where appropriate and measurements taken.			
	Data collected has been displayed in different ways.			
	Data collected has been interpreted.			
	Reference to the advantages of using bioreactors and immobilised enzymes.			

Table 1 Assessment objectives checklist

If you have ticked all the 'Present' boxes your work is probably at Grade E or better.

Have you found any areas where you have left something important out?
Are there any ticks in the 'Missing' column? If there are you may have time to do something about it.

What do you need to do to improve your portfolio?
It is likely that the evidence you have presented in your portfolio can be improved.

Use the information in the Assessment tip margin boxes to increase the chance of your getting a better grade. There is an Assessment tip box for each of the assessment objectives. The advice given, if taken, could improve your grade up to Grade A.

Assessment tip

AO1a and b. Your research work needs to:
- be your own, accurate use of appropriate scientific terms and conventions and from a variety of sources
- include work on genetic engineering and recombinant DNA technology all of which is relevant and logically presented
- show some discussion on the information chosen.

Assessment tip

AO2a, b and c. Your research work needs to include:
- a discussion of how successful recombinant DNA technology is in solving problems associated with food production
- an evaluation of the success of the two chosen examples
- references for source materials used in the discussion
- analysis of the moral, ethical and environmental issues of using recombinant DNA technology in the production of GM plants
- evaluation of *two* types of control placed on scientists and their effectiveness
- complex calculations on financial evidence with answers given to the appropriate degree of accuracy.

Assessment tip

AO3. Production and presentation of investigative work should show an independent approach with:
- detailed risk assessments
- use of a wide range of different techniques of measurement and analysis
- reasons for using particular techniques
- repetition where necessary
- accurate use of scientific terminology
- careful, accurate, precise recording of relevant data
- data displayed, using appropriate precision and accuracy, in a range of ways to best illustrate trends
- interpretation of results using secondary sources to support findings
- conclusions that relate the results to the use of bioreactors and enzyme immobilisation linked to medical/industrial use
- significance of findings linked to how enzymes work and the advantages enzyme technology offers to industry.

Internal assessment

15.1 ② Genetic engineering

By the end of this spread, you should be able to:

* investigate the science of genetic engineering

The science of genetic engineering

Genetic engineering is one aspect of biotechnology. It involves taking DNA from one organism and putting it into the genetic make-up of another. Sometimes an artificial gene may be used instead. Genetic engineering is used to make an increasing range of useful products.

DNA

DNA is a very large organic molecule. It is one of two nucleic acids. The other is RNA. DNA is a polymer formed from monomers called **nucleotides**.

The DNA polymer is organised as a double helix formed by two strands. Each strand has a 'backbone' composed of a sugar–phosphate chain. Nitrogenous bases face each other across the helix. Compulsory, complementary, specific base-pairing occurs between the bases. A purine always pairs with a pyrimidine. Adenine always pairs with thymine and cytosine with guanine. (See spread 4.3.8, Figure 2.)

Genetic code

The order of bases in a piece of nucleic acid works as a chemical code. This ultimately determines the way a cell works. The nitrogenous base-order is read in 'triplets'. There are 64 ways of selecting three bases from four. Each triplet is called a 'codon'. Each codon is specific for a particular amino acid. There are 20 amino acids that commonly occur in proteins. Some amino acids have more than one codon. Three particular codons act as stop-codons. They act as 'full stops' in the message. (In RNA thymine is replaced by uracil.)

Examples of codons and amino acids: AGA codes for the amino acid arginine; GCG codes for alanine; GGG codes for glycine; UAA, UAG and UGA are stop-codons that code for the 'full stops' referred to above.

Protein

The chemistry going on in a cell determines how a cell works, what it can do and how it behaves. Most cell biochemistry is controlled by enzymes. Enzymes are proteins. Therefore whatever controls the proteins a cell can make, controls indirectly the activity of a cell through the enzymes it can produce. Proteins are synthesised inside a cell using DNA as a template. Therefore a cell's DNA controls the production of its enzymes and the chemistry it is 'allowed to perform'.

Activity

If you have studied double award AS you will have worked on some of the material in this unit already. You could be a key-player in discussion groups if you can remember any of it!

Source

Meet up with Tiki the penguin – loads of accessible information and genetic engineering links.

Key definition

Each **nucleotide** is formed from three parts:
• a pentose (5C) sugar molecule called deoxyribose
• a nitrogenous base
• a phosphate group.

Two types of nitrogenous base occur in DNA. They are:
• purines – adenine (A) and guanine (G)
• pyrimidines – cytosine (C) and thymine (T).

Sources

Biotechnology and Biological Sciences Research Council

Biotechnology Online

DNA Interactive

Activity

What polypeptide chain would be produced from the following section of coding?

AGAGGGGCGUGA

Restriction enzymes

Genetic engineers use special enzymes, restriction enzymes, to cut the required 'gene' from a donor organism's chromosome. Each of these enzymes targets a specific sequence of bases in DNA. The specific enzyme used to remove the donor 'gene' is also used to 'make a space', to insert the gene into, by cutting the recipient chromosome. The DNA fragments produced have 'sticky ends'. A sticky end is formed by a single stranded section of nucleic acid. The donor sticky end is complementary to the recipient sticky end.

DNA ligase

Having successfully cut the required 'gene' from a donor and 'made room' to insert it into the recipient chromosome, the genetic engineer then uses another enzyme to produce recombinant DNA strands. The sticky ends are 'glued together' using the complementary base pairing in a process controlled by the enzyme DNA ligase.

Vectors

Plasmids are small circular pieces of DNA found in bacterial cells. Viruses and plasmids are used to insert genes into target cells. Recombinant strands of DNA can be inserted into plasmids using restriction and ligase enzymes. The plasmids are inserted into target bacterial cells which are then cultured to produce large numbers of clones of the recombinant DNA. Viruses and plasmids used in this way are called vectors.

PCR

The polymerase chain reaction (PCR) is used as a means of making large numbers of copies of DNA fragments artificially. The process is carried out in an automated, computer-controlled process. The following are required:

- section of double stranded DNA
- nucleotides containing the bases A, T, G and C
- DNA polymerase
- short pieces of nucleic acid, called primers, to start the process of replication.

Genetic probe

The likely codon (base triplet) sequence necessary for the production of a protein can be worked out from the amino acid sequence of the protein. A short section of compementary, single-stranded DNA can be made using radioactive ^{32}P in the DNA backbone. This is the gene probe. It will hybridise (pair-up) with any complementary base sequence and show us where it is. This enables us to identify specific pieces of DNA – specific genes.

Electrophoresis

Electrophoresis can be used to collect gene probes from restriction enzyme digestion mixtures.

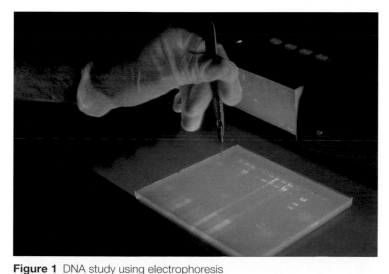

Figure 1 DNA study using electrophoresis

By the end of this spread, you should be able to:

▶ investigate the use of recombinant DNA technology in:
- medicine, and
- agriculture

The use of recombinant DNA technology in medicine

Genetic engineering allows research workers to isolate a gene, purify it and make large numbers of copies. They can then study how it works. This area of research is of great significance to those scientists attempting to find a cure for inherited diseases or create products that will help in the treatment of disease.

Insulin

A diabetic needs an external supply of insulin. In the past this has been provided as purified pig or cow insulin. This sometimes causes immune-response problems. Genetically engineered bacteria can produce human insulin in a fermenter. This product has fewer side effects.

Genetic screening

A sample of cells can be tested to see whether a particular gene is present or not. This technique can be used with organisms that produce useful proteins such as enzymes or hormones. It can also be used in the investigation of inherited disease.

Germ and somatic cell gene therapy

Successful **somatic cell** gene therapy benefits the individual involved but is not inherited by their offspring. Whereas successful **germ cell** therapy could be passed on to future generations. There are ethical and moral issues associated with this line of therapy and it is banned in some countries.

Human genome

The **Human Genome** Project is an international project whose aim is to determine the base sequence of the human genome. Ideally this will lead to the identification, isolation and sequencing of the genes responsible for inherited disease and the discovery of suitable treatments.

Moral and ethical issues

There are many ethical and moral issues associated with the use of biotechnology and genetic engineering in particular relating to individual rights and to environmental issues.

Internal assessment

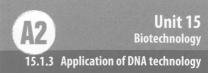

The use of recombinant DNA technology in the production of genetically modified (GM) food plants

Techniques

Useful genes can be transferred to a crop plant using a vector such as *Agrobacterium tumefaciens* or by 'biolistics' using a gene gun. Marker genes are used to check to see whether the transfer has been successful. Antibiotic resistance is often included as the marker gene where a bacterium has been used as the vector. The GM plant is cloned. Field trials see whether the transfer has the desired effect and is genetically stable.

Micro propagation

Cells are taken from the growing point (meristem) of a 'prototype GM plant' and used to produce a clone. Large numbers of identical specimens of a potential GM food plant can be produced as a result.

Two early examples of GM food plants

It is possible to insert genetic material that provides resistance to a particular herbicide. The herbicide glycophosphate is widely used in agriculture. GM wheat plants have been developed that are resistant to glycophosphate.

A natural insecticide called 'T toxin' is produced by the spores of *Bacillus thuringiensis*. The larvae of some species of flies, mosquitoes and leaf-eating caterpillars have gut-enzymes that convert T toxin into toxic proteins. The T toxin gene has been inserted into the Ti plasmid of *A. tumefaciens* and used to produce an insect resistant tomato plant.

Other applications

Recombinant DNA technology can be used to produce a variety of beneficial effects for food producers and for the consumer. Examples include GM food plants showing:

- longer shelf life
- nutritional improvement
- increased yield
- drought tolerance
- tolerance to high salinity
- tolerance to low temperature.

Financial aspects of GM food plant production

There are research and regulatory costs involved in the production of GM food plants.

Concerns about genetically modified organisms (GMOs)

There are many apparent benefits to be gained by the production of GM food plants. At the same time however it is important to be aware of the potential risks. These include:

- genetic pollution (transfer of genes to natural, wild species)
- food chain problems
- farmers and other food producers in different countries having different costs and legislation to comply with and therefore different effectiveness in the market place.

UK legislation

The constraints that scientists work under in the field of genetic food plant development are illustrated in the following texts:

- Food Safety Act
- Advisory Committee on Novel Foods and Processes (ANFP).

EU legislation

Different countries employ different legislation with respect to research, development and implementation of GM products. One example of an EU legislative document is the 'Directive on the release of genetically modified organisms (GMOs)'.

Internal assessment

By the end of this spread, you should be able to:

✳ investigate enzyme technology

Enzyme chemistry

Enzymes are proteins that alter the rate of a chemical reaction. They are 'biological catalysts'. Enzymes are effective in small quantities and remain unchanged at the end of the reaction they catalyse.

Enzymes alter the rate of a chemical reaction by lowering the activation energy for that reaction. (See spread 4.3.5, Figure 1.)

The particular three-dimensional structure of an enzyme is critical in the way the enzyme works. The specific arrangement in space of the protein molecule creates, within it, what is called an active site. This, potentially very small part of the overall structure, is where the interaction between an enzyme and its specific substrate takes place. The enzyme and substrate form an enzyme–substrate complex. There are two ideas you need to have to form some understanding of the way the enzyme and its substrate interact. The first is described by the term 'lock and key' and the second by the term 'induced fit'. In the lock and key analogy the lock is the enzyme (very large molecule) and the smaller substrate molecule is the key. For the pairing to operate the key must fit. Enzymes show specificity. Some enzymes work with one type of molecule only. Some will work with a group of closely related compounds. The lock and key analogy is not perfect. It falls down because the lock is not rigid. It can change its shape and in doing so fits the key more effectively – the idea of 'induced fit'. These slight changes in shape are thought to put strain on the substrate molecule and in doing so lower the activation energy.

Protein structure is affected by temperature and pH. Consequently the activity of an enzyme (protein) is also affected by these factors. The rate of an enzyme controlled reaction is also affected by the enzyme concentration and substrate concentration. These will act as limiting factors. When a variable such as substrate concentration is increased, the rate of reaction increases up to a maximum. During that phase the reaction is limited and the substrate concentration is described as the limiting factor. At the maximum rate some other factor may be limiting.

Enzyme reactions may be affected by inhibitors. A few cause change that disables the enzyme permanently. Most cause a temporary inability to catalyse reactions.

Some inhibitors (competitive inhibitors) have a molecular structure similar to the natural substrate and block available active sites.

Another group of inhibitors attach to parts of the enzyme structure other than the active site. This distorts the molecule and the active site is no longer the correct shape to operate with its substrate.

Some products affect the enzymes that produce them. This is called end-product inhibition.

Activity

If you have studied double award AS you will have worked on some of the material in this unit already. Review the material you have already got and use the planning strategy from the pre-release material for Unit 4 to help you to plan for this part of Unit 15.

Source

Novozymes

Assessment tip

Your task is to plan and run an investigation into the effect of temperature on an immobilised enzyme in a bioreactor you have designed and built yourself.
- You will find a useful planning strategy in spread 4.1.1. There is a 24 point checklist to help organise your work.
- Information in this double page spread should be used to help you to build the bioreactor and immobilise the enzyme.
- Use the generic section of this book to assist in recording, displaying and interpreting your results.

Internal assessment

Bioreactor

Set-up

A bioreactor needs to include the means to:

* supply nutrients
* introduce inoculum of microorganism involved
* remove product(s)
* maintain homogeneity
* monitor and control variables.

Batch and continuous systems

The culture of microorganisms in a bioreactor may be set up in a batch system or in a continuous system. The former involves a 'start – stop – start' approach. The culture is set up with nutrients kept under optimal conditions. Once the culture has gone through its most active productive phase it degenerates. The product sometimes compromises the enzymes in the microorganism and stops the process. Before this happens the product has to be harvested and separated from the rest of the culture. The whole process then has to be set up again with new organisms and more nutrients. Continuous systems provide a much more controlled process. Microorganisms, nutrients and products are introduced and removed in such a way that the process and the equipment are utilised far more efficiently. One feature that makes this easier to set up is the development and employment of immobilised whole cells or immobilised enzymes.

Enzyme immobilisation techniques

Enzyme and cell immobilisation has many advantages including re-use, non-contamination of product and ease of control.

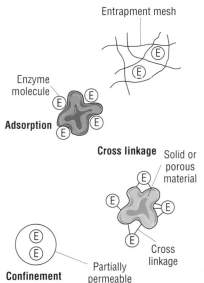

Figure 2 Immobilisation techniques

Medical application of enzyme technology

Medical uses of enzyme technology include:

* production of human proteins including human growth hormone, insulin, factor VIII, erythropoietin
* biosensors.

Agricultural application of enzyme technology

Agricultural applications of enzyme technology include:

* use of lactic acid bacteria and yeasts in the production of silage
* treatment of slurry
* production of biogas.

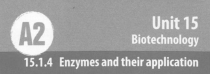

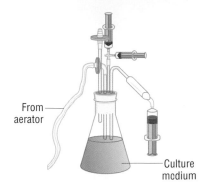

Figure 1 A simple bioreactor

Source

NCBE Bioreactor

Source

Science and Plants for Schools

Internal assessment

By the end of this spread, you should be able to:

✴ describe some of the features common to all waves

What is a wave?

A wave is a special kind of motion. It is a disturbance that transfers energy from one place to another without any permanent effect on the medium in between.

Imagine that you and your friend are holding a rope stretched out between you. If you move your end up and down a disturbance will go down the rope to your friend. This is one kind of wave. You have transferred energy to your friend's end of the rope. However, the particles of the rope will go back to their original positions.

Displacement

The displacement is the distance a wave moves a particle from its rest position. For electromagnetic waves, it is the size of the electric and magnetic fields.

Repeating waves

If you moved your end of the rope up and down *in the same way* lots of times you would send a repeating wave. Some repeating waves have simple shapes such a sine wave (Figure 1) and a square wave (Figure 2).

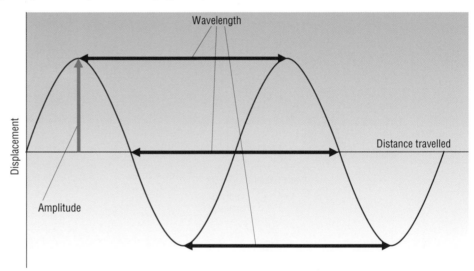

Figure 1 Diagram of displacement plotted against distance travelled for a sine wave

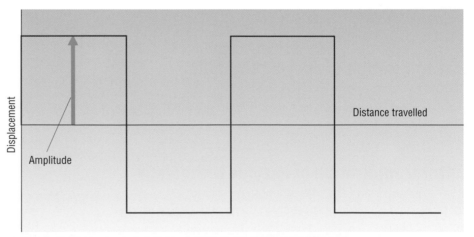

Figure 2 Diagram of displacement plotted against distance travelled for a square wave

Features of repeating waves

You can describe some of the properties of repeating waves by stating their **amplitude, wavelength** (λ), **period** (or periodic time) (T) and **frequency** (f).

The graphs in Figure 1 are like the picture you would get if you took a snapshot of your rope. They show what happens at *all* points along the rope at *one moment in time*. Another way of plotting the graph would be to measure and plot the displacement at *one* point at *different times* (see Figure 3). You use this graph to find the period.

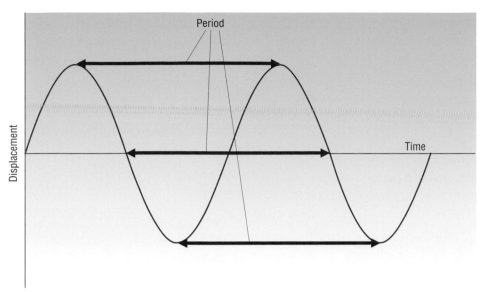

Figure 3 Sine wave plotted against time

The units of frequency are called hertz (abbreviated Hz). This is the same as s^{-1}; it is also called cycles per second. *Note* the unit is written with a lower case letter 'h'. The abbreviation has a capital 'H'.

You can work out frequency from the period using the formula: $f = \dfrac{1}{T}$

e.g. if the period of a sound wave is 0.0035 s

$f = \dfrac{1}{T} = \dfrac{1}{0.0035} = 290$ Hz to two significant figures.

(Notice that the answer is given to 2 significant figures because the information given [$T = 0.0035$ s] is to two significant figures.)

Activity

Figures 4a and 4b are graphs of a repeating irregular wave. From the graphs find the amplitude, wavelength, period and frequency of the wave.

Frequency = $1/(40 \times 10^{-3})$ = 25 Hz
Period = 40 ms
peak to the third.
where the pattern repeats e.g. from the first
NB measurements are made between points
Wavelength = 10 m
Amplitude = 2 cm

Key definitions

The **amplitude** is the maximum displacement. See Figures 1 and 2.

The **wavelength**, λ, is the distance between two similar points on the wave. See Figure 1.

The periodic time or **period**, T, is the time between two similar events. See Figure 3.

The **frequency**, f, is the number of cycles of a wave passing a point in unit time.

Assessment tip

Look at the axes of graphs of waves. Sometimes the horizontal axis is distance, sometimes time. You need a distance axis to measure wavelength and a time axis to measure period.

(a)
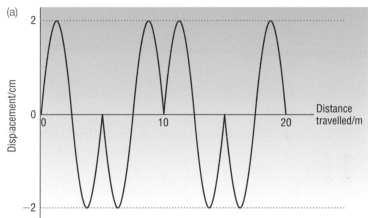

(b)
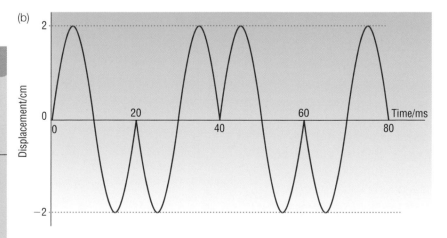

Figure 4 Diagram showing **a** the displacement of an irregular repeating wave against distance travelled and **b** the displacement of an irregular repeating wave against time.

External assessment

By the end of this spread, you should be able to:

✳ describe some more of the features common to all waves

Phase

Imagine that you and your friend are running round a circular running track. You both start at the same time, but your friend starts at a point 100 m ahead of you. If you both run at the same speed the gap between you will stay the same. There is a phase difference between you.

If you both started at the same point and ran together, we would say that you were in phase or had a zero phase difference.

The size of the phase difference can be expressed in different ways, as:
• a distance
• a time difference
• a fraction of a cycle
• an angle in degrees. One complete cycle is 360°
• an angle in radians. One complete cycle is 2π.

If you were running half a circuit behind your friend we would say that you were:
• completely out of phase
• 180° out of phase
• π radians out of phase.

The same idea applies to all kinds of repeating waves.

There is a phase difference between the red and blue waves shown in Figure 1. Notice that the horizontal axis can be shown as an angle not as distance or time.

In Figure 1 the red wave is 45° ahead of the blue wave. The blue wave is 45° behind the red wave.

Activity

In Figure 1:
1 State how many degrees the blue wave is ahead of the red wave.
2 Express the phase difference between the two waves as a fraction of a cycle.
3 Express the phase difference between the two waves in radians.

1 315°. (Imagine you walked into a stadium with a running track and saw two runners, one a short distance behind the other. The runner who appears behind may actually be about to 'lap' the other one so is really a long way ahead)
2 1/8 (or 7/8)
3 π/4 (or 7π/4). Remember one cycle is 2π radians. 1/8th of this is π/4.

Figure 1

Figure 1 Two waves with a 45° phase difference

Wave velocity

Have you ever tried to judge how far away a thunderstorm is by counting the seconds between the lightning flash and the thunder clap? Light travels very much faster than sound. We will meet the exact value of the speed of light later.

For now we can assume that the lightning takes no time at all to travel to where we see it. Any error would be much smaller than our timing error. Sound travels at about 330 m s^{-1}. So if the thunder reaches us 6 s after the lightning, the storm is about 2 km away. This is how we do the calculation:

$$velocity = \frac{distance}{time}$$

Distance = velocity × time = 330 × 6 ≈ 2000 m = 2 km.

Early measurements of the velocity of sound were done in a similar way. They measured the distance between two hilltops. One person fired a gun on one hill and another measured the time between the flash from the gun and the sound.

All waves have a velocity. For repeating waves, we can calculate the velocity from the wavelength and the period. The wavelength is the distance travelled by the wave in the periodic time so:

$$velocity = \frac{distance}{time} = \frac{\lambda}{T}$$

We know from spread 16.1.1 that frequency $f = \frac{1}{T}$, so

$$velocity = f\lambda$$

Worked example

Q: Maria visits her local swimming pool. She estimates that the waves produced by the wave machine are 3 m apart and go past her every 7 s. Find the frequency and velocity of the waves.

Remember to include the units in your answer.

[NB the information in this question is only given to 1 significant figure (s.f.) so answer to 1 s.f.]

A:

$$f = \frac{1}{T} = \frac{1}{7} = 0.14 \text{ Hz} = 0.1 \text{ Hz to 1 significant figure.}$$

The question tells us to answer to 1 s.f. Even if we had not been told we could have judged this because Maria's estimates are only to one significant figure. We normally give our answers to the same number of significant figures as the least precise piece of data we are given.

$$v = f\lambda$$
$$= 0.14 \times 3$$

Notice that for further calculations, we use the value of $f = 0.14$ Hz (to 2 s.f.), then round to 1 s.f. at the end. This is to avoid rounding several times which would increase our errors.

$$v = 0.42 \text{ m s}^{-1}$$
$$= 0.4 \text{ m s}^{-1} \text{ to 1 significant figure.}$$

Activity

Maria hears a sound with a frequency of 512 Hz. She has read that sound travels at 333 m s^{-1} in air but at 1445 m s^{-1} in water. Calculate the wavelength of the sound:
(a) in air
(b) in water.

(a)
$$v = f\lambda$$
$$333 = 512\lambda$$
$$\lambda = \frac{333}{512}$$
$$= 0.650 \text{ m}$$

(b)
$$v = f\lambda$$
$$1445 = 512\lambda$$
$$\lambda = \frac{1445}{512}$$
$$= 2.82 \text{ m to 3 s.f.}$$

External assessment

By the end of this spread, you should be able to:

* describe some features belonging to some waves, but not others

Features belonging to certain types of waves only

Transverse and longitudinal waves

In spread 16.1.1 you imagined that you sent a wave along a rope. The rope moved up and down, but the wave moved horizontally towards your friend. This is an example of a **transverse wave**. Other transverse waves include waves on the surface of water and electromagnetic waves. See Figure 1.

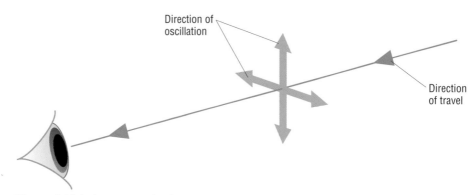

Direction of oscillation

Direction of travel

Figure 1 Light is an example of a transverse wave

Suppose that instead of a rope, you and your friend held a long spring like a 'slinky' spiral. If you moved your end towards and away from your friend you would create a **longitudinal wave**. Other examples of a longitudinal wave are sound and some shock waves.

Polarisation

Think again about the transverse wave you sent along the rope. Instead of moving your end of the rope up and down, you could move it from side to side. The displacement is still at right angles to the wave direction so the wave is still transverse.

You could move your hand at some other angle in between horizontal and vertical. These different directions are called directions of polarisation. A wave that oscillates in all the possible transverse directions at once is called un-polarised.

A wave that oscillates in just one of these directions is called **polarised**.

Electromagnetic waves are transverse, so they can be polarised. For example, light can be polarised by passing it through special materials such as a Polaroid plastic sheet (as used in Polaroid sunglasses). Only light that is polarised in one particular direction can pass through the Polaroid.

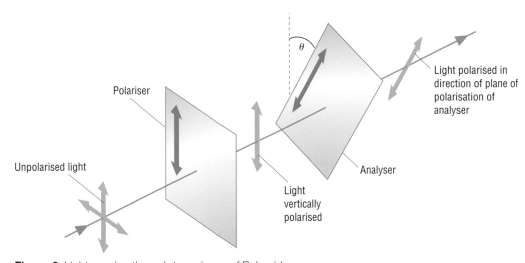

Figure 2 Light passing through two pieces of Polaroid

Light that is polarised at right angles to this direction is completely absorbed by the material and does not pass through.

Light that is polarised at an angle of less than 90° to the direction of polarisation is partly allowed through. We say that the vector components in the direction of polarisation are transmitted. It is probably easier to remember that the closer the direction of polarisation of the light to the direction of the Polaroid, the more light is transmitted.

Figure 2 shows an un-polarised beam of light being polarised by one piece of Polaroid (called the polariser in the diagram) then passing through a second piece of Polaroid (called an analyser in the diagram). Only part of the light transmitted by the first Polaroid also passes through the second. The final ray has the direction of polarisation of the 'analyser'.

Reflected light is partly polarised.

Microwave sources generate polarised waves. A set of metal bars will act on microwaves like a piece of Polaroid acts on light. What happens if you rotate metal bars between a microwave source and detector?

Radio and television transmissions are polarised, because the oscillation of the electric signal is only in the direction of the transmitting aerial. Some transmitting aerials are vertical and others are horizontal. This means that two stations can transmit on the same frequency without interfering with each other. (Usually they will be some distance apart as well.)

It is important to line up your receiving aerial so that:
• it is not only pointing towards the transmitting station; but also
• the bars are lined up vertically or horizontally the same way as your local transmission.

Look at TV aerials near you. Next time you travel to another part of the country look to see if the TV aerials are lined up the same way.

Longitudinal waves cannot be polarised. This is because there is only one possible direction for the displacement. Only transverse waves can be polarised. Sound waves are longitudinal so they cannot be polarised.

Source

For a fuller explanation of your observations in the Polaroid activity see (reference to Physics book in series section 2.4.6)

External assessment

Electromagnetic waves

By the end of this spread, you should be able to:

* describe features unique to electromagnetic waves

You see light which is a type of electromagnetic radiation.

You cook with electromagnetic radiation using a microwave oven or the infrared radiation from a grill. Our long distance telephone calls are carried by microwave links. You use electromagnetic radiation whenever you listen to the radio or watch television. If you have ever had an X-ray image taken in hospital or know anyone who has been examined or treated with gamma rays, these techniques used electromagnetic radiation. If you have been sun tanned, this was done by ultraviolet radiation from the sun – another kind of electromagnetic radiation.

What are electromagnetic waves?

When you speak, the sound waves make air molecules vibrate. The displacement of the wave is the distance moved by the air molecules. With electromagnetic radiation the displacement is not a physical movement, electric and magnetic fields change in size and direction.

You do not need to learn all about electric and magnetic fields, but to help you to understand electromagnetic radiation imagine that you are holding a positively charged object and your friend is holding a similar object a short distance away. Your object would be repelled. (Remember from GCSE that like charges repel.) If your friend swapped his object for a negative one your positively charged object would be attracted. (Unlike charges attract.)

If your friend kept swapping charges you would feel an oscillating force. Oscillating means moving to and fro. (Actually the forces would be very small so you might need some kind of instrument to detect them.) Your friend has sent an oscillating signal and some energy across the gap between you.

A similar effect could be obtained using magnets. In fact, whenever you have an oscillating electric field this creates an oscillating magnetic field and vice versa – hence the term electromagnetic radiation.

Radio waves are one kind of electromagnetic radiation. They are created by sending an oscillating electric signal to a metal rod (a transmitting aerial). This makes electrons (negatively charged) move up and down the rod. This is a bit like your friend swapping positive and negative charges. The receiving aerial in your radio is another metal rod. When the electromagnetic wave reaches your aerial it moves electrons up and down creating a tiny electric signal.

Microwaves can also be made by oscillating electronic signals using special devices.

In practice only radio waves and microwaves are produced by oscillating electric currents. Other types of electromagnetic radiation (ultraviolet, visible light, infrared, X-rays and gamma rays) have frequencies which are much too high. They are produced in other ways. A physicist called James Clerk Maxwell first suggested, in 1873, that light consists of electric and magnetic fields. It was not until some 15 years later that Heinrich Hertz was able to make an oscillator fast enough to produce radio waves and confirm Maxwell's theory. This paved the way for Marconi to develop radio as a means of communication. See Figure 1.

Figure 1 Marconi sent early radio signals

Figure 2 Radio telescope in New Mexico – a modern application of radio

Special features of electromagnetic waves

No medium needed

Electromagnetic waves can travel across a vacuum. For example, light travels across a vacuum from the Sun to reach us. This makes electromagnetic waves different from other kinds of waves you have met.

For example, sound waves need a **medium** to travel in. This is usually air but it can be a solid – have you ever heard your neighbours' music from the other side of a wall? You have already met the idea of sound travelling through water in one of the activities in spread 16.1.2.

Speed

All types of electromagnetic radiation travel at the *same speed in a vacuum*. This is 3.00×10^8 m s^{-1} to three significant figures. You learnt earlier that for examples like lightning, the waves travel across short distances almost instantaneously. This also applies to information carried by radio signals across short distances. However when radio signals are bounced off satellites you sometimes notice a slight delay. The Sun is 1.5×10^{11} m from the Earth, so sunlight takes about 500 s to reach us.

The speed of light is usually represented by the letter c.

In air, electromagnetic radiation travels at almost the same speed as in a vacuum. So for most purposes you can say that all types of electromagnetic radiation travel at the *same speed in air*. The exact values are given in the table below but don't try to remember these figures!

Speed of electromagnetic radiation in a vacuum	299 792 458 m s^{-1}
Speed of electromagnetic radiation in a air	299 702 547 m s^{-1}

Table 1 Speed of electromagnetic radiation

Light slows to about three-quarters of this speed in water, and two-thirds of this speed in glass. The exact speed depends on the type of glass. This difference is important for the study of optical fibres (in a later spread).

Different kinds of electromagnetic radiation and different colours of light slow down by different amounts. The speed of blue light in glass is less than that of red light. One effect of this is that when light goes from air into glass, the blue rays are bent more than the red ones. (See refraction in spreads 16.3.1 and 16.3.2.) This can be used to split white light into the colours of the rainbow.

Frequency and wavelength

You learnt in the previous spread that for all waves, velocity $v = f\lambda$.

For electromagnetic waves we can replace v with c to help us to remember that the whole electromagnetic spectrum has the same speed in a vacuum (and effectively in air). For electromagnetic waves $c = f\lambda$

Different parts of the electromagnetic spectrum vary enormously in frequency, f, and wavelength, λ. As f goes up λ goes down. These differences account for the enormous differences in their properties and how they are made.

Frequencies range from about 100 Hz up to over 10 thousand million million million Hz (10^{22} Hz)

Corresponding wavelengths range from a million metres (10^6 m) down to less than a hundredth of a millionth of a millionth of a metre (10^{-14} m).

Even visible light, which is only a tiny fraction of the overall electromagnetic spectrum varies in wavelength from about 4×10^{-7} m (blue) to about 7×10^{-7} m (red).

Key definition

A **medium** is any material that a wave travels through. Electromagnetic waves are different from other kinds of wave because they don't need a medium.

External assessment

By the end of this spread, you should be able to:

✱ identify and describe qualitatively the similarities and differences of the production, detection, and properties of each of the regions of the electromagnetic spectrum

Regions of electromagnetic radiation

You are familiar with the visible spectrum and the so-called seven colours of the rainbow. The division into seven colours is arbitrary and the spectrum is continuous. The visible spectrum is just one small part of the much wider electromagnetic spectrum. You should recall the regions of the electromagnetic spectrum and their order in frequency and wavelength from your GCSE studies. These are shown in Figure 1. Like the seven colours of the rainbow these regions are arbitrary, there is overlap between them and the divisions are not sharp.

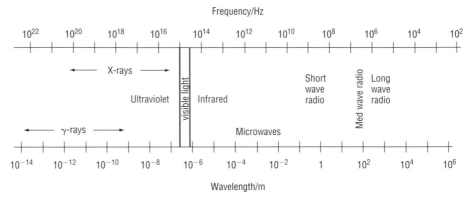

Figure 1 The electromagnetic spectrum

Name	How they are produced	Properties	How they are detected
γ-rays	Produced by nuclear decay in the nucleus of atoms. Large drops between energy levels produce wave packets with large amounts of energy. Also produced in nuclear accelerators.	Although they are produced in different ways, γ- and X-rays are very similar. They have similar properties. They *penetrate objects* – even certain thicknesses of lead or concrete. (This is why they are used in radiography and radiotherapy. We will meet this again in a later spread.) Absorption depends on atomic mass so more is absorbed by bones than by soft tissue. They cause *ionisation*. As we will see later ionisation in living cells is the reason they can be hazardous, but this property can also be put to good use, for example in detectors that use ionisation to produce an electronic signal. Cause fluorescence and *phosphorescence*. Cause *photoelectric emission*. They are *reflected and diffracted by crystals*.	Although they are produced in different ways, γ- and X-rays can be detected in similar ways. Photography – their energy causes chemical changes in film in the same way as light. Special devices detect the ionisation caused by the radiation. These include the ionisation chamber and the Geiger counter. Phosphorescence – for example, zinc sulfide will glow where it has been hit by radiation.
X-rays	Produced when fast-moving charged particles are stopped suddenly. In X-ray machines electrons are fired at a metal target. X-rays are also produced as a by-product in other devices such as cathode-ray tubes. (These are used in older televisions and computer monitors which have special leaded glass screens to protect you.) Two separate processes make X-rays at the same time. In one process it is the actual slowing down of the electrons that converts energy into X-rays. In the other process energy is first given to the innermost electrons in the target atoms. It is then re-emitted as X-rays.		

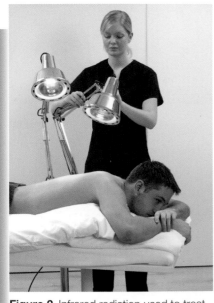

Figure 2 Infrared radiation used to treat sports injuries

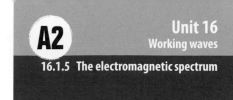

Name	How they are produced	Properties	How they are detected
Ultraviolet	Produced when energy is given to the orbital electrons in atoms. It is re-emitted as ultraviolet radiation. This occurs in high voltage gas discharge tubes such as the mercury vapour lamp. It is also produced by very hot objects such as the Sun.	Absorbed by glass and in the atmosphere by ozone. Passes through quartz and, to some extent, water. Causes chemical reactions such as sun tan. Ionises atoms.	Photography – their energy causes chemical changes in film in the same way as light. Photoelectric cells – their energy causes electrons to be emitted by metals and these can be counted electronically. Fluorescence.
Visible light	Produced when energy is given to the outer electrons in atoms. It is re-emitted as visible radiation. This occurs in gas discharge tubes such as the sodium lamps. It is also produced by hot objects such as a furnace.	Detected by the eye. Causes chemical reactions. Light cannot penetrate most solids because gaps between the energy states of their molecules are equal to the energy carried by the light waves. Penetrates glass and water	Eye. Photography. Photocell.
Infrared	Produced when energy is given to the outer electrons in atoms and molecules. It is re-emitted as infrared radiation. It is also produced by warm and cold objects such as our bodies and our surroundings – in fact any object above absolute zero.	Strongly absorbed by glass and water. Less scattered than visible light by atmospheric particles. Absorbed by water vapour, carbon dioxide and ozone. This limits its usefulness in astronomy. Absorbers of infrared in the atmosphere, such as carbon dioxide, are responsible for the greenhouse effect. Increases in these absorbers cause global warming.	Photography using special film or sensors. Heating effect (e.g. radiometer). Photoconductive cells.
Microwaves	Alternating current in special electronic devices.	Penetrate glass very easily. Strongly absorbed by water, fat and metals. Used for: (a) radar communication (b) analysis of fine details of molecular and atomic structure (c) demonstration of all wave properties on macroscopic scale.	Special electronic devices.
Radio waves	Alternating current in radio aerials.	Absorbed by metals. Do not penetrate far through soils, rocks and materials like concrete. (This is why mobile phones and radios do not work well in tunnels or underground car parks.)	Receiving aerial connected to tuned electronic circuit (i.e. a radio receiver).

Table 1 Properties of the electromagnetic spectrum

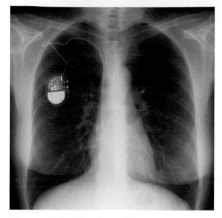

Figure 3 Application of X-rays – image of human chest with pacemaker

Figure 4 Infrared electromagnetic radiation is sent down optical fibres in telephone systems

External assessment

By the end of this spread, you should be able to:

✱ **describe how the spectrum of 'hot-body' radiation varies with temperature**
✱ **describe how the total radiation given off by a surface varies with temperature**

Have you ever seen a blacksmith put a piece of iron into a furnace? If it is taken out of the furnace after a short while it glows red hot and can be seen in the dark.

In this spread you will learn about the radiation given off by cold objects as well as hot ones.

Infrared radiation and temperature

You cannot see infrared radiation but you can sense it – as you will know if you have put your hand near a fire. (Don't do this on purpose!) The radiation heats our skin and the nerve endings in our skin detect the temperature difference.

You have seen objects that are red hot or even white hot. They emit radiation in the visible part of the spectrum as well as infrared.

Cooler objects also emit electromagnetic radiation but only waves with shorter wavelengths that you cannot feel. This is infrared radiation.

Even very cold objects emit infrared radiation. The temperature in space is a few kelvin (around −270°C). The thermal radiation emitted at these temperatures overlaps with the microwave region of the electromagnetic spectrum. It is called cosmic microwave background (CMB).

The remote control on your television uses infrared radiation. So also do some wireless headphones and wireless local computer networks (LANs). You can only go about 10 m from the base station and components need to be in sight of each other.

Spectrum of wavelengths

Objects don't just emit radiation at one wavelength. They emit a wide continuous spectrum of wavelengths and corresponding frequencies.

As temperature goes up, the intensity of radiation at all frequencies goes up.

Figure 2 is a graph showing the spectra of radiation for the Sun and a filament lamp.

Figure 1 TV remote controls use infrared radiation

Activity

Try this experiment with infrared. Hold a glass of water in front of the remote control and try to turn on the television.

Why do you think infrared detectors have difficulty detecting warm bodies in fog?

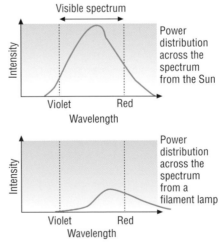

Figure 2 Comparing the spectrum for the Sun with that for a tungsten filament lamp

You may meet these graphs with intensity plotted against frequency. The shape is the same but it is flipped from left to right.

Figure 3 is a graph showing the spectra of radiation emitted at a number of temperatures. Special scales called logarithmic scales have been used on this graph. This is so that wide variations in values can be shown. You do not need to learn exactly how logarithmic scales are drawn but notice that they are more bunched together at higher values. Using a logarithmic scale makes the shape of the graph look slightly different from Figure 2.

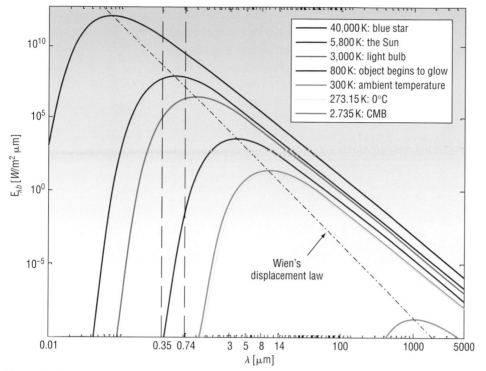

Figure 3 Comparing the spectrum of radiation produced by bodies at a number of temperatures

Peak wavelength

Notice on the graphs in Figure 3, that for each temperature the graph has a peak at a particular wavelength.

The radiation emitted by your body has its peak at a wavelength of about 10^{-5} m.

Objects at a higher temperature have lower peak wavelengths. The formula relating peak wavelength λ_{peak} to temperature T (in kelvin) is called Wien's law and is given below, but you are not expected to remember the exact formula:

$$\lambda_{peak} = \frac{2.9 \times 10^{-3}}{T} m$$

Red hot and white hot

All objects emit electromagnetic radiation. For objects at room temperature and colder this radiation is invisible so we cannot see them in the dark.

In the introduction to this spread, we asked if you have ever seen a blacksmith put a piece of iron into a furnace. If it is taken out of the furnace after a short while it glows red hot and can be seen in the dark. *As well as* emitting infrared radiation the emission spectrum now includes the red end of the visible spectrum.

If the iron is heated to a higher temperature more of the visible spectrum will be emitted *in addition* to the infrared and red. It will become orange, yellow and, if it is hot enough, white. White light includes all the colours of the visible spectrum.

Look again at Figure 3. Notice that the curve for the Sun includes some ultraviolet radiation. You could say it is 'blue-hot'. We normally think of blue as a cold colour. Why do you think this is?

Our eyes have evolved to be sensitive to the radiation reaching us from the Sun. Can you explain why our eyes are not sensitive to ultraviolet?

External assessment

By the end of this spread, you should be able to:

* describe how thermal imaging cameras produce images corresponding to surface temperatures
* outline the advantages of thermal detecting/imaging systems

In this spread we complete our work on infrared spectra then look at how infrared radiation can be used in one of its most important applications.

Black body radiation

The radiation discussed in the previous spread was for a perfect black body. This is an object that would absorb all the radiation falling on it. It is also the most efficient emitter of radiation. Grey or white objects will emit less radiation but the shapes of the curves will be very similar.

The Leslie Cube

The Leslie Cube is a hollow metal cube used in a classic demonstration. It shows the effect of different surfaces on the total radiation emitted. One outside surface is matt black, one is shiny black, another is white, a fourth is a shiny silvery colour.

The cube is filled with water and heated. The infrared radiation given off by each of the sides is measured in turn. This is done using a device called a thermopile. The larger the amount of radiation falling on the thermopile, the greater is its output voltage.

The apparatus can also be used to demonstrate that the total radiation given off varies with temperature.

How thermal images are made

Thermal imaging focuses the infrared radiation given off by an object using a lens. The image is detected by several thousand detector elements arranged in a 'focal plane array'. The more rows and columns (the fill factor), the better is the sensitivity.

The picture of the infrared image is called a thermogram. The image is made into an electronic signal. The signal is processed and then displayed on a standard video monitor. The display uses either different shades of grey or false colours for each temperature (see Figure 1).

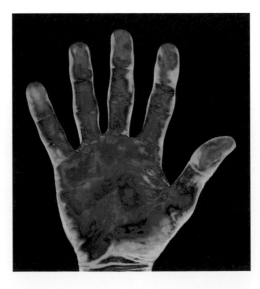

Figure 1 Thermal image displayed in colour

Viewed in a grey scale, hotter things appear whiter, cooler things appear blacker, although that can be reversed (see Figure 2). The sensitivity can be adjusted, so that light greys and white occur at lower or higher temperatures.

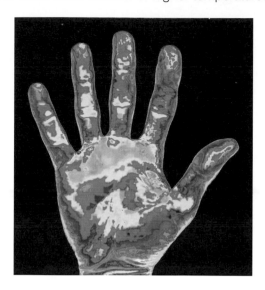

Figure 2 Thermal image displayed in black and white

Interpreting the image

Thermal images show surface temperature. However sometimes surface temperature is affected by what is underneath.

Metal and glass reflect infrared, so some 'hot-spots' may actually be reflected radiation.

If subjects wear glasses, the lenses appear black because glass and optical plastics cannot transmit infrared.

Resolution and range

The resolution of images is a measure of how much detail we can see.

Spatial resolution is a measure of how well we can distinguish between objects at slightly different places. One factor that limits spatial resolution is wavelength. We cannot distinguish between objects closer together than the wavelength we are viewing them with. Infrared wavelengths are longer than visible wavelengths so this can limit resolution.

Thermal resolution is a measure of how you can distinguish between objects at similar temperatures. If two objects are at the same temperature you can't distinguish between them on a thermal image.

Normally, cameras can sense temperatures from –20 to 2000 °C. They can detect 0.2 °C changes in temperature. Specially cooled devices can detect 0.1 °C temperature differences at a distance of 300 m.

One problem is that the camera itself emits radiation. In some cameras cooling is used to reduce this. These 'cryogenically cooled' devices are expensive and more fragile.

Detectors

Thermal detectors respond to incident radiation by raising their temperature. Types include thermocouples, bolometers, pyroelectric detectors and liquid crystals. Their response does not depend on the wavelength. They work well at room temperature.

Photonic detectors are made from semiconductors. Radiation excites electrons in the material. They are more sensitive and respond faster than thermal detectors but normally require cryogenic cooling and are more expensive. Temperatures used are normally between 4 K (liquid helium temperature) and 110 K. Liquid nitrogen is often used. This has a temperature of 77 K.

> **Assessment tip**
>
> Don't confuse thermal imaging with image enhancement.
>
> Image enhancement works by collecting tiny amounts of light, and amplifying them. This is **not** the same thing as thermal imaging which works well in complete darkness.

External assessment

③ Applications of thermal imaging

By the end of this spread, you should be able to:

✳ outline the advantages of thermal detecting/imaging systems
✳ explain applications of thermal imaging

Thermal imaging has a surprisingly wide range of uses. In this spread you are given an overview

Assessment tip

The list of applications of thermal imaging given below is long but not exhaustive. You should learn the principles of, and how to apply, them to any example you come across. Learn details of a few examples of specific applications.

Overview of applications

In all applications you meet consider the following questions:
• Why is a normal image not appropriate?
• What is at a different temperature so will show up in the infrared picture?
• Why is it at a different temperature?

Application	Details
Aerial archaeology	Vegetation covering sites may be at a different temperature as the land underneath has been previously built on.
Agriculture	Different types of trees or crops have different infrared 'signatures'
Animal counts	It can be difficult to count animals on the ground if they are spread over large area, especially in bad weather. The natural camouflage of animals does not work at longer wavelengths. Warm-blooded animals show up against the cooler background of the earth. They can be found and counted from the air.
Astronomy	Telescopes are equipped with infrared sensors to observe dusty regions of space invisible with light e.g. molecular clouds. They can detect planets and highly red-shifted objects. We get information from space in most regions of the electromagnetic spectrum. Look up the Spitzer Space Telescope on the Internet.
Document examination	Different types of inks may have different thermal properties and therefore show up in an infrared image. Similarly: • Areas of a paper where writing has been rubbed out or overwritten can be seen. • Writing on documents that have been burned may be visible to the infrared camera. • Art works can be inspected because we can see through old varnish.
Electrical apparatus inspection	High resistance or high current flow can show problems in electrical systems. They cause heating. This can be detected with a thermal imaging camera.
Energy audits	Where buildings are poorly insulated they will be warmer on the outside on a cold day. Thermal imaging cameras can be used to check the how good the insulation is.  **Figure 1** How good is the insulation?
Environmental impact surveys	If a liquid is released into a river it can be seen in a thermal image because the temperatures are almost always different. It may be possible to follow the path of the liquid back to the source. Applications include: • Finding illegal discharges. • Tracking oil spills or other types of pollution. • Monitoring warm water discharged by power plant cooling towers. • Monitoring the output of rainwater drains. • Monitoring the output from sewage treatment plant. • Checking seepage of ground water into waterways. • Measuring how much fresh water goes into salt water estuaries.
Firefighting	Some parts of a building on fire will be hotter than others. If firemen know where these are it can help them to put out the fire. Thermal imaging will show up the hottest areas.
Fluid levels in containers	The fluid may already be at a different temperature to the container, or the heat capacity of the fluid will make it slower to change in temperature if the surroundings get hotter or colder. Difference in temperature of an opaque container will show up in a thermal image.

Application	Details
Forensic science	Thermal imaging can show where ground or walls have been disturbed e.g. to bury something. This is used by the police to find bodies, money and drugs hidden by criminals.
Hunting	Animals being hunted may be camouflaged in visible light, but their body heat will show up in an infrared camera.
Mechanical inspection	Mechanical systems such as motors, pumps and other rotating equipment and conveyors are likely to overheat if they are not properly oiled, not lined up properly, or if cooling systems have failed. A survey with a thermal imaging camera will show up hot spots.
Medical imaging	Infrared radiation may pass through the skin so that doctors can see underneath. Parts of the body may be hotter or colder than normal as a result of medical conditions. This will show up in an infrared image, where the body may appear normal in visible light. There are many specific medical imaging applications.
Military and police target detection and acquisition	The warmth of people's bodies will show up on an infrared camera. Search and rescue operations use aerial and ground based infrared cameras. They may be disabled or unable to move to an area where they can be seen by visible light. People targets sometimes do not want to be seen.
Mould and moisture detection.	See roofing inspection.
Non destructive testing	Test material is subjected to a wave of infrared radiation. If the wave meets a flaw in the material the progress of the heat energy is disturbed and the uneven temperature can be detected by an infrared camera. This requires a highly sensitive and fast camera.
Observing wildlife	Animals are likely to be at a warmer temperature than their surroundings and different parts of the animal will be at different temperatures. The temperatures of some parts of animals may change at different times of day or night. Thermal imaging is particularly helpful in observing nocturnal animals or animals living underground.
Process monitoring	The temperature of products in a factory can tell us whether the process is going on normally. Examples of processes where this may apply are: • paper manufacture • glass manufacture • plastic manufacture • sheet metal manufacture • food during processing packaging etc. Infrared cameras can be used to monitor this.
Pest control	See roofing inspection.
Product testing	Temperature analysis of systems such as brakes, airbags, electronic controls.
Roofing inspection (especially flat roofs)	Used to find damage before leaks occur. The thermal properties of moist and dry roof areas are different. After dark, the roof cools down, but wet areas of roof insulation stay warm longer. Thermal imaging finds the areas where moisture is trapped below the surface in insulation material. Repairs can be done early and limited to the damaged area. Termites need moisture to survive. Termites bring and create moisture in wall panels and structural and decorative timbers. Thermal imaging can be used to identify the presence of this moisture.
Weather forecasting	Images show the infrared radiation emitted by cloud tops and the surfaces of land or seas.
Wide area thermal mapping	Underground geothermal activity can be a problem in some parts of the world especially if road or building development is planned. Thermal imaging can detect the temperature changes caused by this. Forest fires and fires below ground can be monitored. In the United States Indian trails have compacted the ground where they cross the desert. The compacted ground is likely to be at a different temperature and will show up in a thermal image. The ground above underground streams is likely to be at a different temperature from the surroundings. Surveys can find the paths of such steams and locate leaks.

Table 1 Examples of applications

Figure 2 Weather satellite infrared picture

By the end of this spread, you should be able to:

✻ define refractive index
✻ measure the refractive index of a glass block

Figure 3 Ruler divisions underwater look smaller

Refraction

You may have noticed that objects like sticks appear to bend as they enter water (see Figure 1). Notice that a side view (Figure 2) shows that it really is straight.

Figure 1 Photograph showing a pencil partly immersed in water, viewed from above

Figure 2 Photograph showing a pencil partly immersed in water, viewed from the side

A related effect is that swimming pools look shallower than they really are. Look at Figure 3. The divisions on the ruler below the water level appear smaller than the divisions above.

These effects are due to **refraction**. The direction of light rays changes as they enter or leave different substances such as water, plastic or glass. Refraction is caused by the fact that light travels at different speeds in different materials. You may remember from spread 16.1.2 that light travels at 3.00×10^8 m s^{-1} in air. Light travels at about three-quarters of this speed in water, and two-thirds of this speed in plastics and glass. The exact speed will vary according to the type of glass or plastic.

Refractive Index

How much a ray of light changes direction depends on:
* the two materials
* the **angle of incidence**.

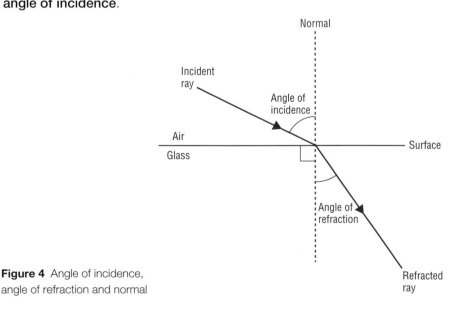

Figure 4 Angle of incidence, angle of refraction and normal

Experiment to measure refractive index

- There are a number of experiments you can do to measure the refractive index of a glass block. This is one of the simpler ones. See Figure 5.
- Put a piece of A3 paper on the bench. Draw a line, a little longer than the block, near the centre.
- Place a ruler on the line. Place the block against the ruler.
- Move the ruler to the opposite side of the block. Remove the block. Draw a line along the edge of the ruler. (This may seem awkward, but is more accurate than simply drawing round the block.)
- Draw a normal to one of the lines.
- Place the block between the lines.
- Arrange a ray box so that a ray enters the block where you have drawn the normal. Make sure that the ray comes out on the other side of the block.
- Mark the paths of the rays going in and out of the block by marking crosses on the rays. The crosses should as far apart as possible.
- Take away the block. Draw lines to show the path of the ray entering, through and leaving the block.
- Measure the angle of incidence, i, and the **angle of refraction, r**.
- You can find the refractive index, n, by calculating $n = \dfrac{\sin i}{\sin r}$.
- For better results repeat with different angles of incidence and plot a graph of $\sin i$ against $\sin r$. The gradient will be the refractive index.

Key definition

Angle of refraction is the angle between the refracted ray and the 'normal'. The refracted ray is the deviated ray that comes from the surface. (See Figure 4.)

Refractive index $n = \dfrac{\sin i}{\sin r}$

A common mistake is to think that the angle of incidence and angle of refraction are the angles between the rays and the surface.

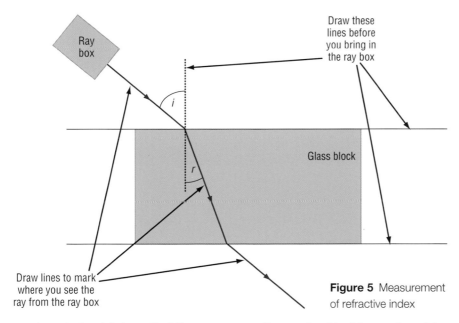

Figure 5 Measurement of refractive index

Draw these lines before you bring in the ray box

Draw lines to mark where you see the ray from the ray box

Ray box

Glass block

Your experiment should show that if you measure the angle of incidence, i, and the angle of refraction, r, for a particular pair of materials, and calculate the value of $\dfrac{\sin i}{\sin r}$ this value will be constant for all values of i. The ratio is called the **refractive index**, n.

Exercise in finding refractive index

Measure the angle of incidence, i, and angle of refraction, r, in Figure 4.

Use the expression refractive index $n = \dfrac{\sin i}{\sin r}$ to calculate the refractive index of the glass.

Note: refractive index is a ratio, so it has no units.

From the diagram: $i = 63°$; $r = 36°$.

---

refractive index $n = \dfrac{\sin i}{\sin r} = \dfrac{\sin 63}{\sin 36} = 1.5$

Assessment tip

By the end of this spread, you should be able to:

✳ calculate refractive index
✳ relate refractive index and wave velocity
✳ describe total internal reflection and critical angle in terms of refraction at glass–air and glass–glass interfaces
✳ measure the critical angle of a sample of glass and relate this to the refractive index

Refractive index and the speed of light

You learnt earlier that refraction is caused by the fact that light travels at different speeds in different materials. In fact the refractive index, n, is equal to the ratio:

$$\text{refractive index of glass } n = \frac{v_{air}}{v_{glass}}$$

Where the:

velocity of light in air = v_{air} = 3.0×10^8 m s^{-1} to 2 s.f.
velocity of light in glass = v_{glass} = 2.0×10^8 m s^{-1} for a typical glass.

(a)
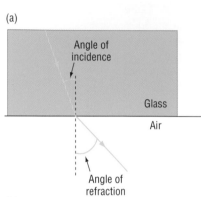

(b)
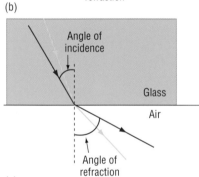

(c)
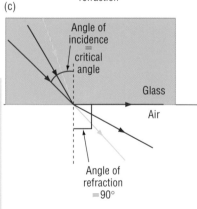

(d)
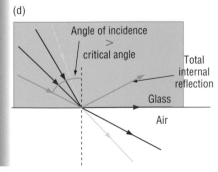

Activity

1 Use the equation and values above to find the refractive index of glass.
2 Find the refractive index for light travelling from air into water.

Velocity of light in air = v_{air} = 3.00×10^8 m s^{-1} to 2 s.f.
Velocity of light in water = v_{water} = 2.25×10^8 m s^{-1} for water.

2 refractive index $n = \dfrac{v_{air}}{v_{water}} = \dfrac{3.0 \times 10^8}{2.25 \times 10^8} = 1.3$

1 refractive index $n = \dfrac{v_{air}}{v_{glass}} = \dfrac{3.0 \times 10^8}{2.0 \times 10^8} = 1.5$

Total internal reflection

Think about a ray of light travelling inside a glass block and meeting the surface.

• As the ray emerges from the block it is deviated away from the normal (see Figure 1a).
• If you increased the angle of incidence inside the glass, the angle of refraction outside the block would increase (see Figure 1b). In practice some of the light is always reflected back into the glass. The angle of reflection is always equal to the angle of incidence.
• If you carried on increasing the angle of incidence inside the glass, the angle of refraction would grow to 90°. This special value of the angle of incidence inside the glass is called the **critical angle**, C (see Figure 1c).
• If you increased the angle of incidence any more, the ray would no longer emerge from the surface. All the energy would go into the reflected ray, which would become a lot brighter. The ray has been totally internally reflected (see Figure 1d).

Figure 1 Diagrams showing **a** light passing from a glass block into air; **b** the effect of a bigger angle of incidence inside the glass – the angle of refraction outside the glass increases; **c** the effect of an even bigger, and special, angle of incidence inside the glass called the critical angle – the angle of refraction grows to 90°; **d** the effect of further increase in the angle of incidence inside the glass – the ray is totally internally reflected

External assessment

Relating critical angle to refractive index

Think about the reverse of the ray shown in red in Figure 1c.

A ray travelling into the block almost parallel to the surface (angle of incidence, $i = 90°$) enters the block at the critical angle (angle of refraction, r = critical angle, C)

You have already learnt that $n = \dfrac{\sin i}{\sin r}$

In this special case $\quad n = \dfrac{\sin 90}{\sin C} = \dfrac{1}{\sin C}$

This can also be written $\quad \sin C = \dfrac{1}{n}$

Measurement of critical angle of a semicircular glass or Perspex block using a ray box

- Lie a piece of A3 paper on the bench and draw a straight line a little longer than the block near the centre.
- Place a ruler on the line and place the straight side of the semicircular block against the ruler.
- Mark the centre of the circle on the paper.
- Aim a ray of light from the ray box through the curved surface of the block so that it meets the straight surface at the *centre of the circle.*
- Notice that the ray passes though the curved surface along the normal. This is so that there is no deviation at the curved surface as the ray enters the block.
- Rotate the paper and block about the centre of the block so that the angle of incidence inside the block increases.
- Continue increasing the angle until the emerging ray just disappears. Mark the path of the ray inside the block and the normal.
- Measure the angle between the ray inside the block and the normal (angle of incidence inside the block). This is the critical angle, C.
- You can use the formula $n = \dfrac{1}{\sin C}$ to find the refractive index of the block.

Activity

Calculate the critical angle for light travelling in glass of refractive index 1.5.

$\sin C = \dfrac{1}{n} = \dfrac{1}{1.5} = 0.667$

$C = 42°$ to 2 s.f.

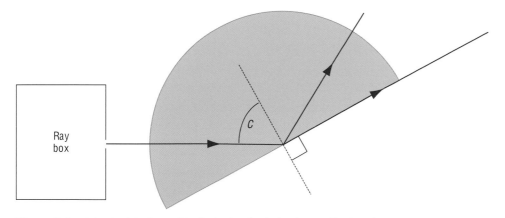

Figure 2 Semicircular block used to find refractive index from critical angle

Ray
box

External assessment

259

By the end of this spread, you should be able to:

✳ describe how total internal reflection prevents light from leaking through the sides of the fibres
✳ describe some applications of optical fibres

How optical fibres work

Under the right conditions, a ray of light can be trapped inside a piece of glass. Each time it meets a surface it is totally internally reflected. You would see none of the light escaping though the surface to the air outside.

Optical fibres are very thin strands of plastic or glass. Light is totally internally reflected each time it meets the curved surface. It is reflected many times as it passes along the fibre, until it comes out at the far end (see Figure 1).

Notice also that the light is refracted as it enters and leaves the fibre i.e. it bends towards the normal as it enters and away from the normal as it leaves.

This only works if:
- The material outside the fibre has a lower refractive index than the glass. This means that light travels more slowly inside the fibre than outside.
- The angle of incidence must be greater than the critical angle. If the angle of incidence is less than the critical angle some of the light escapes through the surface.

Figure 1 Light travelling along a simple optical fibre

Applications of optical fibres

Communications

Optical fibres have revolutionised telecommunications. Optical fibres replace metal cables for data transmission. Signals are coded as high frequency digital pulses of light. These pulses carry data along the fibres. This is used in telephone systems, computer networks and to send video data.

Lasers produce the very short pulses. Infrared wavelengths are used, typically around 1.5 μm or 1.3 μm. These wavelengths are chosen because losses in silica glass fibres are least. Wavelengths of 800–900 nm have also been used.

In some cases data is sent over short distances. For example in local area networking of computers (e.g. within a group of buildings).

Optical fibre systems have also been developed to work over long distances. In this case the fibres are always made of glass, because less light is lost (less attenuation). These systems are used for long distance telephone links and cable television. Attenuation is the reduction in the strength of a signal which occurs, for example, as it passes along a cable or optical fibre.

Even with the best systems, signals get weaker after they have travelled large distances. To correct this, repeater stations are placed every so often along the cable. They detect the signal, amplify it and transmit it along the next section.

Repeater stations are used in both traditional and optical fibre communications. In optical fibre systems the repeater stations can be further apart than in traditional electrical cables. Signals can be sent through optical fibres over distances up to 50 km between repeaters.

Optical fibre systems are used for most long-distance transmissions, but BT still usually uses electrical cables for the final connection to your home.

Case study

The final connection to your home, school or college is sometimes called the 'last mile'. We are beginning to see 'fibre to the home' (FTTH). In Japan, private Internet users can have optical fibre connections with data rates of 100 Mbit s^{-2}. This is much higher than current electrical telephone lines.

Advantages

Optical fibres have the following advantages compared to traditional electrical cables for communications:

- Very large information capacity. The frequency of transmission is very high, sometimes as much as 40 Gb s^{-1}. This means that each fibre can carry many channels.
- Low material costs.
- Small cable size. Fibre saves space in cable ducts because a single fibre can carry much more data than a single electrical cable.
- Negligible crosstalk.
- High immunity to interference.
- Complete electrical isolation.
- Large repeater spacing.
- Wiretapping is more difficult.

Disadvantage

Compared to traditional cables, optical fibres for communications are expensive to produce and install.

Lighting

Optical fibre lighting systems are normally made up of a white or coloured light source, a number of optical fibre cables, joined together at one end to form a harness and end fittings which sometimes have domed lenses so that the light can be focussed and directed. Special fittings are available suitable for submersion in water.

There are three main reasons why optical fibres are used in lighting systems:

- For safety reasons. Electrical wiring can be dangerous in wet areas or where sparks could cause a fire or explosion.
- To light up awkward places.
- For decorative reasons.

Case study

A chemical factory making plastic materials uses large quantities of inflammable solvents.

To reduce the risk of fires and explosions caused by electrical wiring, all telephones and computers are connected by optical fibres rather than wires.

Activity

State and explain *two* reasons why optical fibres are used for carrying telephone signals.

Case study

Optical fibre lighting systems are particularly good for lighting wet areas where electrical cables are hazardous. They are sometimes used to light swimming pools both above and below the water.

A single lamp can be placed in an accessible dry place. Fibres create points of light at a number of end fittings. The end fittings can be in a wet area, under water, and in places high above the ground where it would be difficult to replace lamps.

The system is safe because the electric power source is away from the wet area.

One lamp can be used to light a number of different locations. This saves maintenance costs and energy use.

Figure 2 Swimming pool illuminated by fibre optics

External assessment

By the end of this spread, you should be able to:

* explain the meaning of coherent and incoherent optical fibre bundles
* describe further applications of optical fibres

More applications of optical fibres

Lighting (continued)

Optical fibre systems are used to light instrument panels, display cabinets and rooms.

For example instrument panels in cars include a number of gauges such as a speedometer. In older systems these were lit by filament lamps behind them. If you can imagine trying to reach in behind to replace a bulb in one of these panels you will understand the advantage of a system that is easier to service.

Light emitting diodes (LEDs) are often used as the light sources for applications like instrument panels.

Filters can be fitted in the light sources to remove ultraviolet and infrared wavelengths. Ultraviolet filters are important in applications like museum display cabinets where ultraviolet light could make the colours of specimens or artwork fade. Another benefit is that this lighting causes less heating of the display.

In room lighting systems, just one light source can be used to power a number of emitters (typically between 10 and 25, up to 800) (see Figure 1). This saves on electricity as well as maintenance compared to conventional lighting.

There are disadvantages. If the single light source fails it will affect a number of emitters. The cost of a fibre optic lighting system is usually higher than a conventional system.

Figure 2 A simple example of decorative lighting

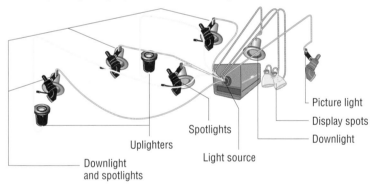

Figure 1 Optical fibres used for room lighting

A simple decorative use of optical fibres is in table lamps such as the one shown in Figure 2. Lamps like these are often used in Christmas decorations.

Endoscopes

In industry, engineers need to inspect places that are difficult or dangerous to reach. For example, they may need to see inside engines, or places that are hot, very cold, radioactive, or contain toxic fumes.

Doctors sometimes need to inspect inside our bodies to carry out a diagnosis. It is much better if this can be done without the surgeon's knife!

Figure 3 A Customs and Excise officer uses an endoscope to check a cruiser water tank for hidden drugs

Endoscopes are used to produce images of inaccessible places (see Figure 3). An **incoherent** (see below) optical fibre bundle takes light from the source to the subject. The same cable includes a **coherent** (see below) optical fibre bundle. This senses the pattern of light at the object and transmits it to the eyepiece. The eyepiece can be replaced by a camera to photograph the image.

In medicine, different kinds of endoscope are used for examining different parts of the body. For example, one application is to examine internal organs such as the digestive tract. In this case a flexible fibre optic instrument is swallowed by the patient. Some endoscopes also include instruments for taking tissue samples from the site being examined.

Some surgical procedures can be performed using fine instruments introduced through the endoscope. Keyhole surgery using endoscopes is safer for some conditions. Recovery times are shorter and it is also cheaper than conventional surgery.

A common misunderstanding is to think that endoscopes have a camera at the far end. In fact there is just a lens at the end of the cable. The optical fibres bring the image to the outside where it can be viewed either with an eyepiece, a display screen or a camera.

Coherent and incoherent optical fibre bundles

Optical fibres are used for many different jobs. In most cases groups of fibres are bundled together.

In cases like optical fibres it does not matter in what order the fibres are arranged at each end. These are called incoherent bundles. The individual strands are normally about 50–100 μm in diameter.

In an endoscope, each strand of fibre detects one pixel of the light from the object. If incoherent bundles were used, the order of the pixels would be randomly arranged at the image end, producing a jumbled up picture. It is important that the fibres are arranged in the same order at each end. These are called coherent bundles. The individual strands in endoscopes are normally about 10 μm in diameter.

Coherent bundles are also necessary for communications. If the arrangement of the fibres was not the same at each end of the bundle there would be chaos! You would find yourself speaking to the wrong person on the telephone. Your computer network would get all the computers mixed up.

Activity

1 Some fibres are made of plastic material called PMMA. This has a refractive index of 1.49.
   (i) Find the velocity of light in PMMA.
   (ii) Find the critical angle for light at a PMMA–air interface
        ($c = 3.00 \times 10^8$ m s^{-1}).

2 A lighting supplier installs optical fibre lighting using unclad glass fibres under water in a pool. Explain why you would expect total internal reflection to occur under water. Describe how the critical angle would change when the fibre goes from air into water ($c_{air} = 3.00 \times 10^8$ m s^{-1}, $c_{water} = 2.25 \times 10^8$ m s^{-1}, $c_{glass} = 2.00 \times 10^8$ m s^{-1}).

3 Suggest *two* applications for which incoherent bundles are unsuitable. Explain why coherent bundles must be used.

---

1 (i) 2.01×10^8 m s^{-1}, (ii) $42.2°$

2 Light travels more slowly in fibres than in water. Difference in speeds is less for glass/water than glass/air so refractive index is less so critical angle is greater.

3 Endoscopes: Picture would be jumbled up if incoherent bundles would be used. Telephone cables: Telephone calls were connected to wrong people if incoherent bundles were used.

By the end of this spread, you should be able to:

* explain why step-index fibres are coated with glass of lower refractive index
* describe how and why the shape of a square wave signal is degraded in multimode fibres
* explain how this degradation can be overcome with graded-index or monomode fibres
* use and understand binary coding
* understand that ASCII code can be used to convert a short text message to binary signals

Construction of optical fibres

You can send light along any piece of glass tube. However there is likely to be leakage through imperfections in the surface. The simplest optical fibres used for communications are made of two layers of glass or plastic. They have a core with a diameter from 50 to 200 μm. This is covered with another layer called the cladding, typically 25 μm thick. The cladding is covered with a protective sheath, usually made of plastic.

This is called a 'step-index' fibre because there is a sudden change (or step) in the refractive index between the core and the cladding. The refractive index of the cladding is lower than that of the core. Total internal reflection keeps the light rays inside the core.

Step-index fibres have the disadvantage that light rays travel different distances as they pass along the fibre. The distance depends on the angle at which they enter. Rays travelling parallel to the axis have a shorter journey than ones that zigzag along. See Figure 1(a). Parts of a signal transmitted at the same moment arrive spread out over a period of time. A sharp square wave signal becomes degraded (see Figure 2). This is called *multimode* or *multipath* distortion.

Step-index fibres are cheap. They are still used for short distances such as in local area computer networks (LANs).

Activity

Connect a piece of optical fibre to a light source and the other end to a photodiode. Observe the effect of switching the light source on and off.

Can you send a Morse code message to your friend?

If you do not have access to a simple fibre optics kit you can send light from a torch along a stream of water. Tape a torch to one end of a jam jar. Punch some holes in the lid. Fill the jar with water and turn it upside down in a darkened room. This experiment is described more fully in one of the weblinks.

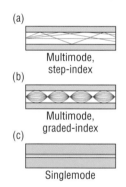

Figure 1 Diagram showing paths of light along:
a step-index fibre;
b graded-index fibre;
c monomode fibre

Figure 2 Diagram showing:
a square wave signal as it enters a fibre;
b a degraded signal as it emerges from a step-index fibre

Multipath distortion can be solved in one of two ways.

In 'graded-index' fibres the refractive index goes down gradually from the core to the cladding. The core diameter is from 50 to 100 μm. The gradual change in refractive index makes the rays of light follow curved paths. See Figure 1(b). The rays that go furthest into the outer layer still travel further, but because the refractive index is less they travel faster. Rays following all the paths reach the end of the fibre together. Unfortunately this only gets rid of distortion perfectly at one wavelength.

A better solution is to make the core much smaller. *Monomode* (or single path) fibres have a core diameter of just 5–10 μm. Only rays parallel to the core are transmitted. See Figure 1(c).

ASCII code

Most data is transmitted as binary code. Binary numbers just use the digits zero and one. Instead of tens, hundreds and thousands that we use in the decimal system of counting, binary numbers count in twos, fours, eights, sixteens and so on. The table below shows how a few numbers are converted.

ASCII stands for American Standard Code for Information Interchange – but you don't need to remember this or the conversion table – just how to use it.

Decimal			Binary						
100s	10s	units	64s	32s	16s	8s	4s	2s	units
		1							1
		2						1	0
		3						1	1
		5					1	0	1
		8				1	0	0	0
	1	0				1	0	1	0
1	0	0	1	1	0	0	1	0	0

Table 1 ASCII number conversion

In fibre optics communications the laser light is either ON of OFF to represent one or zero. The advantage of sending data this way is that even if the light fades, you can still tell whether it is on or off. You don't need to know its exact value. Electronically the ones or zeros are represented by two voltage levels.

ASCII is an agreed code for converting letters, decimal digits and punctuation marks to binary numbers. The code is given in the table below.

Activity

Convert the following decimal numbers to binary: 6, 12.

Convert the following binary numbers to decimal: 0111, 1101.

0111 = 7; 1101 = 13.
6 = 110; 12 = 1100;

Activity

Try converting the word 'Applied' to ASCII.

d-1100100
i-1101001; e-1100101;
p-1110000; l-1101100;
A-1000001; p-1110000;

Char	Binary	Char	Binary	Char	Binary	Char	Binary	Char	Binary	Char	Binary
Space	0100000	3	0110011	F	1000110	Y	1011001	l	1101100
!	0100001	4	0110100	G	1000111	Z	1011010	m	1101101
'	0100010	5	0110101	H	1001000	[	1011011	n	1101110
#	0100011	6	0110110	I	1001001	\	1011100	o	1101111
$	0100100	7	0110111	J	1001010	]	1011101	p	1110000
%	0100101	8	0111000	K	1001011	^	1011110	q	1110001
&	0100110	9	0111001	L	1001100	_	1011111	r	1110010
'	0100111	:	0111010	M	1001101	`	1100000	s	1110011
(	0101000	;	0111011	N	1001110	a	1100001	t	1110100
)	0101001	<	0111100	O	1001111	b	1100010	u	1110101
*	0101010	=	0111101	P	1010000	c	1100011	v	1110110
+	0101011	>	0111110	Q	1010001	d	1100100	w	1110111
,	0101100	?	0111111	R	1010010	e	1100101	x	1111000
-	0101101	@	1000000	S	1010011	f	1100110	y	1111001
.	0101110	A	1000001	T	1010100	g	1100111	z	1111010
/	0101111	B	1000010	U	1010101	h	1101000	{	1111011
0	0110000	C	1000011	V	1010110	i	1101001	l	1111100
1	0110001	D	1000100	W	1010111	j	1101010	}	1111101
2	0110010	E	1000101	X	1011000	k	1101011	~	1111110

Table 2 ASCII conversion chart

You may be required to use this table to convert a short message. For example the word 'Science' is converted as follows:

S-1010011; c-1100011; i-1101001; e-1100101; n-1101110; c-1100011; e-1100101

External assessment

Broadband, and other ways of sending signals

By the end of this spread, you should be able to:

* distinguish between analogue and digital systems
* explain the difference between AM and FM radio transmissions
* explain how broadband transmission increases the speed of data connection to the Internet

Analogue and digital

Have you got an analogue watch or a digital watch?

If your watch has a **digital** display, the time is shown by numbers. This may be very precise – sometimes showing the time to a hundredth of a second – but the numbers change in steps (called discrete values) and cannot show values in between.

Digital signals are represented by numbers, usually binary. Digital signals only have certain values such as 0 or 1. Electronically these are usually represented by the positive supply voltage and zero volts.

If your watch has an **analogue** display, the time is shown by the position of a hand on a dial. The position is continuously variable.

Analogue signals are ones where the size of a variable such as position, amplitude or frequency is proportional to the size of the signal. For example in the output from a microphone, a voltage is proportional to the loudness of a sound. Analogue signals have an infinite number of possible values.

AM and FM

You may remember from spread 16.1.5 that radio waves have a frequency from about 3×10^4 Hz to 3×10^9 Hz. Sound waves have frequencies much lower than this from 20 Hz to 20 kHz. You can test your upper limit in the laboratory by connecting a loudspeaker to a signal generator and increasing the frequency until you can no longer hear the sound. As you get older, this value will go down.

You might wonder why we don't send radio signals at the same frequencies as sound. This would need impossibly long aerials. You can work this out. If you use the equation $c = f\lambda$ to calculate the wavelength of electromagnetic waves with frequencies between 20 Hz and 20 kHz, you will get the answers 15 000 to 15 000 000 m. Since the transmitting and receiving aerials have to be about one quarter of a wavelength long, you can see the problem.

The solution is to vary the radio frequency signal (called the *carrier* wave) according to the sound wave. We call this variation modulation. In analogue radio there are two ways in which this can be done.

Amplitude modulation (AM)

The amplitude of the radio carrier wave is varied according to the sound signal. A loud sound will cause a big change in amplitude and vice versa. The frequency of the modulation will be the same as the frequency of the sound.

The resulting wave is similar to that shown in Figure 1(a).

Frequency modulation (FM)

The frequency of the radio carrier wave is varied according to the sound signal. A loud sound will cause a big change in frequency and vice versa. The amplitude of the wave is constant. The frequency of the modulation will be the same as the frequency of the sound.

The resulting wave is similar to that shown in Figure 1(b).

(a)

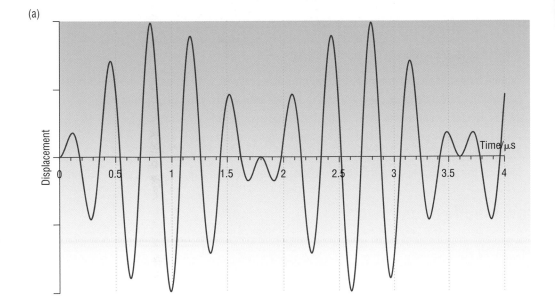

(b)

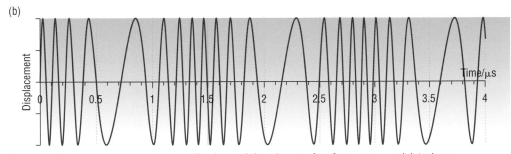

Figure 1 Diagram showing: **a** an amplitude modulated wave; **b** a frequency modulated wave

Broadband

Analogue terrestrial telephone systems carry your voice as an electronic signal that varies at the same frequency as the sound. Modern digital terrestrial phones use the same frequencies. 'Dial-up' computer connections send computer data at these frequencies. Because the frequency is low, the ones and zeroes cannot be too close together so it takes a long time to download your favourite piece of music. Another disadvantage is that you cannot speak on the telephone at the same time.

Broadband works by using the same wires to carry a much higher frequency signal as well as the voice signal. When the signal reaches the box in your house, filters in the box split it up. It sends the lower frequency to your telephone and the higher frequency to your computer. You can use the phone and your Internet connection at the same time.

The higher frequencies are usually in the range 25 kHz–1.1 MHz. Because the frequency is higher the ones and zeroes can be much closer together so your music can be downloaded much quicker.

ADSL

You may have heard your broadband connection described as ADSL. This stands for 'Asymmetric Digital Subscriber line'. The important word is 'Asymmetric', which means unbalanced. In this context it is a way of saying that your Internet provider has given you fast download speeds (getting data *to* your computer) at the expense of much slower upload speeds (e.g. *sending* an email). For most of us this does not matter because we download more data than we upload. It is not so good if you want to run your own web server.

Activity – AM and FM

Figures 1(a) and 1(b) show you how the waves might look, but the difference in frequency between radio and sound waves is so great that it is not possible to show both realistic sound and radio frequencies on the same diagram.

In each diagram:

- Measure the period of both the carrier wave and the modulation.
- Calculate the corresponding frequencies.
- State whether the carrier wave frequencies are realistic for radio waves.
- State whether the modulating wave frequencies are realistic for sound waves.

B: Modulation:
1 complete cycle in 1.45 μs.
$T = 1.5 \times 10^{-6}$ s; $f = 6.9 \times 10^{5}$ Hz.
Not realistic for audible sound.

Realistic for long wave radio.
$T = 1.8 \times 10^{-7}$ s; $f = 5.5 \times 10^{6}$ Hz.
(Note, you get a more accurate answer if you measure the time for a number of cycles.)
B: Carrier:
Approx 20 cycles in 3.6 μs.

A: Modulation:
1 complete cycle in 3.6 μs.
$T = 3.6 \times 10^{-6}$ s; $f = 2.7 \times 10^{5}$ Hz.
(Note, not 1.8 μs.)
Not realistic for audible sound.

Realistic for long wave radio.
$T = 3.4 \times 10^{-7}$ s; $f = 2.9 \times 10^{6}$ Hz.
(Note, you get a more accurate answer if you measure the time for a number of cycles.)
A: Carrier:
Approx 10 cycles in 3.4 μs.

External assessment

By the end of this spread, you should be able to:

* explain how splitting up geographic areas into small cells (0.5–20 miles in radius) increases the number of users a network can carry and the range over which you can communicate
* discuss the factors affecting the distribution of base stations
* state the factors affecting mobile phone signal strength (intensity)
* explain the terms *up-link* and *down-link* bands as applied to mobile phones
* compare the full duplex system used for mobile phones with half duplex devices such as CB radios

How mobile phones work

You probably take mobile phones for granted. Their use has increased tremendously during your lifetime.

Mobile phones use radio signals. The reason they were not in widespread use in the past was because there are only a limited number of radio frequencies available and many of these are used by broadcast radio, emergency services, air traffic control etc.

There are two reasons why it is now possible for many people to make calls using just a few radio frequencies:
* Multiple access technologies have been developed so that lots of people in the same area can share the same frequency.
* Mobile phone masts have been put up all over the country. By dividing the land up into a series of cells, the same frequencies can be re-used by a different set of people in a different cell in a different part of the country. This is why mobile phones are sometimes called cell phones.

Mobile phone cells

The country is divided up into many small cells. Cells vary in size from half a mile to 20 miles across. For each cell there is a base station that transmits (**down-link**) and receives (**up-link**) calls to and from your phone. You will have seen base station masts as you travel about. Some are better hidden than others.

Up-link and down-link in each base station use different frequencies so you can talk and listen at the same time. This kind of system is called **full duplex**.

Some other communication systems, for example CB radios, use the same frequency to talk and listen. This kind of system is called **half duplex**. If you use a half duplex device, you may have to press a button when you want to speak. You have probably heard people in using radio communications in films saying 'Over' when you they have finished talking. This tells the other person that it's their turn.

Signal strength

Base stations are closer together in towns and cities where more people want to make calls at the same time. Each base station can only handle a certain number of calls.

You have probably had a message on your phone saying something like 'no network coverage'. Sometimes if you move a short distance you find that you get a signal. Can you think of examples of when this has happened to you?

Reception often improves if you move outside, away from buildings or hills, up stairs or up a hill. This is because obstructions absorb some of the energy of the signal.

You can also have reception problems if lots of other people are trying to make calls at the same time.

Figure 1 Mobile phone mast

Source

There are very few textbooks written just about mobile phones at this level. This book explains about cells and modulation but it contains a lot of physics that you don't require for this course. Skelding, R. 'Physics Phones Home', 1998, Heinemann, ISBN 0 435 68840.

Key definitions

Down-link is the term used when signals are sent from a base station to your mobile phone.

Up-link is the term used when signals are sent from your mobile phone to a base station.

Full duplex is the term used when signals are sent and received on different frequencies so that you can send and receive at the same time.

Half duplex is the term used when signals are sent and received on the same frequency so that you have to take it in turns to talk and listen.

Even if there are no obstructions, the strength of a signal goes down as you get further away. If cells are too far apart the signal gets too weak. The signal strength is called the intensity. This is the amount of wave energy arriving on unit area each second.

The mathematical equation that tells us how the intensity gets less as you move away from the transmitter is called the inverse square rule.

The inverse square rule states that intensity is inversely proportional to the square of the distance from the source.

For example, this means that if you double your distance from the base station the signal strength goes down to a quarter $\left(\frac{1}{2^2} = \frac{1}{4}\right)$. If you treble your distance from the base station the signal strength goes down to a ninth $\left(\frac{1}{3^2} = \frac{1}{9}\right)$.

The inverse square rule applies when there are no obstructions. If there are obstructions the intensity is even less.

Choice of frequency
No two cells next to each other use the same frequencies. Cells that are separated from each other can re-use the same frequency.

Arrangement of cells and base stations
Networks of cells are usually represented as a honeycomb of equally sized hexagons. How many sides are there in a hexagon? Bees use this arrangement so that no space is wasted between cells. In the same way mobile phone networks want to avoid gaps in reception. As we have seen above cells are not always the same size so real networks can be more complicated.

We often visualise base stations as being placed at the centre of the hexagonal cell as shown in Figure 1(a). In fact they are placed at the corners joining three cells. Each base station transmits and receives three sets of frequencies into three cells. Each cell is served by base stations at three of its corners. Look at Figure 1(b). This helps to keep you connected as you move between cells.

Keeping connected
When you turn on your mobile the signal strength is measured and you are connected, normally to the base station that has picked up the strongest signal.

If you move from one cell to another you are passed on from one base station to another. Your base station sends a special signal to a central switch when your signal drops below a certain level. The system scans to find a stronger signal and switches you over to the next cell. You probably don't even know that this is happening!

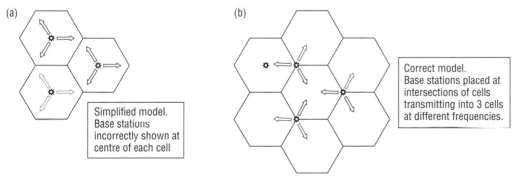

(a) Simplified model. Base stations incorrectly shown at centre of each cell

(b) Correct model. Base stations placed at intersections of cells transmitting into 3 cells at different frequencies.

Figure 2 Diagram showing arrangement of base stations in mobile phone cells:
a simplified model; **b** correct model

By the end of this spread, you should be able to:

* ✳ compare cellular access technologies
* ✳ recognise TDMA as the standard known as the Global System for Mobile Communications
* ✳ compare the advantages of dual-band and dual-mode technologies
* ✳ explain Pulse Code Modulation (PCM), analogue-to-digital conversion and digital-to-analogue conversion

Multiple access

You have probably heard of new phones being described as 3G. The 'G' stands for generation.

FDMA

The first generation of mobile phones (1G) were analogue systems. The available frequencies were shared between users so the system was called Frequency Division Multiple Access (FDMA).

TDMA

Second generation mobile phones (2G) were developed in the 1990s. They use digital signals. More people can use the same frequencies because they are divided up into time slots. Other people use the same frequency as you in different time slots. The base station keeps switching from one user to another on each channel. This all happens so quickly you don't notice. This system is called Time Division Multiple Access (TDMA).

TDMA is used as the access technology for the international standard known as Global System of Mobile Communications (GSM). GSM is the standard in Europe, Australia and much of Asia and Africa. 900 MHz and 1800 MHz bands are used. The United States uses the 1900 MHz band.

Dual band and dual mode

Phones that will work in two frequency bands are called *dual band* phones. For example some phones work on both the 1900 MHz and the 900 MHz bands so that they can be used in both the United States and Europe.

Dual mode phones work with both FDMA and TDMA. This means they can work in countries where analogue systems are used as well as countries using digital systems.

It is possible to buy phones that are both dual band and dual mode.

Frequencies around 900 MHz were used for both 1G and 2G in Europe. For this reason 1G systems were closed down to make space for 2G systems.

CDMA

Third generation mobile phones (3G) commonly use Code Division Multiple Access (CDMA). Calls use frequencies over the whole band. Each call has a unique code to identify it. CDMA is a development of earlier military coding systems.

Analogue–digital conversion

Digital signals are better for transmission. There are two reasons for this:
* We can send more information using a limited range of frequencies.
* Digital signals can be recovered if they become slightly degraded.

However the sound that we speak and listen to is analogue. We need to be able to convert from one to the other.

Figure 1 Mobile phones keep us in touch

A device that converts a signal from analogue to digital is called an analogue to digital converter. An analogue to digital converter is used to convert the output that your voice creates in the microphone of your mobile, to a signal we can send across modern networks.

A device that converts a signal from digital to analogue is called a digital to analogue converter. This is what we need to convert the signal that arrives at your mobile phone into one that will create sound in the phone's speaker.

Pulse Code Modulation

One form of analogue to digital conversion is called Pulse Code Modulation (PCM).

The analogue signal is sampled at many points within each cycle. The samples are taken at equal time intervals. The size of this voltage is converted electronically to a number.

The infinite number values that an analogue signal can have are rounded to a specific, predetermined set of numbers. This process is called quantising.

This number is expressed in binary form ready for transmission.

At the receiving end the numbers can be reconverted back to an analogue signal. A smooth curve will now appear as a series of steps. As long as the samples were taken closely enough together you will not hear the steps.

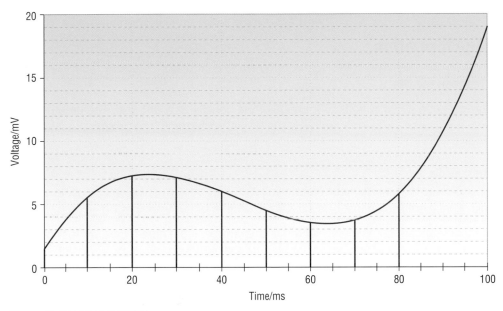

Figure 2 Sampling for PCM

Activity

The vertical bars on the wave in Figure 2 are samples drawn for you.

For each bar record the voltage to the nearest mV.

Draw in the remaining bars up to 100 ms and record these voltages to the nearest mV.

Convert your values to binary numbers.

Draw a reconstructed graph consisting of a series of steps at your recorded values.

1, 6, 7, 7, 6, 5, 4, 4, 6, 11, 19

00001, 00110, 00111, 00111, 00110, 00101, 00100, 00100, 00110, 01011, 10011

Reconstructed graph will be a series of steps rather than a smooth curve.

By the end of this spread, you should be able to:

* state qualitatively the differential absorption of X-rays by air, fat, other soft tissues and bone and the appearance of X-rays on film after passing through these media
* explain techniques for improving quality of X-ray images; use of a grid, narrow beam, filtration
* describe how the use of image-intensifying screens reduces dose rates

This spread builds on what you learnt about **X-rays** in Unit 3. Knowledge of this foundation work will be assumed in the examination. Here, you will learn various ways in which X-ray images can be improved.

Digital X-ray images

In modern machines digital imaging is replacing film. The digital X-ray camera converts the image into a digital signal. The image can be sent for display and storage through a fibre optic link.

Image formation

X-ray films are 'negative' images. The bone areas look bright, because the X-rays have not reached the film.

X-rays produce a two dimensional image of the density of your body. The greater the atomic number of the part of the body the X-rays go through, the greater the absorption of X-rays.

Contrast media

It is possible to make organs or blood vessels lighter on X-ray pictures by using contrast media. These are liquids that absorb X-rays, often a barium compound.

Contrast media are sometimes injected. For example, if the health care professionals want to examine a patient's blood vessels. An iodine based substance is injected into blood vessels to study blood flow. The iodine is later excreted by the kidneys so can be used to check that the kidneys are working properly, or whether they are blocked e.g. by kidney stones.

Improving the quality of X-ray images

The quality of X-ray images depends on a number of factors. We will concentrate on just three of these.

Point source produces a narrow beam

Wider beams produce blurred images. The width of the beam can be limited by lead placed just outside the X-ray machine and before the beam reaches the patient. Lead absorbs X-rays.

One method uses two pairs of adjustable lead sheets that can be moved in and out at right angles to the direction of the beam. A beam of visible light is used to set up the sheets according to the area to be scanned. An alternative method uses a cone of lead.

In order to reduce blur and keep the beam narrow we would ideally like the X-rays to come from a single point. This produces the sharpest shadow.

Activity

In spread 3.5.1 you learnt about the different shades of grey produced in X-rays by different parts of the body. Copy out the table from 3.5.1 and add a column for the effective atomic number values as follows:

Bone, contains calcium: 14.

Fat, contains carbon and oxygen: 6 to 7.

Other soft tissues: 7 to 8.

Air: 1 to 2.

Case study – Barium meal

Ana's doctor thinks she may have a stomach ulcer. She is referred to hospital so that her stomach can be examined with the aid of a barium meal.

Ana is then given some barium compound liquid to drink. Next, she is asked to lie on a couch while X-ray pictures are taken.

Some patients are given an injection as well as the barium meal. This is to make their muscles relax.

It is not possible to have a point-like X-ray source. You may remember that X-rays are produced when electrons hit a metal target. If all the electrons hit the target at the same place too much heat would be produced there. The target might melt. The process of producing X-rays from electron beams is not very efficient. All but a few percent of the electron energy is wasted as heat in the target and has to be conducted away.

We have to spread the electrons out over a small area of target.

To compensate for this we can reduce the effective area of the target. The X-ray beam is taken at an oblique angle to the target surface. This is called reducing the *focal spot size*.

The effect of this blurring is reduced if the patient is close to the film or detector.

Filtration

X-ray machines produce X-rays with a range of frequencies. Lower frequencies (sometimes called low-energy X-rays) are either absorbed by the skin giving an unnecessary dose of radiation to no useful effect, or scattered, so blurring the image.

Filters are used to remove X-rays with lower frequencies, increasing the proportion of useful higher frequency waves. For diagnostic X-rays aluminium filters are used.

Use of a grid

Blurring is also caused by radiation that has been scattered (sent in random directions) within the patient. Scattered radiation may still reach the film or detectors, but in the wrong place. Radiation scattered by tissue may arrive at a part of the image that is supposed to correspond to bone.

To prevent this scattered radiation from reaching the film or detector a grid is placed *between the patient and the film/detector*. The grid is made of strips of lead with gaps that allow direct (unscattered) radiation to pass but block scattered radiation. See Figure 1. Typically the strips are 5 mm long, 0.05 mm thick and 0.05 mm apart. They are separated by material transparent to X-rays.

One problem is that the grid itself may affect the image. To avoid this, the grid is sometimes moved from side to side. To absorb radiation scattered parallel to the grid, a second grid is sometimes used. The second grid has the strips at right angles to the first.

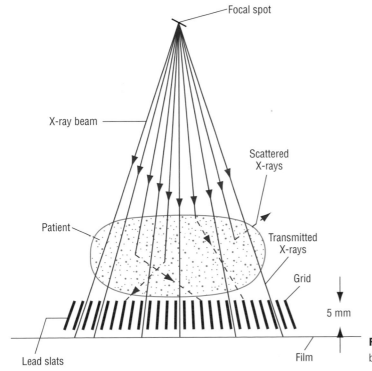

Figure 1 Grid to reduce blur on X-ray image

Case Study – Contrast media

Peter had an arteriogram. Colourless dye called 'contrast' was injected into one of his arteries to allow X-ray images to be taken of the flow of blood in his legs.

John had an arthrogram. John was suffering from pain in his hip. Arthrograms are used to examine the soft tissue in a patient's joint. Contrast material was injected into his hip joint. Soft tissue does not show up well on an ordinary X-ray. This helps the doctors to decide if John needs a hip replacement. Arthrograms can be also used for problems in ankles, wrists, shoulders, hip, and knees.

Source

Martin Hollins, 'Medical Physics', Macmillan Education Ltd., 1990, ISBN 0-333-46657-8, describes a simple investigation with visible light. Compare the shadow of your hand when lit by a tungsten light bulb, with the shadow when a card with a pinhole is placed in front of the bulb. The point source (the pinhole) gives a sharper image.

Assessment tip – Diagnosis and radiotherapy

Don't confuse diagnosis and radiotherapy. Diagnosis is finding out what is wrong with you. Radiotherapy is using radiation to treat disease, usually cancer.

External assessment

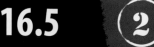

Health hazards of X- and γ-radiations

②

By the end of this spread, you should be able to:

✳ explain how X- and γ-radiations damage cells through ionisation
✳ evaluate the consequent health hazards

In this spread you will learn why ionising radiation can be harmful. You will learn about how much radiation is likely to cause damage. There is a difference between what we need to think about when dealing with radioactive sources inside rather than outside your body. You will learn about how long a radioactive isotope might stay inside a patient's body.

Health hazards

Unlike other parts of the electromagnetic spectrum, X- and γ-rays cause ionisation. Ionisation is the process of stripping electrons from atoms leaving them negatively charged. This property can be useful, because it helps us to detect this kind of radiation. It also makes it hazardous.

Ionisation in living cells can kill them. It can also cause them to change (mutate).

The damaging process

In the first small fraction of a second, ionisation of water molecules in living cells causes chemical reactions. These cause, for example, hydrogen peroxide to be formed.

Over a period of a few seconds, this attacks the organic molecules in the cell. Sometimes the organic molecules are broken. Sometimes molecules are modified.

The next biological stage may take minutes or years. It leads to either:
• early cell death
• cell division being prevented or delayed
• modification of the cell and its daughter cells.

An alternative possibility is that instead of ionising water molecules, the radiation may directly ionise the DNA molecules.

The damage caused

If this happens in our bodies it can cause both short term (acute) effects and long term effects.

Some of these effects are somatic. They damage the ordinary cells in our bodies. Somatic means that they damage the person receiving the radiation.

Some effects are genetic. This means that they damage subsequent generations.

Somatic effects

Acute effects are caused by very large doses. They include:
• changes in the blood
• vomiting
• tiredness
• loss of appetite
• loss of hair
• damage to the gut
• damage to central nervous system (this is fatal within hours).

Long term effects include leukaemia and cancer.

Cancer causes cells to divide more rapidly than a normal cell. The defect is transmitted to daughter cells, so the population of abnormal cells builds up to the detriment of the normal cells in the organ.

Genetic effects

The genetic (hereditary) effects are caused by damage to the cells in the reproductive organs.

The damage may be passed on to children and grandchildren.

How much radiation is safe?

All ionising radiation is potentially hazardous – but you take a chance whenever you cross the road!

Health care professionals have to weigh up the risks and benefits of using X-rays and γ-rays in diagnosis and therapy with the benefits to patients. Remember that many medicines have side effects.

Background radiation

We are all subjected to background radiation all the time.

Natural background radiation comes mainly from local γ-radiation from rocks and cosmic radiation. On average these add up to around 1.25 mSv per year. This figure varies according to the kind of rocks where we live. Smaller amounts come from carbon-14, radon and potassium in our bodies. (The sievert (Sv) is the unit of radiation dose. It is linked to the energy it can impart to our body.)

Irradiated and radioactive

People and objects that have been exposed to α, β, γ, or X-ray radiation (irradiated) may be damaged in the ways described above. *They do not become radioactive.*

Things *do* become radioactive if a radioactive source becomes attached to them. People working with open radioactive substances have to take very careful precautions not to get the material on their skin or clothes.

In medicine, radioactive substances are sometimes injected, swallowed or implanted inside patients' bodies as part of their diagnosis or treatment. In such cases the patient *does* become radioactive and the radiation they emit may be monitored with a Geiger counter. They may be advised to keep away from other people, especially children for some hours afterwards. The isotopes used are chosen to be ones that decay quickly. They may also be excreted.

In choosing isotopes for purposes like this, doctors have to take into account a number of factors:

- The dose must be big enough to do its intended job, such as killing off a cancer.
- The dose must be small enough to avoid unnecessary harm to the patient or hospital staff.
- The chemical toxicity.
- The **half-life** of the substance must be long enough for the procedure to work.
- The half-life must be short enough for the patient to resume normal contact with others within a few hours or days.

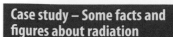
Case study – Some facts and figures about radiation

In addition to *natural* background radiation we receive a further dose of about, on average, 1½ % of the above figure due to non-medical *manmade* background radiation such as the fall-out from past nuclear weapons tests. For comparison, it has been estimated that it would take eight times the average natural background radiation to cause up to one extra case of cancer per thousand people exposed. This is half the number of cases of cancer that occur spontaneously. The probability of genetic effects due to background radiation is far less.
It would take a much, much larger dose of 5000 mSv to kill half the people exposed to such a dose.

Key definitions

The **half-life** of a radioactive substance is the time taken for the number of active nuclei to be halved.

The physical half-life relates to the decrease in active nuclei due to their radioactive disintegration. The number of active nuclei in a patient's body also decreases if the substance is excreted.

The biological half-life is the time taken for the number of active nuclei to be halved due to excretion.

Case study

For tracers such as technetium-99m ($^{99}Tc^m$) both physical and biological half-life must be taken into account. The physical half-life T_P of $^{99}Tc^m$ = 6 hours. Not all the $^{99}Tc^m$ remains in the body of the patient. If the biological half-life, T_B, is also 6 hours, the effective half-life T_E can be calculated using:

$$\frac{1}{T_E} = \frac{1}{T_B} + \frac{1}{T_R}$$

$$\frac{1}{T_E} = \frac{1}{6} + \frac{1}{6}$$

$$= \frac{2}{6}$$

$$= \frac{1}{3}$$

$$T_E = 3 \text{ hours}$$

External assessment

By the end of this spread, you should be able to:

* identify the radiological protection measures taken in X- and γ-ray imaging and radiotherapy treatment areas, to monitor and minimise the dose received by staff and the damage done to healthy tissue of patients
* evaluate the half-thickness value of lead screening used
* describe how the use of image-intensifying screens reduces dose rates

In the last spread you learnt about the hazards of ionising radiation. Now we will discuss what precautions we can take to guard against these hazards.

Regulations

Work with radiation and radioactive substances must follow a risk assessment. This will take into account special regulations for radiation and radioactive materials.

In the past, limits were set on the maximum radiation dose permitted for members of the public. Higher limits were set for people exposed to radiation as part of their job. Special rules applied to people under 18 and to pregnant women.

Today, the golden rule is that doses should follow the principle of being *as low as reasonably achievable.* In addition maximum limits still exist.

Precautions

You are not expected to be able to write a full risk assessment for this kind of work. This should be done by someone with specialised knowledge. You should understand some of the principles on which a risk assessment is based.

The following should be considered in order. For example it is better to use a smaller source than to have an unnecessarily large source with lots of lead shielding:

* Consider whether the procedure is necessary (e.g. could ultrasound imaging be used instead?).
* Reduce the size of source used.
* Increase the distance from the source. (You met the inverse square rule in the spread about mobile phone strength. The same principle applies to the intensity of X- and γ-radiation.)
* Reduce the exposure time.
* Use shielding materials such as lead or concrete between the source and the person.
* Wear protective clothing. Sometimes it is not possible for a radiographer to go behind a screen, because they have to be with the patient. They may wear a lead apron instead.

Open sources

Sources injected into patients are open sources. Additional precautions are needed to make sure that the member of staff is not contaminated with radioactive material. Typical precautions for handling open sources include:

* Wear plastic or rubber gloves, goggles and a nylon coat or overalls. Note that these would be ineffective at providing shielding from closed X- and γ-sources, but will help to prevent contamination from open sources.
* Use a plastic tray to contain the source in case of spillage.
* Wash work surfaces after use.
* Dispose of waste materials (gloves etc.) as radioactive waste.
* Wash your hands afterwards.
* No eating, drinking or smoking. (It is unlikely that these would be permitted anyway! It is particularly important not to put your hands near your mouth if you are handling open radioactive sources.)

Case study – Radiographer

A recent job advertisement on the Internet for a hospital radiographer practitioner included in the list of Main Purposes and Responsibilities: that the practitioner should make sure that radiation doses are as low as reasonably achievable to patients, staff and visitors. It goes on to qualify this by recognising the need to balance clinical needs with the dangers of exposure.

Patients

Health care professionals have to decide whether to expose a patient to radiation as part of medical diagnosis or treatment. They have to balance the risks and benefits.

Careful planning can reduce dose to parts of the body not being investigated or treated.

Image-intensifying screens

If you go for an X-ray, the dose you receive is much less than it would have been in the past. This is due to advances in technology, e.g. more sensitive films and detectors, and the use of filters.

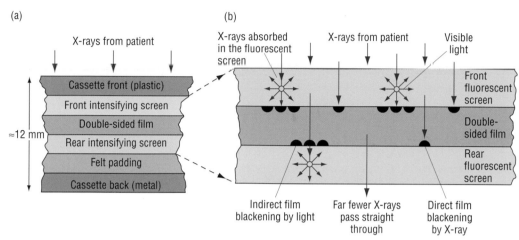

Figure 1 Image-intensifying screen

Another way of getting the same image with a lower amount of radiation is by using an image-intensifying screen.

Only a small percentage of the X-ray energy is absorbed by the film. One way of capturing some of the remaining energy is by converting it into visible light and using this light to increase the exposure of the film.

The intensifying screens are layers of fluorescent material, usually zinc sulfide. They are placed on either side of the film. Double sided film is used to catch the light from both screens. The atoms in the fluorescent materials absorb the X-ray energy and re-emit it as tiny flashes of light (see Figure 1).

Another name for the fluorescent material is a scintillator.

Image-intensifying screens can increase exposure by up to 250 times. One disadvantage is that resolution is slightly poorer.

Phosphorescent layers are commonly used in modern digital systems (see Figure 2).

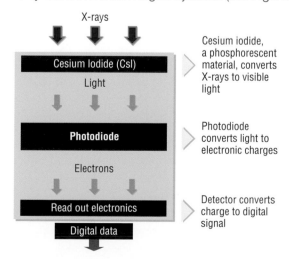

Figure 2 Digital detector

By the end of this spread, you should be able to:

* describe the principle of the gamma camera used to image radioactive tracers administered to the body
* identify the advantages of technetium-99m as a radioactive tracer

X-ray images are made using an X-ray machine, which, of course, has to be outside the patient's body. These images are shadow photographs of parts of the body with high atomic numbers such as bones. You have learnt how other parts of the body can be made to show up as shadows by adding contrast media.

Another way of getting images of parts that don't show up on normal X-rays is to use a radioactive tracer, inside the body. The radiation from these tracers is detected using a gamma camera.

Tracers

The tracer is normally a γ source, because this is easiest to detect from outside the body. Radiation from α and β sources would be absorbed before it escaped from the patient's body. The tracers are radioactive isotopes of chemicals that tend to concentrate in the particular organ to be examined. The source may be swallowed, injected, administered as an enema or implanted surgically.

The most commonly used isotope is technetium-99m ($^{99}Tc^m$ the 'm' stands for metastable). Technetium is an artificially produced element. It has half-life of six hours.

Isotopes of an element are versions of it with different numbers of neutrons in the nucleus. All elements have isotopes. For most elements, some isotopes are stable and some are radioactive. In everyday language we often use the term isotope when we mean a radioactive isotope.

Technetium is good as a medical tracer because:
* The half-life of six hours is long enough to carry out an examination but short enough to keep the radiation dose the patient receives low.
* Technetium can form compounds in a range of biologically active substances. This makes it possible to concentrate it in the tissue or organ the doctor wants to examine.
* It does not produce high energy β particles. These would increase the radiation dose without helping to produce the image.
* It can be produced in the hospital when needed using special 'generators' of molybdenum-99. This decays to technetium-99 with a half-life of 66 hours. After two weeks the generator is returned for recharging.

Technetium is used to get images of:
* skeleton
* heart muscle
* brain
* thyroid
* lungs
* liver
* spleen
* kidney
* gall bladder
* bone marrow.

External assessment

Case Study – Iodine Tracer

Radiographers can find out about a patient's thyroid gland by using ^{131}I tracer. The patient swallows a dose of $Na^{131}I$. This tends to accumulate in the thyroid gland. Radiographers monitor the uptake over a period of time.

^{131}I has a physical half-life of eight days and a biological half-life of 21 days.

$$\frac{1}{T_E} = \frac{1}{T_B} + \frac{1}{T_R}$$

$$\frac{1}{T_E} = \frac{1}{8} + \frac{1}{21}$$

$$= 0.173$$

$$T_E = 5.8 \text{ days}$$

The gamma camera

The device used to build up a map of the radiation given off is called a gamma camera.

The gamma camera has several features in common with a digital X-ray detector (see Figure 1):

- A collimator is placed between the patient and the detector. This is similar to the grid used with X-ray machines.
- A scintillator, made of sodium iodide, converts the γ-ray energy into visible light. This is typically 40 cm in diameter and 1 cm thick.
- A photomultiplier tube converts the light into a pattern of electrons. The tube includes an array of dynodes that detect the electrons and convert them into an electronic signal.
- Circuitry to display and store the image.

The collimator

The collimator is a lead disc placed between the patient and the detector. The disc has thousands of holes drilled through its face.

These holes are normally parallel to each other. Special collimators have diverging or converging holes:

- Diverging holes spread out on the patient side to give a wide angle of view.
- Converging holes are closer together on the patient side to give an enlarged image of a small part of the patient's body.

Discs can also be chosen with more holes closer together:

- Advantage – a better resolution (you can see more detail).
- Disadvantage – less sensitivity (less γ-rays get though to the detector because there is more lead separating the holes).

Collimators of different thicknesses are needed for different tracers, depending on the energy of the γ-rays.

The radiographer can swap the discs attached to the camera for different purposes, but you would find them very heavy to lift in and out!

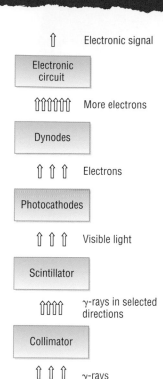

Figure 1 Block diagram of gamma camera

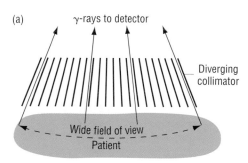

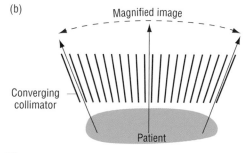

Figure 2 Diagram showing: **a** diverging, and **b** converging collimators for gamma camera

By the end of this spread, you should be able to:

* describe how CAT scanners can produce much more detailed information than conventional X-rays
* describe how X- and γ-radiations are used therapeutically

This spread builds on what you learnt about CAT scanners in Unit 3. Knowledge of this foundation work will be assumed in the examination.

Computerised axial tomography

The computerised axial tomographic scanner, CAT or CT scanner, uses X-rays to produce images of the body, slice by slice.

The intensity of an X-ray beam that has passed through a body has been affected by all the layers it has passed through. It is much more helpful to the health care professionals if they have an image of each individual layer.

To do this, the machine takes lots of X-rays images from different directions. A computer works out what bits of the image are where.

A simplified CAT scanner would consist of a source and detector, placed on opposite sides of the patient, and rotated around the body, measuring the intensity at each position.

Some early versions had an X-ray tube and a film cassette that moved in straight lines in opposite directions on either side of the patient.

In modern machines, the X-ray beam is shaped like a fan. The tube is rotated about an axis – hence the word 'axial' in the name. The film is replaced by a ring of many fixed detectors (see Figure 1).

As the X-ray tube rotates, the patient lies on a bed that moves through the machine. The combined effect is a spiral.

Patients are warned in advance that they will have to stay very still and hold their breath while this is happening. If they move the image may be blurred.

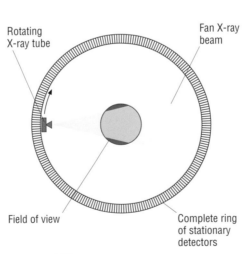

Figure 1 CAT scanner

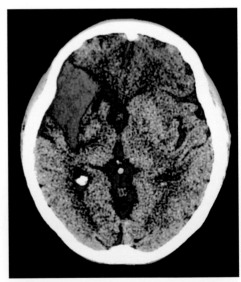

Figure 2 CT image of the head showing right sided infarction (stroke). CT and MRI images are viewed as if the patient's feet point towards the viewer, so the left side of the image represents the patient's right

Uses of CAT scanners

CT scanners are very sensitive to small differences in X-ray intensity. This means that they can distinguish between layers of soft tissue. Uses include making images of:
- the brain (see Figure 2)
- chest
- abdominal or pelvic organs e.g. lungs, liver, kidneys, bladder.

Contrast CT is used to examine the gut.

Figure 2 shows a CT scan of a head.

Disadvantages

CAT scanners have some disadvantages:
- significantly higher radiation doses
- much more expensive than conventional X-rays
- requires a cooperative or sedated patient.

Therapy using X-rays and γ-rays

Therapeutic applications of these radiations use the same destructive properties that make them hazardous. The radiation is used to kill off cancer cells so that they don't spread.

The challenge faced by radiographers is to kill off the unwanted cells while doing as little damage as possible to nearby healthy cells.

Radiation therapy can involve the use of external or internal sources of radiation.

If an external X- or γ-ray source is used, the beam is aimed at the tumour from a number of different directions. Ideally the source is rotated round the body. This is not always possible if particularly sensitive organs such as the eyes are in the way. Only the tumour gets a constant dose of radiation. Other tissue is exposed to radiation, but the dose is spread out. There is some risk of damage being caused.

Therapeutic doses are typically much higher than diagnostic X-rays. This has to be weighed up against the greater risk of death if the tumour is not treated. It is important to get the dose right. If the dose is too high there will be unnecessary damage to surrounding tissue – possibly causing further cancer. If the dose is too low it may not kill off the diseased cells.

Healthy cells recover from radiation treatment faster than cancerous cells. For this reason the patient is given many (typically 20) small doses at (typically) daily intervals, to give the healthy cells time to recover in between.

The X-rays used for therapy have frequencies hundreds of times higher than those used for diagnosis. There are two reasons for this. Firstly, higher frequencies are better at penetrating deep sites in the body. Secondly, the main mechanism of X-ray absorption is different at high frequencies. You have learnt that low frequencies are absorbed more readily by bone. High frequencies are equally absorbed by different materials, so are better when we want absorption by soft tissue.

High frequency X-rays are often called high energy X-rays. The higher the frequency, the higher is the energy of each photon. The special X-ray machine that produces these high energy X-rays is called a 'megavoltage machine' or a 'linear accelerator'. The electrons have to be travelling very fast when they hit the target to produce the X-rays.

The advantage of using an X-ray machine is that it can be switched off when not in use. If large γ-sources are used, they have to be very well shielded. They are still used in places where maintaining a linear accelerator might be difficult. The most common source used is ^{60}Co (cobalt-60).

Internal sources may be injected, swallowed or surgically implanted to kill off cancer cells. They are more likely to be sources of α or β radiation and therefore beyond the scope of this specification.

Case study – Radiotherapy for breast cancer

Mrs Brown has been diagnosed with breast cancer.

As part of her treatment she undergoes radiotherapy.

She travels to hospital for treatment in the radiotherapy outpatient department each day Monday to Friday, with a rest at the weekend, over a period of three weeks. Each treatment only takes a few minutes. During that time the staff move into another room so that they are not irradiated. She has to lie very still.

External assessment

Exam-style questions

Unit 3 Monitoring the activity of the human body

1 (a) The graph below shows blood pressure in different blood vessels within the circulatory system.

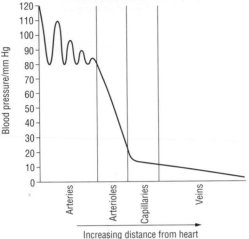

Use information in the figure above and your own biological knowledge to complete the table below. [8]

Feature	Artery	Capillary	Vein
Range of blood pressure/ mmHg		21–13	
Blood flow		Smooth flow	
Structure of walls			
Presence of valves in wall		Not present	

(b) An individual's blood pressure was recorded by a technician before and after carrying out a period of heavy manual work in a factory.
What piece of equipment would have been used to measure blood pressure? [1]

2 Most people are familiar with conventional X-ray machines. More recently CAT and MRI scanners have been used. These are large machines that look very similar.
(a) State **one** similarity shown by a CAT scanner and a conventional X-ray machine in the way that they produce images?
(b) State **one** difference between an MRI scanner and a CAT scanner in the production of images.
(c) (i) A radiographer leaves the room once the patient has been set up for a CAT scan.
Explain why this is necessary.

(ii) Explain why the source rotates during a CAT scan.
(d) State **one** advantage and **one** disadvantage of using a CAT scanner rather than a conventional X-ray machine.
(e) MRI scans are considered to be a safe form of diagnosis. However, all medical procedures carry some risk. Complete the following table.

Hazard	Risk	Safety precaution(s)
Noise		

(f) MRI scans are in high demand and short supply. Discuss the ethical issues that arise as a result.

Unit 4 Cells and molecules

1 Imagine that you are given some plant cells suspended in water.
(a) Describe how you would prepare a temporary microscope slide, for use with a light microscope, to investigate the structure of these plant cells.
(b) Name **two** structures you might expect to see in the plant cells you observe and **two** additional structures that could only be observed using an electron microscope.

	Structure 1	Structure 2
Light microscope		
Electron microscope		

(c) Name **three** structures found in **both** plant and animal cells and describe their functions.

Name	Function

2 Microbiological research scientists use electron microscopy in their work.
(a) List **two** advantages and **two** disadvantages of electron microscopy.
(b) The figure below shows a B lymphocyte and a plasma cell drawn to the same scale.

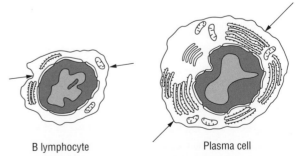

B lymphocyte   Plasma cell

(i) Use label lines and letters **W–Z** to label the diagram of the plasma cell.
Label the following structures:
W endoplasmic reticulum
X Golgi apparatus
Y mitochondrion
Z nuclear membrane

(ii) What is the function of a mitochondrion?

(iii) The actual distance between the two arrow heads on the B lymphocyte is 4.0 μm.
Calculate the actual distance between the two arrow heads on the plasma cell.
Show your working.

(iv) Plasma cells secrete antibodies.
Monoclonal antibodies are extremely useful in biotechnology.
1 What are monoclonal antibodies?
2 Explain how monoclonal antibodies can be used to identify genetic diseases.

(v) Susan discovered that her grandfather and his sister died of Huntington's disease (Huntington's chorea). Susan's father is in his early 40s and is still unaffected.
Now, 21 years old and pregnant, she wants to know if she is affected and has decided to undergo a series of diagnostic tests.
Outline the moral and ethical implications of diagnostic testing for genetic disorder.
In this part of the question, 2 marks are available for the appropriate use of English, spelling, punctuation and grammar.

Unit 16 Working waves

1 The regions of the electromagnetic spectrum have a number of features in common. However, they differ widely in frequency and wavelength. This means that they also differ a lot in how they are produced and how we use them.

(a) State **two** properties that are common to all regions of the electromagnetic spectrum.

(b) Figure 1 shows the wavelengths of the electromagnetic spectrum. Indicate the letter corresponding to the point that lies within:

Wavelength/m

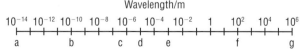

Figure 1 Electromagnetic spectrum

(i) the visible region of the spectrum

(ii) the X-ray region of the spectrum.

Indicate the letter corresponding to the point that best indicates the wavelength of maximum intensity of radiation from:

(iii) a block of melting ice

(iv) cosmic background radiation.

(c) A radio station broadcasts at a frequency of 98 MHz. Calculate the wavelength of this signal.
[Velocity of radio waves = 3.0×10^8 m s^{-1}]

2 A thermal imaging camera is used to observe wildlife after dark.

(a) Explain how the image is formed.

(b) Suggest why the thermal image of an animal's ears might appear different in the middle of the night compared to shortly after sunset.

3 Optical fibres and microwave links are replacing copper wire for carrying telephone calls from city to city.

(a) Explain why monomode optical fibres have replaced step index multimode fibres for this type of application.

(b) In some data transfer applications multimode step index fibres are still used.
(i) Suggest a data transfer application where multimode step index fibres might still be used.
(ii) Explain why there is no problem with using multimode fibres in this case.
(iii) State why multimode step index might be preferred in this case.

4 (a) Peter's modern mobile phone uses digital signals, but his father tells him that early mobile phones were analogue.
(i) Explain what you understand by the terms digital and analogue in this context.
(ii) State why digital systems are now preferred.

(b) Peter's broadband connection uses a terrestrial telephone line. Explain how this system allows much higher data transfer rates than a dial-up Internet connection over the same landline.

(c) Peter's DAB digital radio has a switch that allows him also to listen to analogue FM transmissions. However it does not allow him to tune into analogue AM radio stations.
(i) Explain the difference between AM and FM radio transmissions.
(ii) Explain why one of these gives better reception than the other.

5 X-rays and γ-rays are widely used in hospitals for diagnosis and therapy.

(a) Explain briefly how these radiations can cause damage in the human body.

(b) Suggest why it is justifiable to use these hazardous tools in medical applications.

(c) Give two examples of precautions taken to reduce the dose received by hospital staff.

Exam-style answers

Unit 3 Monitoring the activity of the human body

1 (a) Blood pressure: artery 120–80; vein 13–3; blood flow: (artery) pulsing/uneven/fast; (vein) smooth/slow; structure of walls: (artery) thick/more muscular/more elastic/more contractile tissue; (capillary) single celled wall/*very* thin/thinnest; (vein) thin/little muscle/little elastic tissue; presence of valves: (artery) not present AND (vein) present.

(b) Sphygmomanometer.

2 (a) Both use X-rays to generate images

(b) MRI uses magnetism (to generate images);

(c) (i) *two from:* high levels of radiation; accumulative; hazardous/cause mutation/cancer/fetal damage;

(ii) to build up an image of a thin slice through the body/to generate 3D outcome;

(d) *advantage:* better resolution of soft tissue or organs/ obtain 3D image; *disadvantage:* expense/higher levels of radiation necessary/not portable/not widely available;

(e) e.g.s [Hazards] noisy (given) [Risk] deafness/ear damage/panic; [S.Prec] ear-plugs/muffs/ headphones/music/calming music/protection of ears; [Haz] magnetism (and metal) e.g. staples, earrings, pacemaker; [Risk] MRI not allowed therefore diagnosis may be incomplete/jewellery may be 'sucked into' machine/cause damage to machine and/or patient; [S.prec] interview/medical records/ remove jewellery;

(f) *three from:* Age of patient; patient rating/cost-benefit; medical need; quality of life outcome; 'post code'; private vs NHS.

Unit 4 Cells and molecules

Planning exercise

It is not possible to present examples of whole investigation reports because of their size. However one particular issue that should be raised here is to remind students of the need to distinguish between 'preliminary work' and 'main work' in their report. Preliminary work should relate directly to the task involved and precede it in the written report. Preliminary work could include deciding on appropriate apparatus, concentrations of reagents to use, size of cell populations, counting techniques, identifying control variables, time factors. Any appropriate, advanced preparation that relates to and makes the main investigation function correctly is acceptable.

Test questions

1 (a) *four from:* serial dilution/described; place coverslip over drop; explain how; attempt to exclude air bubbles; use an appropriate stain/named.

(b) light microscope: *two from:* nucleus; cytoplasm; cell wall; vacuole; chloroplast; electron microscope: *two from:* ribosomes; smooth endoplasmic reticulum (SER)/rough endoplasmic reticulum (RER); mitochondria; membrane/plasmalemma/surface membrane/tonoplast; Golgi (apparatus).

(c) *three from:* cytoplasm and site of many reactions/e.g. glycolysis; Golgi and produces vesicles to transport material out of cell/processes molecules; mitochondria and aerobic respiration/Krebs cycle/ oxidative phosphorylation/electron transport chain/ ATP synthesis; nucleus and control centre of the cell/ refer to DNA/chromosomes/genes; plasmalemma and selects/controls movement in and out of cell/ across membrane; RER and involved in protein synthesis/exportation/holds ribosomes; ribosomes and protein synthesis; SER and involved in lipid synthesis/transport.

2 (a) advantages: *two from:* magnifies objects (over 500 000 times)/higher magnification/can see cell ultra-structure; has a higher resolving power; possible to investigate greater depth of field; disadvantages: *two from:* cost; special accommodation; needs skilled operative; preparation of specimens lengthy/ complex; material may be distorted/produces artefacts/distorts image; high vacuum required; living material cannot be viewed.

(b) (i) four correctly placed labels and lines;

(ii) aerobic respiration/release of ATP/release of energy/Krebs cycle/TCA cycle/oxidative phosphorylation/electron transport chain;

(iii) correct measurement between arrows; correct conversion from mm to µm/proportionality process; answer range 6.6 to 6.9; correct unit;

(iv) identical/all from the same clone/hybridoma/ single/pure antibody; which combines with one specific antigen only;

(v) *five from:* possibility of error arising during testing; human rights issues including employment; insurance: mortgage facilities; the mother may need to know because of possible problems with her long term care of the child; she may need to consider termination; she may need to consider how serious a defect has to be before selective abortion is considered; the disease is incurable so does she want to know; she/the child could have many years of normal life before symptoms show; if she is positive should she tell her close genetic relatives; cost-effectiveness of screening. Appropriate use of English is apparent. Spelling, punctuation and grammar.

Unit 16 Working waves

1 (a) *any two* from: velocity in vacuum (velocity/speed in air acceptable); transverse; can be polarised; can travel through a vacuum; consist of changing electric/magnetic fields.

  (b) (i) visible = c,
   (ii) X-ray = b,
   (iii) block of melting ice = d,
   (iv) cosmic background radiation = e.

  (c) $c = f\lambda$; $3.0 \times 10^8 = 98 \times 10^6 \lambda$; Wavelength, λ, = 3.06 m = 3.1 m to 2 s.f.

2 (a) All objects emit infrared radiation. Cannot see infrared with naked eye. Warmer objects emit at higher (peak) frequency/lower wavelength. Animals warmer than their surroundings. So emit different higher frequency/lower wavelength. Sensors in thermal imaging camera detect infrared radiation. Display on screen as false colours/different shades or grey. Very hot – bright/red; cold – darker/blue. Switching on visible light would disturb animals.

  (b) Animals ears likely to get colder as night progresses.

3 (a) Multimode step index fibres allow light to travel down the fibre along different paths. Some paths are at a greater angle to fibre axis than others; so longer distance; so signals take longer time to travel; so signals don't arrive at same time. Sharp edge of square wave signal becomes rounded/signal becomes degraded. Repeater stations need to be closer together to refresh the signal. Monomode fibres have much smaller diameter core; so only one path is possible.

  (b) (i) Local area networks (LANs) [alternative short distance data transfer application acceptable]
   (ii) short distance, so not too much signal degradation
   (iii) cheaper.

4 (a) (i) (Mobile phones use radio signals.) In analogue signals the carrier wave is modulated/varied continuously. In digital signals the modulation is either present or absent/1 or 0.
   (ii) digital systems can carry more data/phone calls.

  (b) Broadband uses much higher frequency carrier signal than the audio telephone signal. Higher frequency systems can carry more data.

(c) (i) In analogue radio signals the audio signal is superimposed on a high frequency carrier wave. AM = amplitude modulated. The amplitude of the signal is varied according to the audio signal at a particular frequency. FM = frequency modulated. The amplitude is constant but the frequency is varied according to the audio signal.
   (ii) FM is less prone to interference because changes in amplitude due to external noise will not be confused with the signal.

5 (a) Cause ionisation. Ionisation in body cells causes chemical changes. The chemicals produced by ionisation modify the cells. The cells are killed or the way they reproduce is changed. Cause cancer.

  (b) Benefit to patient outweighs risk. Doses kept as low as possible. In diagnostic applications this is normally very low. In therapeutic applications higher dose is balanced against known risk of non-treatment. Alternatives such as chemotherapy are also hazardous.

  (c) Appropriate answers include: Leave room while radiation administered. Wear lead apron if this is not possible.

Glossary

abundance The frequency of occurrence of plants in a sampled area, such as a quadrat.

acceleration (*a*) The rate of change of velocity, measured in metres per second squared ($m\ s^{-2}$); a vector quantity.

acid A species that is a proton donor.

activation energy The minimum level of energy required to enable a reaction to take place. Enzymes reduce the amount of energy required to allow a reaction to proceed.

active site The area on an enzyme molecule to which the substrate binds.

active transport Movement of substances across membranes against their concentration gradient, requiring the use of energy in the form of ATP. Active transport usually involves the use of transport proteins.

addition polymer A very long molecular chain, formed by repeated addition reactions of many unsaturated alkene molecules (monomers).

addition reaction A reaction in which a reactant is added to an unsaturated molecule to make a saturated molecule.

adenine A nitrogen-containing organic base found in nucleic acids. It pairs with thymine in DNA and with uracil in RNA.

alkali A type of base that dissolves in water, forming hydroxide ions, $OH^-(aq)$ ions.

alkanes The homologous series with the general formula C_nH_{2n+2}.

alkyl group An alkane with a hydrogen atom removed, e.g. CH_3, C_2H_5; alkyl groups are often shown as 'R'.

allele A version of a gene.

alpha-helix A protein secondary structure – a right-handed spiral held in place by hydrogen bonds between adjacent C=O and NH groups.

alveoli Small air sacs in the lungs.

amino acid An organic compound that contains both an amino group ($-NH_2$) and a carboxyl group ($-COOH$). Amino acids form the monomers of protein molecules.

ammeter A device used to measure electric current, connected in series with the components.

amount of substance The quantity whose unit is the mole. Chemists use 'amount of substance' as a means of counting atoms.

ampere SI unit for electric current, e.g. 4 A.

amplitude (x_o) The maximum displacement of a wave from its mean (or rest) position, measured in metres (m).

amylase An enzyme that catalyses the hydrolysis of starch to maltose.

angle of incidence The angle between an incident ray and the normal.

angle of refraction The angle between the refracted ray and the normal.

anion A negatively charged ion.

antibiotics Molecules produced by microorganisms that kill or limit the growth of other microorganisms.

antibodies Protein molecules released by the immune system in response to an antigen, which are capable of neutralising the effects of the antigen.

antigen Foreign molecule (which may be protein or glycoprotein) that can provoke an immune response.

assay The use of comparative studies or samples to determine the concentration or quantity of a substance in a sample.

atomic (proton) number The number of protons in the nucleus of an atom.

ATP Adenosine triphosphate – a molecule used to store energy temporarily in organisms. The molecule is broken down to adenosine diphosphate + phosphate to release energy to drive metabolic processes.

atrioventricular node (AVN) A patch of tissue in the septum of the heart that conducts the electrical stimulus from the atria in the heart through to the Purkyne fibres.

atrioventricular valves Valves between the atria and ventricles of the heart that prevent backflow of blood.

atrium One of the upper chambers in the heart.

attenuation The reduction in the strength of a signal which occurs, for example, as it passes along a cable or optical fibre.

autotroph An organism that makes its own food from simple inorganic molecules, such as carbon dioxide and water.

Avogadro constant, N_A The number of atoms per mole of the carbon-12 isotope.

base A species that is a proton acceptor.

base-pairing rules Complementary base-pairing between nitrogenous bases in nucleic acids. Adenine pairs with thymine (or uracil). Guanine pairs with cytosine.

Benedict's test Test for reducing sugars. The substance is heated to 80°C with Benedict's reagent. If a reducing sugar is present, the Benedict's reagent changes from blue to red/red precipitate.

biodegradable material A substance that is broken down naturally in the environment by living organisms.

biodiversity The number and variety of living things to be found in the world, in an ecosystem or in a habitat.

Biuret test A biochemical test for the presence of proteins.

body mass index Numerical value found by dividing an individual's mass in kilograms by their height in metres. It is used to assess if the individual is underweight, acceptable weight, overweight or obese.

Bohr shift/Bohr effect The effect of carbon dioxide concentration on the affinity of haemoglobin for oxygen.

brittle A material that distorts very little even when subject to a large stress and does not exhibit any plastic deformation, for example, concrete.

bronchi Airways in the lungs that lead from the trachea to the bronchioles.

bronchioles Airways in the lungs that lead from the bronchi to the alveoli.

buffer A chemical system that resists changes in pH by maintaining a constant level of hydrogen ions in solution.

calibration To determine the quantity of a substance in a solution by taking readings from solutions containing known amounts of the solution (e.g. by colorimetry) and constructing a calibration curve on a graph. This can then be used to determine the amount of that substance in solutions of unknown concentration. Also to determine the value of intervals of a scale on an instrument, such as a thermometer.

cambium Plant tissue in the stem and root that contains dividing cells.

carbaminohaemoglobin The molecule resulting from combination of carbon dioxide and haemoglobin.

carbohydrate A class of biological molecules with the general formula $C_n(H2O)_n$. It includes sugars, starches, glycogen and cellulose.

carcinogen A substance that causes cancer.

cardiac cycle The sequence of events making up one heartbeat.

cardiac muscle The muscle found in the heart. It has its own intrinsic heartbeat (it is myogenic).

carnivore An animal that eats meat.

carrier protein A protein found in membranes, which is capable of carrying a specific molecule or ion through the membrane by active transport.

cartilage A flexible, slightly elastic connective tissue.

cartilage ring A flexible ring of cartilage that holds the airways open.

catalyst A substance that increases the rate of a chemical reaction without being used up in the process.

cation A positively charged ion.

CDMA Code Division Multiple Access.

cellulose A carbohydrate polymer (of $C_6H_{12}O_6$-glucose) that forms plant cell walls.

centriole An organelle from which the spindle fibres develop during cell division in animal cells.

centromere The region of a chromosome where two sister chromatids are joined together, and where the spindle fibre attaches during cell division.

channel protein A protein pore that spans a membrane, through which very small ions and water-soluble molecules may pass.

chloroplast An organelle found in plants, which contains chlorophyll and is responsible for photosynthetic activity in the plant.

cholesterol A lipid-like molecule found in all cell membranes and involved in the synthesis of steroid hormones.

chromatin Material staining dark red in the nucleus during interphase of mitosis and meiosis. It consists of nucleic acids and proteins.

chromosome A linear DNA molecule wrapped around histone proteins found in the nucleus. Chromosomes become visible in prophase of cell division.

cilia Short extensions of eukaryotic cells, typically 2–10 μm long and 0.03 μm in diameter. They may be used for locomotion or to move fluids or mucus over a surface, for example in the mammalian respiratory tract.

ciliated epithelium Epithelial cells that have cilia on their cell surface.

cis–trans isomerism A special type of E/Z isomerism in which there is a non-hydrogen group and a hydrogen atom on each C of a C=C double bond: the cis isomer (Z isomer) has the H atoms on each carbon on the same side; the trans isomer (E isomer) has the H atoms on each carbon on different sides of the bond.

clones Genetically identical cells or individuals.

coenzyme An organic non-protein molecule that binds temporarily with substrate to an enzyme's active site. It is essential for enzyme activity.

coherent and incoherent optical fibres Coherent bundles have their fibres arranged in the same order at both ends. Incoherent bundles have randomly arranged fibres.

competitive inhibitor A substance that reduces the rate of an enzyme-controlled reaction by binding to the enzyme's active site.

complementary (base/structure) Refers to structures that fit together because their shapes and/or charges match up. For example, adenine and cytosine are complementary bases in DNA.

concentration The amount of solute, in mol, per 1 dm^3 (1000 cm^3) of solution.

concentration gradient The difference in concentration of a substance between two regions.

condensation A type of chemical reaction in which two molecules are joined together by means of a covalent bond to form a larger molecule, and at the same time a water molecule is released.

conductor   A material with a high number density of conduction electrons and therefore a low resistance.

connective tissue   A type of tissue that consists of separate cells held together by a ground substance (matrix).

conservation *ex situ*   Conservation in areas other than the natural habitat.

conservation *in situ*   Conservation in the natural habitat.

constrict   To make narrow. For example, vasoconstriction is the narrowing of blood vessels.

control   Part of an experimental investigation. The control is set up to show that the variable being investigated is responsible for the change observed.

conventional current   A model used to describe the movement of charge in a circuit. Conventional current travels from + to –.

coronary arteries   Arteries that carry blood to the heart muscle.

cotransporter protein   A protein in a cell membrane that allows movement of one molecule when linked to the movement of another molecule in the same direction by active transport.

coulomb   Unit of electric charge (C), e.g. 1.6×10^{-19} C. 2 coulomb is the amount of electric charge moved by a current of 1 ampere in 1 second.

couple   Two forces that are equal and opposite to each other but not in the same straight line.

covalent bond   A bond formed by a shared pair of electrons.

cracking   The breaking down of long-chained saturated hydrocarbons to form a mixture of shorter-chained alkanes and alkenes.

crenation   State of animal cells when they have been immersed in a solution of lower water potential and have lost water by osmosis. They become shrivelled.

cristae   The folds found in the inner membrane of a mitochondrion. Stalked particles containing ATP synthase are found on cristae.

critical angle   The angle of incidence such that a ray will just emerge from a medium.

cytosine   A nitrogen-containing organic base found in nucleic acids. It pairs with guanine in DNA.

cytoskeleton   The network of protein fibres and microtubules found within the cell that gives structure to the cell and is responsible for the movement of many materials through it.

dehydration   An elimination reaction in which water is removed from a saturated molecule to make an unsaturated molecule.

delocalised electrons   Electrons that are shared between more than two atoms.

denaturation   An irreversible change in the tertiary structure of a protein molecule. It leads to loss of function in most proteins.

density (r)   The mass per unit volume, measured in kilograms per cubic metre (kg m^{-3}); a scalar quantity.

deoxygenated   Blood with haemoglobin that carries no or little oxygen.

deoxyribose   The 5-carbon sugar in DNA nucleotides.

diaphragm   A sheet of muscular and fibrous tissue separating the chest cavity from the abdominal cavity.

diastole   The period when the heart muscle in the ventricles is relaxing and blood pressure is at its lowest.

diffraction   When a wave spreads out after passing around an obstacle or through a gap.

diffusion   The net movement of molecules or ions in a gas or liquid from an area of high concentration to an area where they are less concentrated.

diffusion gradient   The gradient in molecular concentration (the difference in concentrations) that allows diffusion to occur.

dilate   To make wider. For example, vasodilation is when the lumens of blood vessels become wider.

dipeptide   A molecule consisting of two amino acids joined by a peptide bond.

disaccharide   A molecule consisting of two monosaccharide sugars joined by a glycosidic bond.

disease   A departure from full health.

displacement reaction   A reaction in which a more reactive element displaces a less reactive element from an aqueous solution of the latter's ions.

displayed formula   A formula showing the relative positioning of all the atoms in a molecule and the bonds between them.

dissociation   The breakdown of a molecule into two molecules, atoms or ions. For example, the release of oxygen from oxyhaemoglobin.

diversity   Being diverse – usually used in the context of biodiversity – where there are many different types of organisms present, or genetic diversity within a population of organisms that have genetic variation.

DNA   Deoxyribonucleic acid – a polymer of nucleotide molecules that form the instructions for the synthesis of proteins found within organisms. These nucleotides contain the 5-carbon sugar deoxyribose.

double circulatory system   A transport system in which blood travels twice through the heart for each complete circulation of the body.

double helix   Describes the structure of DNA as a twisted helix of two strands with bases joining the strands.

down-link   The term used when signals are sent from a base station to a mobile phone.

dynamic equilibrium   The equilibrium that exists in a closed system when the rate of the forward reaction is equal to the rate of the reverse reaction.

ecosystem   All the living organisms and all the non-living components in a specific area, and their interactions.

efficiency   The ratio of useful output energy to total input energy.

electric charge (Q or q)   Physical property, measured in coulombs (C); a scalar quantity.

electric current (I)   A flow of charge. An SI quantity, measured in amperes (A); a vector quantity.

electrocardiogram   Trace (graph) showing the electrical activity of the heart muscle (atria and ventricles) during a cycle.

electrolyte   A fluid that contains ions that are free to move and hence conduct electricity.

electromagnetic wave   A self-propagating transverse wave that does not require a medium to travel through.

electromotive force, e.m.f.   The electrical energy transferred per unit charge when one form of energy is converted into electrical energy, measured in volts (V).

electron configuration   The arrangement of electrons in an atom.

elimination reaction   The removal of a molecule from a saturated molecule to make an unsaturated molecule.

empirical formula   The simplest whole-number ratio of atoms of each element present in a compound.

emulsion   A suspension of one material in another as droplets, because it does not dissolve. For example, fat droplets dispersed in water.

endoplasmic reticulum (ER)   A series of membrane-bound, flattened sacs extending from the outer nuclear membrane through the cytoplasm. It may appear rough (rough ER) when ribosomes are attached to the outer surface, and it is involved with synthesis of proteins. It may appear smooth (smooth ER) when ribosomes are not attached, and it is involved with lipid metabolism or membrane formation.

endothermic reaction   A reaction in which the enthalpy of the products is greater than the enthalpy of the reactants, resulting in heat being taken in from the surroundings (ΔH +ve).

end-product inhibition   The regulation of metabolic pathways where the last product in a sequence of enzyme-controlled reactions becomes an inhibitor of one of the enzymes earlier in the sequence.

enthalpy, H   The heat content that is stored in a chemical system.

enzyme   A protein molecule that acts as a biological catalyst.

enzyme–substrate complex   The intermediate structure formed when a substrate molecule binds to an enzyme molecule.

erythrocytes   Red blood cells.

ester bond   The bond formed when fatty acid molecules are joined to glycerol molecules in condensation reactions.

esterification   The reaction of an alcohol with a carboxylic acid to produce an ester and water.

ethanol emulsion test   A biochemical test for the presence of lipids.

exothermic reaction   A reaction in which the enthalpy of the products is smaller than the enthalpy of the reactants, resulting in heat loss to the surroundings (ΔH –ve).

E/Z isomerism   A type of stereoisomerism in which different groups attached to each carbon of a C=C double bond may be arranged differently in space because of the restricted rotation of the C=C bond.

fat   A mixture of lipids, mainly triglycerides with saturated fatty acids, that is solid at body temperature. In living organisms they act as an energy store, insulation, waterproofing for the outer layer, and may give buoyancy.

fatty acid   A molecule consisting of a fatty (hydrocarbon) chain and an acid (carboxylic acid—COOH) group.

FDMA   Frequency Division Multiple Access. Available frequencies are shared between users. 1G technology

fermenter   A vessel used to grow microorganisms in large numbers.

fibrillation   A state in which the chambers in the heart contract out of rhythm.

fibrous protein   A protein with a relatively long, thin structure, which is insoluble in water and metabolically inactive, often having a structural role within the organism.

flaccid   A term used to describe plant tissue where the cells have lost turgor and are not firm.

fluid mosaic (model)   The model of cell membrane structure proposed by Singer and Nicholson – a phospholipid bilayer with proteins 'floating' in it.

fluorescence   A process that causes light to be given off by atoms or molecules a very short time after they have been given extra energy by γ-rays, X-rays or ultraviolet light.

frequency   The number of cycles of a wave passing a point in unit time.

full duplex   The term used when signals are sent and received on different frequencies so that you can send and receive at the same time.

functional group   The part of an organic molecule responsible for its chemical reactions.

gamete   Sex cells, usually haploid (one set of chromosomes). Male and female gametes can fuse during sexual reproduction to form zygotes (diploid).

gas-liquid chromatography   A technique that separates volatile components in a mixture in the gas phase.

gene   A length of DNA that carries the code for the synthesis of one (or more) specific polypeptide.

general formula   The simplest algebraic formula of a member of a homologous series. For example, the general formula of the alkanes is C_nH_{2n+2}.

giant covalent lattice   A three-dimensional structure of atoms, bonded together by strong covalent bonds.

giant metallic lattice   A three-dimensional structure of positive ions and delocalised electrons, bonded together by strong metallic bonds.

globular proteins   Proteins with relatively spherical molecules, soluble in water, often having metabolic roles in organisms.

glucose   A 6-carbon monosaccharide sugar.

glycerol   A 3-carbon (alcohol) molecule. It forms the basis of lipids when fatty acids are bonded to it.

glycogen   A polysaccharide found in animal cells. Formed from the bonding together of many glucose molecules, used as a store of glucose.

glycolipid   A lipid with carbohydrate molecules bonded onto it.

glycoprotein   A protein with carbohydrate molecules bonded onto it.

glycosidic bond   The covalent bond formed when carbohydrate molecules are joined together in condensation reactions.

golgi body   Membrane-bound organelle in eukaryote cells. Its functions are: to modify proteins made at the rough endoplasmic reticulum into glycoproteins; to package proteins for secretions to outside the cell; to make lysosomes; to secrete carbohydrates that make up the cell walls (in plant cells).

guanine   A nitrogen-containing organic base found in nucleic acids. It pairs with cytosine.

habitat   The place where an organism or population lives. It includes the climatic, topographic and edaphic factors as well as the plants and animals that live there.

haemoglobin   The red pigment that carries oxygen in the red blood cells.

haemoglobinic acid   The acid produced when haemoglobin takes up hydrogen ions.

half duplex   The term used when signals are sent and received on the same frequency so that you have to take it in turns to talk and listen.

health   Complete mental, physical and social wellbeing.

hectare   An area of land 100 metres square.

herbivore   An animal that eats only plant material.

heterogeneous catalysis   A reaction in which the catalyst has a different physical state from the reactants; frequently, reactants are gases whilst the catalyst is a solid.

heterotroph   Organism that has heterotrophic nutrition – it gains nutrients from complex organic molecules. These molecules are digested by enzymes to simple soluble molecules and then built up into the complex molecules that the organism requires. Heterotrophs are consumers or decomposers in a food chain.

homogeneous catalysis   A reaction in which the catalyst and reactants are in the same physical state, which is most frequently the aqueous or gaseous state.

homogeneous samples   Samples that are the same throughout the whole location.

homologous series   A series of organic compounds with the same functional group, but with each successive member differing by CH_2.

Hooke's law   The extension of an elastic body is proportional to the force that causes it.

hormone   Chemicals made in endocrine glands that are carried in the blood to target cells/tissues/organs. They act as chemical messengers and are associated with developmental changes of the organism. Most are polypeptides but some are steroids.

hydrocarbon   A compound of hydrogen and carbon only.

hydrocarbon chain   A chain of carbon atoms bonded together with hydrogen atoms bonded onto the carbons.

hydrogen bond   A weak bond formed when partially positively charged groups come close to partially negatively charged groups. It is seen in water molecules, and in the secondary and tertiary structure of proteins.

hydrolysis   A reaction in which a molecule is broken down into two smaller molecules by the addition of a water molecule and the breaking of a covalent bond.

hydrophilic   Water-loving (associating with water molecules easily).

hydrophobic   Water-hating (repelling water molecules).

hydrostatic pressure   Pressure created by a fluid pushing against the sides of a container.

immiscible   Two or more liquids that are insoluble in each other and do not mix.

induced fit (hypothesis)   The theory of enzyme action in which the enzyme molecule changes shape to fit the substrate molecule more closely as it binds to it.

infrared   A form of electromagnetic wave with wavelengths between 7.4×10^{-7} and 10^{-3} m. Used in remote controls.

inhibition/inhibitor   The slowing of an enzyme-controlled reaction. An inhibitor slows down or prevents the formation of enzyme-substrate complexes.

initial reaction rate   Rate of reaction at the beginning of the reaction.

insulator   A material with a small number density of conduction electrons and therefore a very high resistance.

intensity   Energy per unit area.

intercostal muscles   Muscles between the ribs, responsible for moving the rib cage during breathing.

ion   An atom (or group of atoms) carrying a positive or a negative charge.

ionic bonding   The electrostatic attraction between oppositely charged ions.

ionisation   The process of stripping electrons from atoms leaving them negatively charged.

isotopes   Atoms of the same element with different numbers of neutrons and different masses.

keratin   Fibrous protein found in skin, hair and nails.

kilowatt   Unit of power (kW), e.g. 3.5 kW. 1 kW = 1000 W.

kilowatt-hour   Unit of energy (kWh), e.g. 3 kWh. Used by electricity companies when charging for electricity. 1 kWh = 3.6 MJ.

kinetic energy   The work an object can do by virtue of its speed, measured in joules (J); a scalar quantity.

lactate   A compound containing lactic acid – the product of anaerobic respiration in mammals and some bacteria.

Le Chatelier's principle   When a system in dynamic equilibrium is subjected to a change, the position of equilibrium will shift to minimise the change.

leaching   A process where a liquid (often water) washes through a solid and dissolves soluble materials.

leucocytes   White blood cells.

limiting factor   A variable that limits the rate of a process. If it is increased, then the rate of the process will increase.

limiting reagent   The substance in a chemical reaction that runs out first.

lipase   An enzyme that catalyses the breakdown of lipid molecules.

lipids   A diverse group of chemicals that includes triglycerides, fatty acids and cholesterol.

lock and key hypothesis   The theory of enzyme action where the enzyme active site is complementary to the substrate molecule, like a lock and a key.

longitudinal wave   A wave where the oscillations are parallel to the direction of wave propagation, e.g. sound.

lumen   A cavity surrounded by a cell wall in cells such as xylem vessels which have lost their cell contents. Also used for the central cavities of blood vessels.

lymphocyte   A type of white blood cell activated as part of the immune response.

lysosomes   Membrane-bound vesicles made by pinching off from the golgi body. They usually contain digestive enzymes.

macromolecule   A very large molecule.

magnification   The number of times greater an image is than the object.

maltose   A disaccharide molecule consisting of two α-glucose molecules bonded together.

marker-assisted selection   A mechanism used by animal and plant breeders to help select individuals with the desired genotype. The desired gene is linked (marked) to a section of DNA that is easy to identify in a young individual.

mass (m)   SI quantity, measured in kilograms (kg), e.g. 70 kg; a scalar quantity.

mass (nucleon) number   The number of particles (protons and neutrons) in the nucleus.

medium   Any material that a wave travels through.

messenger RNA (mRNA)   A type of RNA polynucleotide involved in protein synthesis. Carries the information coding for a polypeptide from the nucleus to the ribosomes in the cytoplasm.

metabolism   All the chemical reactions that take place in an organism.

metallic bond   The electrostatic attraction between positive metal ions and delocalised electrons.

microwaves   A form of electromagnetic wave with wavelengths between 10^{-4} and 10^{-1} m. Used in mobile phones.

mitochondrion   The organelle found in cells in which most of the ATP synthesis occurs. It is the site of aerobic respiration. The plural form is mitochondria.

molar mass, M   The mass of a mole of a substance. The units of molar mass are g mol^{-1}.

molar volume   The volume per mole of a gas. The units of molar volume are dm^3 mol^{-1}. At room temperature and pressure the molar volume is approximately 24.0 dm^3 mol^{-1}.

mole   The amount of any substance containing as many particles as there are carbon atoms in exactly 12 g of the carbon-12 isotope.

molecular formula   The number of atoms of each element in a molecule.

moment of a force   The turning effect due to a single force, measured in newton metres (N m), e.g. 4 N m; a vector quantity.

monoculture A crop of plants of a single species bred to be very similar.

monocytes Large, phagocytic white blood cells.

monomer A small molecule that is one of the units bonded together to form a polymer.

monosaccharide A simple sugar molecule. The monomer of polysaccharides.

mucus A slimy substance secreted by goblet cells in animal epithelial tissues. It is made up mostly of glycoproteins (proteins bonded to carbohydrates) and is used to protect and/or lubricate the surface on to which it is secreted.

myogenic Describes tissue (heart muscle) that generates its own contractions.

neutrophils Phagocytic white blood cells. They engulf and destroy bacteria. Neutrophils have a many-lobed nucleus, and a granular cytoplasm due to the large numbers of lysosomes present.

niche The exact role of an organism in the ecosystem – its use of the living and non-living components of the ecosystem.

non-aqeous A system that uses a liquid that is not water.

non-competitive inhibitor An inhibitor of an enzyme-controlled reaction that binds to the enzyme molecule in a region away from the active site.

normal An imaginary line at right angles to the surface.

nuclear envelope The double membrane structure surrounding the nucleus in eukaryotic cells.

nucleic acid A polymer of nucleotide molecules.

nucleotide The monomer of nucleic acids consisting of a phosphate, a sugar and an organic base.

nucleus A large, membrane-bound organelle found in eukaryotic cells. It contains the genetic material in the form of chromosomes.

omnivore An animal that eats plant and animal material.

optical density A measure of how slowly light travels in a medium, a way of expressing refractive index.

optimum (temperature/pH) The condition that gives the fastest rate of reaction in enzyme-controlled reactions.

organ A collection of tissues that work together to perform a specific overall function or set of functions within a multicellular organism.

organelle Structure inside a cell. Each organelle has a specific function.

organic base Nitrogenous base in nucleic acid: adenine, thymine, uracil, cytosine, guanine.

organisms An individual living system (e.g. a plant or animal) that can reproduce and grow.

osmosis The movement of water molecules from a region of higher water potential to a region of lower water potential across a partially permeable membrane.

oxidation Loss of electrons or an increase in oxidation number.

oxidation number A measure of the number of electrons that an atom uses to bond with atoms of another element. Oxidation numbers are derived from a set of rules.

oxidising agent A reagent that oxidises (takes electrons from) another species.

oxygenated Describes blood carrying oxygen in the form of oxyhaemoglobin.

oxyhaemoglobin Haemoglobin with oxygen molecules attached.

partially permeable membrane A membrane that will allow some molecules to pass through but will not allow others.

peptide A molecule consisting of a small number of amino acids bonded together by (covalent) peptide bonds.

peptide bond The covalent bond formed when amino acids are joined together in condensation reactions.

percentage yield $\dfrac{\text{Actual yield}}{\text{Theoretical yield}} \times 100\%$

period time or period The time between two similar events in a wave.

pH The measure of acidity/alkalinity of a solution. It is the reciprocal of the logarithmic value of the hydrogen ion concentration. So pH 1–6 are acidic (lots of hydrogen ions), 7 is neutral, and 8–14 are alkaline.

phagocyte Cell that can carry out phagocytosis and ingest bacteria or small particles. Macrophages and neutrophils are phagocytes.

phagosome A vacuole inside a phagocyte which is created by an infolding of the plasma (cell surface) membrane to engulf a foreign particle. The foreign particle is held inside the phagosome.

phospholipid A molecule consisting of a glycerol molecule, two fatty acid molecules and a phosphate group covalently bonded together. Phospholipids form the basis of cell membranes.

phosphorescence A process that causes light to be given off by atoms or molecules that lasts some considerable time after they have been given extra energy by γ-rays, X-rays or ultraviolet light.

photoelectric emission A process that causes electrons to be given off by atoms or molecules that have been given extra energy by γ-rays, X-rays, ultraviolet, or even visible light.

placebo An inactive substance used as a control in an

experiment or trial to test the effectiveness of a medicinal drug.

plane polarised wave A transverse wave oscillating in only one plane.

plasma membrane/cell surface membrane The membrane that surrounds every cell, forming the selectively permeable boundary between the cell and its environment. It is made up of a double layer of phospholipids with embedded proteins.

plasma proteins Proteins made in the liver that are found in blood plasma.

plasmid Small, circular piece of DNA present in some bacterial cells. Plasmids may have genes for antibiotic resistance. Plasmids can also be used as vectors in genetic engineering.

plasmolysis Detachment of the plasma membrane from the cell wall as the cytoplasm shrinks when water is lost from a plant cell.

platelets Fragments of cells in the blood that play a part in blood clotting.

polarisation The process of turning an unpolarised wave into a plane polarised wave (for example, light passing through a Polaroid filter).

polarised wave A wave where the displacement is only in one of the possible transverse directions.

polymer A large molecule made up of many/repeating similar, smaller molecules (monomers) covalently bonded together.

polynucleotide A polymer consisting of many nucleotide monomers covalently bonded together (DNA and RNA are polynucleotides).

polysaccharide A polymer consisting of many monosaccharide monomers covalently bonded together.

potential difference, p.d. The electrical energy per unit charge when electrical energy is converted into some other form of energy.

potential energy A form of stored energy (see gravitational potential energy and elastic potential energy).

power (P) The rate of doing work, measured in watts (W); a scalar quantity.

precipitation reaction The formation of a solid from a solution during a chemical reaction. Precipitates are often formed when two aqueous solutions are mixed together.

pressure (p) Force per unit area, measured in pascals (Pa), e.g. 100 000 Pa. 1 Pa = 1 N m^{-2}; a scalar quantity.

primary source (of information) An original document containing firsthand information about a topic. This would include own experimental material, interview notes, original research papers.

primary structure The sequence of amino acids found in a protein molecule.

principle of moments For a body in rotational equilibrium, the sum of the clockwise moments equals the sum of the anticlockwise moments.

protease An enzyme capable of digesting proteins.

protein A polymer consisting of many amino acid monomers covalently bonded together.

pulmonary circulation The circulation of the blood through the lungs.

pulse code modulation (PCM) A form of analogue to digital conversion.

purine Cytosine and guanine – nitrogenous bases consisting of a double ring structure.

Purkyne tissue (Purkinje tissue) Specialised tissue in the septum of the heart that conducts the electrical stimulus from the sinoatrial node to the ventricles.

pyrimidine Thymine, adenine and uracil – nitrogenous bases consisting of a single ring structure.

quadrat A square frame used for sampling in field work.

quaternary structure Protein structure where a protein consists of more than one polypeptide chain. Haemoglobin and insulin both have a quaternary structure.

radio waves A form of electromagnetic wave with wavelengths between 10^{-1} and 10^4 m. Used in telecommunications.

rate of reaction The change in concentration of a reactant or a product in a given time.

redox reaction A reaction in which both reduction and oxidation take place.

reducing agent A reagent that reduces (adds electron to) another species.

reducing sugar A carbohydrate monomer or dimer that gives a positive result in Benedict's test because it is able chemically to reduce copper sulfate in solution.

reduction Chemical reaction involving transfer of electrons from one reactant to another. The substance that gains electrons is reduced.

reflection When waves rebound from a barrier, changing direction but remaining in the same medium.

refraction The effect that causes the change of direction of light when it goes from one medium to another in which it travels at a different speed.

relative molecular mass, M$_r$ The weighted mean mass of a molecule compared with one-twelfth of the mass of an atom of carbon-12.

representative samples Samples taken from different areas in a location where the composition varies.

resolution The ability to distinguish two separate points as distinct from each other.

respiration The process in which energy is released from complex molecules such as glucose within cells and transferred to molecules of ATP.

ribose The 5-carbon (pentose) sugar found in RNA nucleotides.

ribosomal RNA (rRNA) Ribosomal RNA (rRNA) – mRNA and tRNA are included.

ribosome The organelle on which proteins are synthesized inside the cell.

RNA Ribonucleic acid – a single-stranded polynucleotide molecule that exists in three forms. Each form plays a part in the synthesis of proteins within cells.

salt A chemical compound formed from an acid, when a H^+ ion from the acid has been replaced by a metal ion or another positive ion, such as the ammonium ion, NH_4^+.

saturated hydrocarbon A hydrocarbon with single bonds only.

secondary source (of information) This contains commentary or discussion about a primary source. It might include abstracts, reviews, material from textbooks, commentaries.

secondary structure The coiling or folding parts of a protein molecule due to the formation of hydrogen bonds formed as the protein is synthesised. The main forms of secondary structure are the α-helix and β-pleats.

semi-conservative replication The replication of a DNA strand where the two strands unzip, and a new strand is assembled onto each 'conserved' strand according to the complementary base-pairing rules. The replicated double helix consists of one old strand and one newly synthesised strand.

semilunar valves Valves between the ventricles and the main arteries leading out of the heart, which prevent backflow of blood.

septum The wall separating the ventricles of the heart.

sexual reproduction The production of a new individual formed by the fusing of cells from two different parent organisms. The offspring have unique combinations of alleles inherited from both parents.

sinoatrial node (SAN) The patch of tissue that initiates the heartbeat by sending waves of excitation through the Purkyne tissue to the ventricles.

smooth muscle A type of muscle (involuntary muscle) found mostly in certain internal organs and involved in involuntary movements such as peristalsis.

spectrum A collection of waves with a range of frequencies, for example, visible spectrum and electromagnetic spectrum.

standard conditions A pressure of 100 kPa (1 atmosphere), a stated temperature, usually 298 K (25 °C), and a concentration of 1 mol dm^{-3} (for reactions with aqueous solutions).

standard solution A solution where the concentration of solute is known.

standing wave An alternative name for a stationary wave.

starch A polysaccharide found in plant cells. It is formed from the covalent bonding together of many glucose molecules.

stationary wave A wave formed by the interference of two waves travelling in opposite directions.

stem cells Undifferentiated cells that are capable of becoming differentiated to a number of possible cell types.

stereoisomers Compounds with the same structural formula but with a different arrangement of the atoms in space.

strain The extension per unit length.

stress The force per unit cross-sectional area, measured in pascals (Pa).

structural formula A formula showing the minimal detail for the arrangement of atoms in a molecule.

structural isomers Molecules with the same molecular formula but with different structural arrangements of atoms.

substitution reaction A reaction in which an atom or group of atoms is replaced with a different atom or group of atoms.

substrate The substance that is used up in an enzyme-controlled reaction, leading to the formation of product. It fits into the active site of the enzyme at the start of the reaction.

surfactant A chemical that can reduce the surface tension of a film of water.

suspension A liquid that contains insoluble particles throughout the liquid, for example muddy water.

sustainable development Development that does not cause excessive harm to the surrounding environment. The local biodiversity (species diversity, habitat diversity and ecosystems) and the local people are able to continue to live and operate alongside the development.

systemic circulation The circulation that carries blood around the body, excluding the circulation to the lungs.

systole The stage of the cardiac cycle in which heart muscle contracts to pump blood.

TDMA Time Division Multiple Acess. Available frequencies are divided into time slots and shared between users. 2G technology.

temperature (*T* or θ)   SI quantity, measured in kelvin (K), e.g. 273 K. Also measured in degrees celsius (°C).

tendinous cords   String-like tendons used to attach the atrioventricular valves of the heart to the sides of the ventricle wall. Sometimes called heart strings.

tensile force   Usually two equal and opposite forces acting on a wire in order to stretch it. When both forces have the value *T*, the tensile force is also *T*, not 2*T*.

tensile stress   The tensile force per unit cross-sectional area.

tertiary structure   The overall three-dimensional shape of a protein molecule. It is the result of interactions between parts of the protein molecule such as hydrogen bonding, formation of disulfide bridges, ionic bonds and hydrophobic interactions.

testosterone   Steroid hormone made in the testes.

thin layer chromatography   A technique where the components are separated using an absorbent solid mounted on a glass or plastic plate.

thrombus   A blood clot.

thymine   A nitrogen-containing organic base found in DNA. It pairs with adenine.

trachea   The windpipe leading from the back of the mouth to the bronchi.

transcription   The assembly of an mRNA molecule that is a copy of the DNA coding strand (and complementary to the template strand).

transect   A line through a habitat used to help take samples and study the habitat.

transfer RNA (tRNA)   A type of RNA polynucleotide involved in protein synthesis. It transports amino acids to the ribsomes to be added to the growing polypeptide chain.

transgenic   An organism that has genetic material from another organism, usually by genetic engineering.

transverse wave   A wave where the oscillations are perpendicular to the direction of wave propagation, e.g. water waves, electromagnetic waves, etc.

triglyceride   A molecule consisting of a glycerol molecule and three fatty acid molecules covalently bonded together.

turgid   Describes a cell that is full of water as a result of entry of water due to osmosis. When the pressure of the cell wall prevents more water entering, the cell is said to be turgid.

ultrastructure   The detailed structure of the internal components of cells as revealed by the electron microscope rather than by the light microscope. Sometimes called fine structure.

ultraviolet   A form of electromagnetic wave with wavelengths between 10^{-9} and 3.7×10^{-7} m. Causes sun tanning.

unsaturated hydrocarbon   A hydrocarbon containing carbon-to-carbon multiple bonds.

up-link   The term used when signals are sent from a mobile phone to a base station.

uracil   A nitrogen-containing organic base found in RNA. It pairs with cytosine.

urea   Chemical made in the liver from amine groups from deaminated amino acids and carbon dioxide. It is toxic and is removed from the body in urine.

vaccine   A preparation of antigens given to provide artificial immunity.

variation   The differences between individuals.

vascular tissue/bundle   The transport tissue in a plant – usually found as a bundle containing both xylem and phloem.

velocity (*v*)   The displacement per unit time, measured in metres per second ($m\ s^{-1}$), e.g. $330\ m\ s^{-1}$; a vector quantity.

vena cava   Either of two large veins that carry deoxygenated blood from the body back to the heart.

ventilation   Breathing – movement of the diaphragm and rib cage that bring air into and out of the lungs.

ventricles   The lower chambers in the heart.

volatile   A liquid that turns easily into a gas, for example ethanol.

volatility   The ease with which liquid turns into a gas. Volatility increases as boiling point decreases.

volt   Unit of potential difference and e.m.f (V), e.g. 230 V. $1\ V = 1\ J\ C^{-1}$.

water potential (Ψ)   A measure of the ability of water molecules to move freely in solution. Measures the potential for a solution to lose water – water moves from a solution of high water potential to one of lower water potential. Water potential is decreased by the presence of solutes, and increased by applying pressure.

watt   Unit of power (W), e.g. 60 W. $1\ W = 1\ J\ s^{-1}$.

wave   A series of vibrations that transfer energy from one place to another.

wavelength (λ)   The smallest distance between one point on a wave and the identical point on the next wave (e.g. the distance from one peak to the next peak), measured in metres (m).

weight (*w*)   The gravitational force on a body, measured in newtons.

X-rays   A form of electromagnetic wave with wavelengths between 10^{-12} and 10^{-7} m. Used in X-ray photography.

Young modulus (*Y*)   The ratio of tensile stress to tensile strain, measured in pascals (Pa).

Index